FROST BYTES

Dedicated to Paul Myers
and to women with aspirations

for Marion,
I hope this gives you a better idea of life in Antarctica — no doubt complementary to your son's stories. regards Pene Greet

FROST BYTES

Pene Greet and Gina Price

DOUBLEDAY

Sydney   Auckland   New York   Toronto   London

FROST BYTES

A DOUBLEDAY BOOK

First published in Australia and New Zealand
in 1995 by Doubleday

National Library of Australia
Cataloguing-in-Publication Entry.
Greet, P. A. (Penelope A.)
  Frost bytes.

  ISBN 0 86824 554 2.

  1. Greet, P. A. (Penelope A.) — Correspondence. 2. Price, Georgina D.
  — Correspondence. 3. University of Adelaide. Mawson Institute
  for Antarctic Research. 4. International correspondence. 5. Polar
  regions. I. Price, Georgina D. II. Title.

530.092

Doubleday books are published by

Transworld Publishers (Aust) Pty Limited
15–25 Helles Avenue, Moorebank, NSW 2170

Transworld Publishers (NZ) Limited
3 William Pickering Drive, Albany, Auckland

Transworld Publishers (UK) Limited
61–63 Uxbridge Road, Ealing, London W5 5SA

Bantam Doubleday Dell Publishing Group Inc
1540 Broadway, New York, New York 10036

Edited by Deb Brown
Cover and text design by Reno Design Group 14013
Calligraphy by Ingrid Urh
Cover photographs of authors by Pene Greet and Gina Price;
background by Jonathan Chester/Extreme Images
Back cover photographs by Pene Greet (top), Sue
Steinacher (centre) and Gina Price (bottom)
Typeset by Bookset Pty Ltd
Printed by Australian Print Group
Production by Vantage Graphics, Sydney
10 9 8 7 6 5 4 3 2 1

CRADLE OF DAWN

Go to sleep, welcome the night
I will be here in the morning light
Slip into dreams, you've done all that you can
I'll hold you here in the dawn.

Sunset in your country, sunrise in mine
Lay down your body, feel mine begin to rise
Sunset in my country, sunrise in yours
I feel you there in the dawn.

The forces facing us are terrible indeed
My hope may flicker in the night
But in the morning I will plant another seed
And while you sleep it seeks the light

There are no promises that we will see the day
The dreams we live for will succeed
But I can promise you that halfway round the world
I'll hold the light up while you sleep

We need a quiet place to let our spirit be
Somewhere that we are safe from harm
So my beloved, as the moonbeams touch the sea
Rest in the cradle of the dawn.

Go to sleep, welcome the night
I will be here in the morning light
Slip into dreams, you've done all that you can
I'll hold you here in the dawn.

Sunset in your country, sunrise in mine
Lay down your body, feel mine begin to rise
Sunset in my country, sunrise in yours
I feel you there in the dawn.
I'll hold you here in the dawn.
Rest in the cradle of dawn.

Words and music by Libby Roderick (From *If You See a Dream*, Turtle
Island Records, PO Box 203294 Anchorage, Alaska, 99520, USA.
© Libby Roderick Music 1990.)

1959 must have been a good year. It marked the peak of the solar cycle and an end to a decade. That year Pene and Gina were born and the Mawson Institute for Antarctic Research was established.

CONTENTS

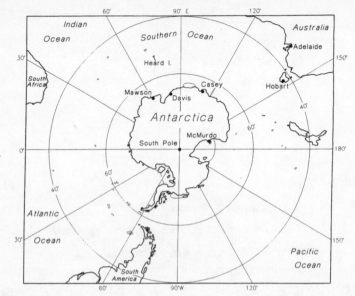

Authors Pene Greet and Gina Price conquered the tyranny of distance between Mawson Base, Antarctica (above), and Fairbanks, Alaska (below), with technology. E-mail (electronic mail) formed a vital link between the two friends as they adapted to their new lives at opposite ends of the earth. MAPS: JOHN COX

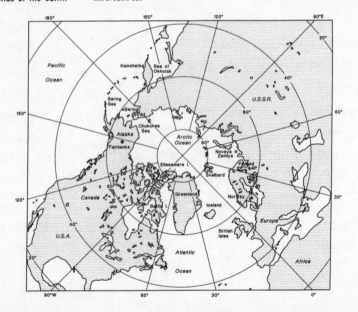

ACKNOWLEDGMENTS

To reveal details of your life, however mundane or momentous, in a book is a daunting prospect. We hope others may enjoy sharing our pleasures and sorrows without being too critical or damning of the people whose lives have crossed paths with ours. We would like to thank those who have supported us along the way and who have made our lives more rich and interesting. We particularly thank the 1990 and 1985 Mawson expeditioners; the Hidden Hillbillies; Hig and Art; special women friends Kim, Cathy, Sue and Sharon; the Fairbanks women's circle; the women of ANARE; and others too numerous to name individually. The Mawson and Alaskan huskies, our firm and unquestioning friends and accomplices, deserve a special mention.

The late Dr Fred Jacka inspired us as young scientists and encouraged us as women in a male-dominated field. His enthusiasm and work through the Mawson Institute for Antarctic Research enabled us to achieve something in our lives and gave us the chance to pursue our work in Antarctica. The Australian Antarctic Division provided access to the environment that has engendered this book. We thank them for the chance to fulfil scientific endeavour and experience Antarctic adventure, and for the safety and comfort of Mawson Base. Through the Geophysical Institute at the University of Alaska Prof. Roger Smith gave Gina the opportunity to further her scientific career, for which she is grateful. The computing facilities at the University of Adelaide, the University of Alaska and the Australian Antarctic Division gave us the means to exchange our letters, offer mutual support and discuss details of our work. The opportunity to communicate ensured that we were happier and more productive in our working environment.

Many have encouraged us while we have been developing this book, by reading various drafts and offering criticism and encouragement. We would particularly like to thank Fred and Eleanor Jacka for their encouragement and Franchesca Rendell-Short for helping us to turn a series of letters into a coherent form. We thank Caro Kaye and Malcolm Robb for their ready ears and sound advice and all those who read the manuscript and offered support and suggestions. We also thank Mark Conde for allowing us to use his letter and John Cox for producing the maps.

We thank our families for their part in putting us where we are today, and all those who accepted the excuse that we were writing a book when we have not been able to do other things.

INTRODUCTION

Gina and I had our last meeting in Perth, lolling on the beach at Cottesloe in the heat of December 1989, with hats and sunburn cream to protect us from the 32°C heat. Sam, Gina's 5-year-old nephew, kept us active playing in the surf and building castles and moats in the sand. Talk was mostly of the coming year: what we hoped to achieve and what we expected. Gina was to depart for Fairbanks to take up a job at the Geophysical Institute in the University of Alaska. I was on my way to Mawson, Antarctica, for 12 months. It was our work, upper atmospheric physics, which would take us to these remote places.

Gina and I had a solid friendship based on many shared experiences over a number of years. We were both facing changes in our personal lives. After recently ending a relationship with Tod, Gina was beginning another with Art, an Alaskan she had met on her travels the previous year. He was a jeweller and owned and ran a gallery at Chitina in the Alaskan bush. Art was visiting Australia to see Gina and meet her family; I was in Perth to try to resolve problems in my relationship with Brian. Our relationship was strained after 14 months' separation and now the prospect of another 14 months apart. For me it was confronting and unsettling. Time with Gina was relaxing, undemanding.

Gina and I were going to opposite ends of the world but

planned to keep in touch through the computer 'e-mail' (electronic mail) network. Australian Antarctic bases are visited by ship only three or four times a year, hence normal mail deliveries are infrequent. E-mail permits rapid communication between scientists on a global basis, facilitating collaboration and dissemination of information. I would be able to access the international network through the computer at Adelaide University. To get on to that system I could use a satellite link to log in to the computer at the Antarctic Division Headquarters in Kingston, Tasmania, and from there use telephone connections to Adelaide. This book contains e-mail Gina and I exchanged after our time together in Perth until we met again two years later.

I was to leave Perth and travel to Hobart to catch the ship to Mawson, one of Australia's three Antarctic bases. It would take 20 days to get there on rough seas, heading south-west against the roaring forties, furious fifties and screaming sixties. My ship left on 6 January and Brian was not coming to see me off. Gina had to start work in Fairbanks in February.

For both of us the year ahead held big challenges. I would be the only woman in a group of 24 wintering at Mawson, a position I would have to deal with thoughtfully and carefully. I had an important research project in atmospheric physics to carry out. If this ran successfully I would be able to spend a couple of weeks on a dog-trip visiting emperor penguin rookeries west of Mawson at Taylor Glacier, Fold Island and Kloa Point. This was a traditional dog-trip completed many times over the last 20 years when there was enough enthusiasm from those working the dogs and when sea-ice conditions allowed. Such a trip would require much preparation. For it to be achievable I would need the support of most of the station. I would need to learn much about working with dog-teams before we left. In Antarctica I would have to be confident about my work, my field skills and my social interactions in a small isolated group of men.

Life in Antarctica is a microcosm of today's society, although a strangely stark microcosm at times. The year was to initiate the whole gamut of life's experiences, from sheer pleasure to the depths of despair, in ways I could never have imagined. A year in Antarctica is not a life's dream but part of a life, a continuance, a set of experiences on which to build. My correspondence with Gina provided me with an outlet, a contact with another part of the world, a firmer sense of reality.

Gina was striding out into the international research community and establishing her reputation as an atmospheric physicist. In Alaska she also had problems to face and a new environment to adjust to. For both of us balancing our workloads, our personal relationships and our social responsibilities was a challenge.

The letters we exchanged were not intended for publication; they were our way of sharing our experiences and maintaining our friendship. At times our letters were short: a few details of routine life, the weather, a simple observation on our environment. The thread of communication was maintained and thus the telling of adventures was made easier. The letters are of a personal nature and contain our personal appraisal of people and events. In the interests of privacy, some names have been changed. These appraisals reflect our own feelings and moods and show, at times, the stresses of the environments in which we were living and working.

As the letters were usually quickly 'bashed out', they have been edited and spelling and grammar have been corrected for ease of reading. Work discussions have been severely edited, the deletions being mainly descriptions of specific instrumental details or analysis procedures. The date at the top of each letter is the date on which the letter was written or started. In places several letters were received at once due to problems in the computing network. The letters have been arranged in approximate chronological order and where there was some doubt as to what the order should be they have been ordered to facilitate the flow for the reader.

Finally, as in all specialised subjects, the text is embedded with a lot of jargon, both in our work discussions and of a general Antarctic and Alaskan nature. Rather than grossly modifying the text a glossary has been included to explain specialised vocabulary and slang Australian terms. If a word is not included in the glossary the standard English meaning is implied. (Appendices list the names of most people and dogs mentioned in the text, as well as imperial–metric conversions and measures for wind-scales.)

Knowing I would get a quick response from someone who understood me and my position at Mawson prompted a steady stream of correspondence through the months that followed. I looked forward to Gina's replies and the balance they gave to my perspective on the world. By sharing our experiences we are able to learn from each other, sweeten our joys and share our sorrows.

Pene Greet

PART ONE

TWO WOMEN TO SCIENCE

GINA PRICE:
POLAR EXPERIENCE
DIVERTED TO ALASKA

Science is the use of logical reasoning to explain the world around us. It works surprisingly well. To me the role of science is not to conquer or mimic nature or to fly the flag for a lost society. The world of 'experts', 'answers' and 'jargon' is dangerous and misleading. I don't believe that science alone can provide a sound recipe for our society's survival. However, it has become an essential tool of modern life. Science satisfies a certain curiosity, a passion for learning about and understanding the world around me. It is a teacher which creates a reverence for life itself.

Growing up, I was treated as an equal among my three brothers although my father referred to me as his favourite daughter. As a family we took camping trips each September through the outback where dad had sold sheep showers in his younger days. These trips were about listening to the birds, breathing fresh air and discovering vast horizons. Dad was a real estate agent and his life values were established in the marketplace although his heart was on the land and his talents with people. Communication at the dinner table was an important part of the day, even if it was just to learn what Dad had eaten for lunch. My mother is more academic, the staple of her world being words, books and ideas. She had started an arts degree, then worked as a journalist, enabling her to travel to Europe before marrying my father at 27 and devoting herself to four children. We were all encouraged to follow 'careers', although as children of the '60s we have been more concerned about lifestyle than salaries. This led my oldest brother on to the land, the second youngest to a career in music, and the third to an array of jobs, travels and, more recently, photography.

My motivations for pursuing a scientific career come from the gut level. I have loved physics since high school, and in my final two years there wasn't much else that I liked about St Hilda's Girls School. My physics teacher, Mr Prince, had mastered the art of cracking open doors, enlightening minds and encouraging questions without the promise of answers. At the University of Western Australia I continued with physics and a second major in electronic music. My father would ask regularly what sort of job physics would lead to. I couldn't answer him, only reassure him that it was what I wanted to do.

After two years at university I was disillusioned and left to work as a governess–jillaroo on a sheep station. Quobba station is situated 1200 km north of Perth and stretches for 80 km along the coast. I loved life on the land and left knowing that if I didn't make anything else of my life I'd happily return. I was finding my feet and a taste for adventure. I moved to Tasmania to complete a science degree. With my blue heeler–kelpie cross, Taj, in tow I soon became known as 'the girl with the dog'. Taj would accompany me to classes and wait outside the refectory or pub. She prided herself in being more popular than me. It was in Tassie that I met Tod, who soon took Taj's position as number one in my life.

The two years after gaining my degree was a time of restlessness, working in bars, jillarooing and travelling between Tod and home in Perth. I bought a kombi 'pop top' to support my nomadic lifestyle and Tod and I travelled across the Gunbarrel Highway, the dry heart of Australia. I got my first professional job, field geophysicist with a contracting firm. It was during the minerals boom of the early 1980s and they'd employ anyone who could demonstrate an ability with numbers. I spent months at a time camping in remote areas with just a few male companions. I was the first woman they had employed and so as not to risk disapproval from head office in Sydney I was entered on the payroll by first initial only. I survived eight months and the experience I gained later proved to be invaluable.

I eventually emerged from my restless period. Tod had decided to move to Canberra for a job, alone, although we continued our toing-and-froing and support for each other over the distance. I found myself in Adelaide with not only Tod out of my life but also Taj, who had died after taking a dog bait. I felt 'rock bottom' and decided it was time for me to pursue what I felt to be my calling. I wanted to go to Antarctica. It came to me when I was working in the factory of a silver-plating company in Sydney. It was 1981, the year of the royal wedding, and there I was putting cardboard sleeves on the boxes of mail-order Prince Charles and Lady Di souvenir teaspoons. Working in a factory where some of my workmates didn't know where Perth was and who thought Tasmania was another country made me realise that I wanted more from life. Suddenly I had direction and I had a goal.

The Mawson Institute for Antarctic Research (MIAR) won me immediately. I was in the public library gathering information on the agencies involved in Antarctic science when I saw Pene's picture and an article on MIAR. They study physics of the upper atmosphere, I discovered, and they'll send down women. That was all I needed. Meeting the director, Fred Jacka, I was further inspired: the pictures on his wall from Mawson's early expeditions; a certain air of dignity. I felt that working for Dr Jacka would be a challenge, a challenge to gain the respect of a man I already admired — and I was a sucker for a challenge. I knew nothing about Fabry-Perot spectrometers (FPSs) but on seeing all the racks of electronics and hearing the stories of those who had been 'south' I was fascinated, enthusiastic and in my element. I worked hard. I asked a lot of questions; I felt foolish when I asked stupid ones. I read Phil Wilksch's thesis over and over again until I started understanding how he had put the FPS together. Sometimes I think I run on sheer determination and I guess a hidden confidence, or stubbornness, that says if someone else can understand this, then so can I.

I learnt a lot from the people around me. I loved talking interferometers with fellow students Mark Conde and Norm Jones. We'd return from an evening jog, look in through the office door window and wonder what we would see if the window was an etalon, transmitting only selected wavelengths. Living physics and thinking creatively is what I love to do, and an important part of science.

An honours degree from the Mawson Institute and practical experience gained from working in remote locations in the bush won me a job with the Antarctic Division. I was going to study aurorae, about which I knew very little. I recognised myself in the story of a now well-known Australian colleague, Robert Eather. He was interviewed for the position of auroral physicist with Australian National Antarctic Research Expeditions (ANARE) back in 1963. It wasn't until after he had been offered the position that he decided he better look up the dictionary for the meaning of the word 'auroral'! I too felt very green as I headed off to Antarctica.

I remember seeing my first aurora, a greenish, faint blob in the twilight sky, not exactly impressive but exciting enough for a newcomer. Aurorae still take my breath away. They are dynamic, ethereal and awe-inspiring. Brilliant displays swirl, loop, and cartwheel across the sky. It's a moving artform and a symphony of lights. All these things — and at heart, it's physics.

Antarctica didn't let me down. It fascinated me and I still maintain that the hardest part of overwintering is returning to Australia; being forced to leave the people and the place that have been everything to you for a year and return to normality, ready or not. I was lucky in that Tod had volunteered to work on the marine science cruise and so got to visit me at Mawson, for one day. The day itself was emotionally charged; however, at least he glimpsed my world, which helped us immensely in maintaining a strong bond over the time. A lot of people go to Antarctica to escape their home lives for one reason or another and these folks usually do multiple trips. I felt from the start that I was a one-timer, although Antarctica and the high latitudes had rubbed off on me more than I realised.

Several years later when Tod and I took off to travel the world I found it was Alaska that was tugging at me. We arrived in Fairbanks in midwinter, looked hard to see aurorae through cloudy skies and drove to the rocket range, Poker Flat, with some of the Geophysical Institute staff. Again I found myself in my element. It took the subsequent break-up of my relationship with Tod for me to realise that Alaska was beckoning. That's what they say up here: 'You don't pick Alaska, Alaska picks you'. In no time I was back. Alaska in summer reminds me of Australia; and in winter, of Antarctica. Here I can have the best of both worlds, the northern lights to soothe my soul, and a fairly normal lifestyle. Alaska used to be called a male domain, like Antarctica, but this is hardly the case any longer. There seems to be an abundance of women mushing dogs, flying planes, climbing mountains, working in trades and doing their own thing. Rather than feeling like an anomaly as a female upper-atmospheric physicist, in Alaska I feel like 'just one of the gals'.

Sometimes I ponder my path from Perth to Mawson, to Alaska, and the study of auroral phenomena. How did I get started on all this? It certainly wasn't a childhood ambition and these weren't places I had heard stories about. Recently a clue was revealed to me. My second name is Dawn, after my aunt, who was born at dawn (her elder sister June, my mother, being born in June). When my aunt joined an Italian class they insisted on calling her by a Latinised name: Aurora, 'the goddess of morning, or dawn deified', as it is defined in the dictionary. So now I am proud of my middle name and think perhaps I was destined to be an auroral physicist after all.

Catching the light from the sky

Fabry-Perot spectrometers (FPSs) are high-precision optical instruments designed to measure light intensity as it varies with wavelength, or colour. They are so precise they can measure the shape of an atomic emission line. By observing such emission lines produced in the upper atmosphere, winds and temperatures in regions 90–250 km above the Earth's surface can be determined. The FPSs that Pene and I worked with were designed and built by Dr Jacka and the technical staff of the Mawson Institute. The instruments are based on two optically flat (flat to within 6 nanometres, or less than 6 millionths of a millimetre, basically very flat) pieces of glass called an etalon or, due to its particular configuration, a Fabry-Perot etalon. If the distance between these pieces of glass is varied slightly the wavelength, or colour, which is transmitted can be controlled. (This effect is due to interference of light and is similar to the interference produced by a thin film; a thin film of oil on a puddle will appear a different colour depending on the position of your eyes.) This is done by mounting the etalon on piezoelectric ceramic tubes. By varying a voltage applied between the inside and outside of the tubes their height varies slightly. The instrument is very sensitive and must be temperature-controlled and mechanically isolated from the building in which it is housed to remove vibrations, and allowances must be made for normal variations in air pressure. Thus there are many sections of the interferometer that must be operational for successful measurements to be made. This also means that if the instrument is not working properly the problem could be in many places. In order for the instrument to run well the operator must be familiar with all the parts of the FPS.

The emissions we observe are very weak; most are below the threshold of human vision. Aurorae are the only exception to this. Light is composed of discrete packets of energy. In large quantities these discrete packets blend together, forming light as we perceive it. As the light intensity decreases the packet nature can become evident. These so-called 'packets' of light are called photons. To observe weak emissions each photon must be counted and so photomultipliers, which convert photons of light into electronic pulses, are used instead of photographic film or video recorders. These electronic pulses are recorded using a personal computer. Output from the FPS is described as a 'profile' as it records the shape of the emission being observed. This profile is then analysed in conjunction with calibration profiles of laboratory lamps and lasers to determine the motion and temperature of the emission region.

I ran the FPS and other UAP (upper-atmospheric physics) experiments at Mawson during 1985. In my thesis I analysed data from two of these experiments and described in detail a number of auroral events where I had measured vertical winds associated with the deposition of energy by the aurora. I was observing the green oxygen emission which is the dominant feature of the aurora. Aurorae can be vibrant active lights, twisting across the sky, or soft stable glows. Their activity and motion is controlled by the Earth's magnetic field and the amount of energy that particles carry into the atmosphere. The energy is obtained both from the sun and from the interaction of the solar magnetic field and the Earth's magnetic field. On most nights at Mawson, aurorae can be seen if the sky is dark and clear of cloud. No aurorae are seen in summer as the sky is not sufficiently dark so summering expeditioners do not become familiar with this polar phenomenon.

Pene's thesis work had involved observations of an emission from a layer of neutral sodium atoms near 90 km. This emission can be seen most easily at dawn or dusk when the sun is shining at 90 km but not on the lower layers of the atmosphere. She had spent many evenings and early mornings at Mt Torrens, collecting the observations for her thesis work. This sodium emission originates below the regions that auroral particles reach. The advantage in measuring the sodium emission at Mawson was that twilights are much longer at polar latitudes than at lower latitudes. Studying atmospheric phenomena in polar regions completes our understanding of the global picture.

PENE GREET: FROM NORTH QUEENSLAND TO ANTARCTIC PHYSICS

I do not believe in the ability of science to completely explain the world. The world is characterised by change, change we can describe and understand but not control. For me atmospheric physics is a way of studying what I am good at, physics, while learning about the Earth.

My father was an accountant in the ANZ Bank and my mother, a physiotherapist. When I was asked at school 'What does your father do?' I always mentioned my mother's occupation as well. Dad was transferred every two to three years and, as our family shifted through some of the smaller Queensland towns, hospitals would ask if Mum would work. The services of physiotherapists in country towns were difficult to obtain. Both my parents were from farming families; Dad's father had been a dairy farmer in southern Queensland and Mum's family had a sugarcane farm in Home Hill, the town where I was born. There were four children in our family; I have two older sisters and a younger brother. We eventually settled in Townsville when Dad left the bank and took a job with another company. My sisters and I had been brought up expecting to follow our mother's example and pursue a career. In my second year of high school I saw a notice on the board about studying rural science at the University of New England (UNE) at Armidale in New South Wales. I nurtured this idea through my high school years and went to UNE in 1977.

First-year rural science studies were straight science courses. As always I found physics the most stimulating and challenging course. Chemistry and biology involved too much rote learning of names and formulae. Maths I could do well but it seemed to have no practical purpose. I was also impressed by the physics professor, Neville Fletcher, with whom I had chatted when he occasionally gave me a lift from the university colleges to the main campus area. He put a human face on what can seem a somewhat scholarly, technical discipline. He also mentioned that physics could do with more female students.

I found university life a bit disconcerting and decided to take a 12-month break after first year. During this time I worked as a laboratory attendant in the science labs at my old secondary school, Heatley State High School in Townsville, and I studied philosophy externally from UNE. I got to know my school teachers as people and I decided I wanted more from my life than the prospects of this job. I returned to university to study physics and philosophy because I had found these subjects interesting. I had no idea where such studies would lead me and what sort of employment I would eventually get. After second-year philosophy I decided not to pursue that discipline any further. What was the point of arguing for the sake of arguing? Philosophy certainly wasn't going to answer any of the questions life posed for me. I had also realised that science wouldn't either, but physics was a challenging study with practical applications.

I completed my degree majoring in physics and then did an

honours degree including a research project in upper-atmospheric physics under the supervision of Professor Frank Hibberd. Professor Hibberd had a deep monotone voice and put most students to sleep in the first five minutes of his lectures but I could see his enthusiasm and interest in his subject. It was more than just the formulae and another lecture to him; it was a life's work to be shared with us. After I completed honours Professor Hibberd recommended that I apply to study for a PhD at a number of Australian universities. When offered a scholarship at the University of Adelaide to work in the Mawson Institute for Antarctic Research, I accepted. The Mawson Institute was run by Dr Fred Jacka, who would supervise my further studies in upper atmospheric physics. I planned to base my research on data I was to collect over a winter at Mawson.

In 1981 Dr Louise Holliday became the first woman to winter on an Australian Antarctic base, as medical officer at Davis. In 1982 the medical officer at Mawson was another woman. In 1983 I was to be one of two women overwintering; again the doctor was a woman and I was to be the first female scientist to winter on an Australian Antarctic base. In 1983 there was still resentment among some male expeditioners and, apparently, among some of the bureaucrats in the Antarctic Division towards women wintering. Antarctica was one of the last frontiers where some men liked to think they were intrepid heroes. Admitting that women could cope in such places denied the men this glory. It also forced them to face up to issues which some were going to Antarctica to escape. I was young, 22 years old, and naively expected that the bureaucrats would be reasonable in their attitudes towards women. What I found was an unwritten agenda where I was expected to behave quite differently to my fellow expeditioners.

I had an affair with one of the mates on the ship and this was used as a reason to make things difficult for me on the voyage down. The ship went via Casey and Davis to Mawson, a five-week voyage with much time spent in the splendours of the pack-ice. We arrived off Mawson with 20 km of fast ice between us and the station. As it seemed the ship might not be able to reach the base, it was decided to send dog-teams out to pick up the wintering expeditioners and their bare necessities. After weeks of sedentary ship life, running with the dogs into Mawson was an exciting initiation into polar travel. West Bay was dubbed the international dog-port as we swept up the snowdrifts and jumped the tide-cracks on arrival.

My excitement was soon cut short. After I had been at Mawson little over a week I found out through Norm Jones, a MIAR colleague at Mawson for the summer, that I would have to return to Australia on the same ship. Despite attempts by myself and my fellow expeditioners, the director of the Antarctic Division would not reconsider the decision. Dr Jacka did at least manage to convince the division that I should be allowed to stay at Mawson for the remaining six weeks of summer.

The reasons cited for my enforced return were not consistent with my own experiences. Yet on my arrival back in Hobart no attempt was made to debrief or consult me. My research project would not be completed. I did not know if I wanted to continue my work in science or even if the opportunity would be there for me to do so. I spent some weeks in Adelaide during which time Dr Jacka assured me I would be welcome to take up another project if I so chose. At least he was interested to hear my account, which differed somewhat from the stories he'd been told. But now that I was back in Australia there seemed little point in dwelling on what might have happened. I wanted to consider my life and its direction so I decided to spend some time travelling. After four months visiting friends and relatives I went to Sri Lanka for a two-week meditation course run by a Western Buddhist nun. This gave me some purpose for my travels; however, after three months in Asia I was ready to return to work.

Although I was denied the chance to work in the Antarctic I had seen enough of Dr Jacka's work at the Mawson Institute to want to return and pursue my studies in atmospheric physics. I respected the thoroughness and preparation of the equipment developed by the institute. Dr Jacka also had my respect for the support he had offered me on my return home the previous summer. In the years that followed I had further lessons to learn about Australian Antarctic bureaucracy but eventually I did return to Mawson. However, my primary aim at this time was to pursue my studies in atmospheric physics and to continue learning about the Fabry-Perot spectrometer.

An experimental upper atmospheric physicist's job has many facets: early morning rises or even all-night stints collecting data, instrument maintenance, calibrations and modifications, and then many hours at the computer analysing and presenting data to colleagues. The data collected and published can then be used by theoreticians, who try to model the atmosphere and phenomena occurring within it. Their models can be compared with measurements to test our understanding of what is going on. These many facets of the job make it interesting and challenging although, as with all jobs, it can become boring at times. When you are rising at 4 a.m. for the 10th morning in a row, or you run a computer program for the 50th time in a week, you sometimes wonder if it's all worthwhile. A sense of fulfilment and purpose does come when a task is completed and your work is presented as a paper in a journal or at a conference.

Sometimes I think I should have completed the rural science degree I started, or possibly the degree in natural resources that many of my undergraduate friends at Armidale were doing. But I have enjoyed and still enjoy my physics studies. My experiences in pursuing them have in many ways enriched my life. It is through this combined experience of science and life that I have grown in understanding of my place in the world.

Seeds of friendship

Gina and I first met in Adelaide in 1983 during my short stay after my first trip to Mawson. I encouraged her to go 'down south', hoping she could learn from my experiences and achieve what I had not been able to. Despite my troubles I'd been most impressed by Antarctica and the friendship of the average expeditioner. To winter there would certainly be an exciting experience.

Gina completed her honours degree at the Institute in 1983 and was accepted to winter at Mawson with the 1985 ANARE. She was employed by the Australian Antarctic Division as a physicist. Gina and Peta Kelsey, a geophysicist, were the first

female scientists to winter in Antarctica. Five of the 28 expeditioners at Mawson that year were women. The 1987 expedition
to Mawson also included five women. The UAP physicist that
year was Maria de Deuge and she wrote her masters at the
Mawson Institute on her return. Now there are usually women
on Australian bases over winter. They are still very much a
minority because the large proportion of expeditioners are tradespeople and there are very few Australian women with trade
qualifications. Over summer there are often women scientists
carrying out field programs, improving the ratios of both scientists to support staff and females to males.

In 1985 there was no e-mail (electronic mail) network and
communication with Antarctic expeditions was limited. Telexes
and rad-phones, prone to the vagaries of ionospheric disturbance of high-frequency (HF) radio communications, were all
that were available. Mail from the ships was very important for
the morale of expeditioners. I found a particularly bright calen-
dar, produced by the *New Internationalist*, with photos of life in
Third World countries to send Gina on the last ship before
winter closed in. Having been at Mawson I knew the things
she'd appreciate most in the long cold months before her.

After Gina's return from Mawson in 1986 she remained a
student of the Mawson Institute, visiting Adelaide regularly while
working at the Australian Antarctic Division in Kingston, Tasmania. The instrument common to Gina's and my work is the
Fabry-Perot spectrometer. Through work our friendship developed. In later years Gina stayed with me and we shared an office
when she visited. There are few women working in physics and
it was good to find another woman working in my particular
area of research who also shared a similar lifestyle and values.
We were comfortable together in our office and at home.

Early in 1988 Gina and I banded together when she suggested we apply to do a summer project together at Mawson. I
could extend the concepts of my thesis work to measurements
made at Mawson. Gina and Mark Conde, who had spent two
winters (1984 and 1986) working on the same instrument, were
also interested in returning to Mawson. Between us we would
have considerable expertise in obtaining and analysing the measurements. This project did come to fruition but Gina chose not

to participate, opting instead to travel in America and Europe. However, her incentive had provided me with the opportunity to return to Mawson for the summer.

All thoughts of travel were banished until we completed our PhD theses. In its final stages writing a thesis tends to overwhelm most other facets of your life. Gina and I deliberated about various points of the work: what style we should use for chapter headings, what colour the covers should be, whether a section should be included here or there or left out altogether. Working long hours seven days a week and collapsing in front of the television to watch the Olympics for an hour or two, we were too exhausted to think more than work required. Cycling in to uni and back home each day provided some exercise and a sense of freedom. Gina went swimming regularly and I attended yoga classes once or twice a week. Work filled our days. Every minute away from our theses was counted as lost time.

In October 1988 we both completed and submitted our doctoral theses. Gina had an international flight to catch and I, a ship to Mawson. We finished within days of each other, having managed to live through the stress and tension of the final few months together. Finishing did give us both a tremendous sense of relief and satisfaction; we had each completed a significant project. It would take some time for us to appreciate this as we both moved on to new ventures in our lives.

My summer at Mawson was enjoyable. Mark Conde taught me the finer points of dog-sledging and together we ran a very successful observing program. We'd spend many days discussing the intricacies of interferometers and the data analysis. If we were observing I'd often work through the night and Mark would take over for observations through the day. Somehow on most days we also managed to take a team of dogs out for a run after tea. I experienced the pleasure of cruising the sea-ice, watching ice-cliffs and reeling snow petrels against the blue summer sky. It was with much reluctance that I left Mawson when the *Icebird* called for the last time that year on 25 March 1989. The dogs had won a place in my heart and I'd made some good friends.

Gina was still travelling overseas and sent me enticing and colourful postcards from Nicaragua, Alaska and Europe with stories of her travels. While in Nicaragua Gina and Tod's relationship came to an end. They parted and Gina returned alone to Alaska, where she met Art. From Alaska she went to a conference in England where she was able to arrange to work at the Geophysical Institute at the University of Alaska. Professor Roger Smith leads a group there studying upper-atmospheric physics. Gina's experience with the Mawson Institute Fabry-Perot spectrometer stood her in good stead to work with a similar instrument at Poker Flat, near Fairbanks. It also gave her an opportunity to pursue a relationship with Art. On his return to Australia Tod became involved with Claire, a mutual friend of his and Gina's. Meanwhile my relationship with Brian had also foundered. He had moved to Perth and was having a relationship with a woman called Carol. Gina and I both felt some anger and frustration about these other women: something else we shared.

Dr Jacka applied for support for another summer program at Mawson in 1989–90. By August it became evident that no one was available to go for the summer. I suggested that instead of sending two people for the summer, perhaps we could change the proposal to be one person for a winter — myself. I had promised my brother that I'd be at his wedding in early November, which precluded a summer trip, but the previous summer had again whetted my appetite to see what an Antarctic winter would be like. After the usual bureaucratic deliberation and hesitation, at the last minute we obtained approval for my participation in the 1990 winter ANARE.

PART TWO

LOGGING IN

i left Hobart for Antarctica on 6 January 1990. We were sailing into prevailing westerlies and the weather didn't drop below a force 7 gale for the 11 days it took to reach Heard Island. There we had a two-day stop before proceeding to Mawson.

The *Polar Queen* was a small ship with 11 crew and on the voyage to Heard Island and Mawson there were 23 passengers. I was fortunate to have a cabin to myself. The ship rolled much of the time and, although I was not really ill, the continual movement prevented me from working effectively. By the time we reached Atlas Cove, boredom and seasickness had me wondering, 'Was this really what I wanted to do?'

It helped enormously to spend time ashore inspecting the abandoned ANARE station, established in 1948, and investigating the penguins and seals. It was a bleak morning with snow squalls and low cloud, but I knew that was typical weather at Atlas Cove. Dr Jacka had told us about some of his experiences on Heard Island and now I had the opportunity to see the place for myself and photograph the retreating Jacka Glacier. Mountains and islands generally stay the same but during periods of global warming, glaciers decrease in size and even disappear. As such they're not a good monument to mark the deeds of our forebears. That afternoon we cruised down the eastern side of the island and the clouds of the morning lifted to give us excellent views of the summit of Big Ben. The wind dropped so we were able to lounge in the fresh air on deck and enjoy the vista before us. This was more like it!

On 22 January, after 16 days on the Southern Ocean, we arrived at the edge of the fast ice, about 14 km off Mawson. The big red and green buildings could just be identified on rocky outcrops in the distance. Most of the passengers alighted for a game of football as the ship advanced and reversed, slowly cutting through the ice. It was good to get some exercise. The sky, stretching endlessly from horizon to horizon, was the deep blue of Antarctic summers. Adelie penguins were passing by on a march from their rookeries on the islands just off Mawson, to feed in open water. It was tempting to walk in to the base for tea but we couldn't be sure what the ice would be like close inshore, where it rots more quickly due to rock particles and debris warming it.

We arrived off the end of West Arm that night and had to wait there until late next afternoon as 45-knot winds prevented the ship from mooring safely. There was Mawson, just out of reach. Not much had changed since I left 10 months ago. There is comfort in familiar things, like the sign in front of us at the end of West Arm: 'It's home, it's Mawson'.

Mawson was established as an Australian base in 1954. It is a conglomeration of buildings that can not be described as beautiful or inspiring. The old station is a series of grey tin-clad boxes tied down with numerous guy ropes. Most of these buildings are still in use. The old kitchen, mess and club form the focus of the base. Below them are workshops for the carpenter, plumber and electrician. Various other buildings are used as stores and workshops. The old dongas or sleeping quarters are fully occupied in summer when the base population swells from 25 to 30 over winter up to 70 at the height of the summer programs. In the late 1970s three buildings were erected to house radio transmitters and science projects. These buildings are adequate and functional. In the 1980s a major construction program commenced and large gaudy buildings sprang up. The three-storey 'red shed' is now the accommodation block. While each person has a separate bedroom, shower, toilet and laundry facilities are communal. Plant and store rooms are located below the ground floor. The large 'green store' building also dominates the landscape. The 'blue box' houses the power station, and smaller red and green buildings are dotted around for various uses. Three domed structures house radar dishes: one for the Anaresat satellite link (6 m dish), the second for the met. (meteorological) radar used to track radiosonde balloons sent up twice a day, and a much smaller, almost inconsequential, dome behind the radio shack for Inmarsat communications. All these buildings are connected by cable trays and pipes for water, sewerage and electrical services. Roads and paths around the station have to cross these service lines numerous times. Almost all flat areas around the base have been used to store boxes of material for further buildings in the construction program. The end result is a sprawl of pipes, wires and boxes of varying sizes. The only relief is where an inspired expeditioner has painted murals on some of the older buildings. The beauty in Antarctica lies beyond the confines of Mawson.

On Australia Day, 26 January 1990, we were finally able to go ashore. I was greeted by some of the friends I had left behind the previous summer. There were six weeks before the last ship for the season was to visit Mawson. My friends from last summer would then be leaving. I had met the 23 men with whom I would be wintering, at field training in Hobart in September. Just how we would all work together at Mawson I'd find out soon enough. I did anticipate some difficulties in being the only woman in a group of 24. It had originally been intended that the wintering party would be all men. Some of the men had chosen to go to Mawson for that very reason. I had joined the expedition at the last minute but was confident that I would get along well with some of the people. Base personnel were a chef, a carpenter (or 'chippie'), an electrician, a plumber, a doctor, the station leader, four radio operators, two met. observers and a met. technician, four diesel mechanics ('diesos') and the plant inspector, three radio technicians, a geophysicist from the Bureau of Mineral Resources (BMR), an upper atmospheric physics (UAP) electronics engineer and myself, the Mawson Institute UAP physicist. We had diverse interests and backgrounds, and different motivations for electing to spend a winter in Antarctica.

Bob Parker, also known as 'the Major' because of his second-ment from the Australian Army, was the nominal station leader. His task was to coordinate station activities and to liaise, by phone and telex, with Australian Antarctic Division headquarters in Kingston, Tasmania. There, Tom Maggs was Mawson Station Manager providing continuity for station policy from year to year. Tom had been voyage leader for the trip down on the *Polar Queen* and in that time I had come to know and like him. He had wintered three times before: as a radio operator at Mawson in 1977 and 1980, and in 1988 as station leader at Casey.

My motivations for wintering were twofold. My work in upper atmospheric physics was my primary aim. In addition I had a strong desire to see and live in the Antarctic, to under-stand more about this remote part of the Earth. How cold is cold and how do you cope in those circumstances? What are blizzards really like? How would I adapt to the darkness of winter? I enjoyed living in a small community where frequent interactions with people from all walks of life add interest beyond that usually obtained in a university environment. I dislike city life because you do not feel part of the whole society. On an Antarctic base the whole society is easily comprehended and your part and dependence on others is obvious. Although you may at times feel isolated, in some ways you can be more lonely in a large city surrounded by thousands of faceless, busy people than on an Antarctic base where there is usually someone want-ing a hand with a job or a partner for a game or evening trip; and at Mawson there were always the dogs.

Mawson had two dog-teams. On my recent summer trip I had learnt much about dog-handling and by the time I left I felt confident about driving a team. Being the only person with experience and enthusiasm for working with the dogs I had been appointed as dog-handler. Rod Ledingham, the Antarctic Division's field operations officer, was responsible for manage-ment of the dogs. It was my job to keep him informed of the activities of the Mawson teams. Fortunately there were several others interested in the dogs so that the workload was shared. Time is required for running teams, for breeding, raising and training of puppies, feeding, occasional veterinary problems, and maintenance of the dog-lines, sledging and camping equipment.

The dogs were huskies, originally from Greenland and Labrador stock. They were brought to Mawson in 1954 when the station was established and were the principal form of land transport in the 1950s and 1960s. The teams were maintained after that with occasional new blood and used for sea-ice and plateau travel until they were removed altogether in 1993.

As working animals, the dogs were kept on a chain line overlooking the station. In 1990 there were 23 dogs and six puppies. Once a dog became too old to work it was culled, so few lived much beyond seven years. The younger dogs Gina had run with in 1985 were still present as good old reliable workers in 1990. Team size varied depending on the purpose of the run and the load to be pulled. An evening run of 15–20 km around the station would use a team of five or seven. On an overnight run, requiring considerable camping and emergency gear, a team of nine would pull a load of about 300 kg.

I was thrilled to be dog-handler as I hoped to spend most of my spare time with them. It gave me an opportunity to get away from the base, and I felt safer and more self-reliant travelling with the dogs than in a vehicle. It also gave me an incentive to escape the laboratory for some exercise for both myself and the 'boys'. (All the dogs and bitches are referred to collectively as 'boys'. Typically three or four bitches were kept for breeding purposes and to be used in the working teams. The term was used as an endearment and I ask forgiveness from anyone who finds it offensive.)

Any trip away from an Antarctic base is described as a 'jolly', although for those on traverse or doing field work the name is more appropriate for short trips, principally for rest and recreation. Such trips provide expeditioners with relief from base life and can be useful for honing field skills and learning about the Antarctic environment. Expeditioners are usually keen to see something of Antarctica, especially the penguins, seals and bird life. Some, however, make surprisingly little effort to experience the vast wilderness which surrounds them.

There is no requirement for modern expeditioners to excel in field skills as mechanised vehicles are used for transport and few work programs necessitate leaving the base. While stringent medical tests are given to expeditioners as part of selection procedures, these tests are to screen for serious illnesses rather than fitness. Abundant good food, usually at least two 3-course meals per day, and a lack of regular exercise results in a significant number of expeditioners gaining weight. Leaving the warmth of buildings does require some preparation and several extra layers of clothing. Exercising outdoors by skiing, running or dog-sledging is possible and an indoor gym with a variety of equipment is available.

Station limits are well defined and any movement beyond these limits is monitored. For a short trip, emergency sleeping requirements, clothing and food are taken. A VHF radio is an essential requirement for emergency communication. The proposed route, party members and estimated time of departure and return are recorded in a book. An overnight trip requires emergency food and equipment for at least three extra days. Trip plans and details are supposed to be submitted three days before departure for approval by the station leader. Any trips over 40 km from base or of more than four days' duration require permission from the Antarctic Division bureaucracy in Australia.

Long trips require considerable planning. Travelling in the Antarctic environment can be extremely dangerous if adequate precautions and preparations are not taken. A blizzard or 'blizz', during which any travel is impossible, may blow up without warning and can last anything up to a week. Travel on sea-ice has its own hazards including thin ice and possible break-out. The sea ice around Mawson is usually connected to the continent and held firmly in place by a large number of islands scattered along the coast. This is known as 'fast ice'. A blizz accompanied by large ocean swell can break up the sea-ice, thus allowing it to float away as pack-ice. On the plateau some routes are marked to avoid crevassed areas.

There are five refuge huts in the vicinity of Mawson and these are popular destinations for jollies. Travel beyond the station is usually by Hagglunds (a tracked, all-terrain vehicle), quike (four-wheeled motorbike) or dog-sled. The Hagglunds are specially designed for sea-ice travel. They will float, if properly sealed, in case they break through the sea-ice. Sea-ice 50 cm or more thick will hold a Hagglunds; around Mawson the sea-ice is usually over one metre thick and has been used for landing Russian DC3s and other jet aircraft. For longer trips two parties must travel together for safety reasons. A multi-volume operations manual lists all the rules and regulations governing Australian Antarctic operations, including travel away from stations. Most of the rules and regulations are common sense and the manual is rarely, if ever, consulted by the average expeditioner. Field and first-aid manuals are given to all expeditioners and they contain most of the relevant information for field travel.

When sledging with dogs camping is often necessary. Polar pyramid tents are large, relatively comfortable, and withstand the rigours of a blizzard. When travelling by dog-sled luxuries such as generators, microwave ovens and toasters must be spurned for a more simple outdoor life. HF radio is always carried for overnight trips and daily radio contacts, or skeds, with the station are required. If radio contact is not made for two days, no matter what the reason, the worst is assumed and a search-and-rescue is mounted for the 'lost' party.

There is no travel between stations once the last ship departs as Australia does not maintain any aircraft in the Antarctic during winter. Helicopters deployed in summer do not have the range required for inter-station travel. The nearest base to Mawson is Davis, 600 km to the east. The Lambert Glacier and Amery ice-shelf make land and sea-ice travel between these two Australian bases virtually impossible. Moladeznhaya, a large Russian base, lies 900 km west of Mawson and occasionally Russian aircraft, bound for or from there, call in.

It took a few weeks to settle in to work and station life and it was a while before I found time to sit down at the computer. Gina was to start work in Alaska in early February so I would be able to contact her then.

16 FEBRUARY 1990

Dear Gina,
Well, I guess you must have started work in Fairbanks by now. I hope everything is going OK for you. I arrived here at Mawson on 26 January. It has taken me a while to settle in. The lab was in a terrible mess. There'd been a new air-conditioning unit put in last year and

25

there was plaster dust all over everything. I had to wipe down every-thing in the lab from the ceiling to the floor. Managed to get tendonitis from too much cloth-squeezing and had to have my wrist bandaged for a week. I finished up by polishing the floor. I don't think it had been done since I left last summer! I'm finally getting some FPS observing done today. It took me a few days to get the system up and running. I've also been doing some maintenance on it with the engineer from last year.

We had a blizz for a couple of days last week. It was great to get some snow. We haven't been able to get the dogs out for a run yet. The plateau ice is sharp and they were cutting their paws on it when we were taking them for evening walks. Would've been too hard to try and get them to pull a sled. Needless to say, there's no sea-ice. The last of it blew out when I came in with the *Polar Queen*. We had to break in through about 12 miles of fast-ice. Once the ship was in, it all started breaking up and blowing out.

I was the last of the 1990 people to arrive. There's been a lot of people out in the field. There's a big party out at the PCMs [Prince Charles Mountains]. Pete Crosswaite, last year's dog-handler, is due back in this evening with the next helicopter flight. I'm looking forward to catching up with him. The Lambert traverse got back in last Tuesday. [1] They'd been out three and a half months. Paul Myers, a 1990 dieso, was with them, so now with us both on the base all the 1990 people are here. I haven't got to know many of them very well, though, as I've been spending most of my time with the '89-ers I knew from last summer.

I did manage to squeeze in a jolly to Mt Henderson last weekend. Four of us walked up. We had to wear crampons all the way — the ice was really slick. They reckon at least a metre of ice has gone off the plateau around Gwamm. There's still lots of melt-streams running up there. Hopefully now that we've had a blizz and things are cooling down the plateau ice will get a bit smoother and we'll be able to start running the dogs. It was good to get away from the base before the ship arrived. I knew that if we didn't get away last weekend we wouldn't until the ship had been and gone. It's the major resupply voyage so things will be pretty busy. You know what the bureaucrats are like when there's a ship around. You just can't get away from the base for an overnight trip. I'm looking forward to settling in with the new crew and farewelling all the extra bods from summer.

Well, time to change another profile.
Peace and happiness, love, Pene.

Gina was living at Hidden Hill, a community set up by the

Religious Society of Friends, or Quakers. Quakers are a Prot-
estant sect active in peace and aid projects on local, national and
international levels. Community members are not required to
take an active role in the larger community, but they are encouraged to do so.

21 FEBRUARY 1990

Dear Pene,
Well, hi from frosty Fairbanks at 40°F below. First impressions of the
life and job up here are pretty positive. The community is just great. It
consists of seven folks; two couples and three singles, living in separate
cabins with a common cabin. We take it in turn to cook each night so
we eat well and mealtimes are nice and relaxed and lively. It sure makes
full-time work more palatable. Hidden Hill is situated on the outskirts
of town, as is the Geophysical Institute, and once I've worked all the
trails out I should be able to ski home crossing only one road and barely
seeing a house. It's good to be out of the city centre as at this time of
year it gets covered in 'ice-fog'. With very cold temperatures and no
wind the moisture from car exhausts and building air-conditioners turns
into a very dense smog. The air is so dry at these temperatures that
moisture is just sucked out of everywhere and freezes instantly.

I had forgotten how hospitable and welcoming people are up here —
especially to foreigners who arrive in the middle of winter at 30°F
below. I realise Tod and I were lucky not to hit the headlines of the
News Miner [Fairbanks' daily newspaper], or *News Minus* as it is called,
with our trip here last winter. As one tourist was discovered here
recently, they did an article trying to recall when the last tourist was
seen in Fairbanks in winter.

We are surrounded by skiing and dog-mushing trails but there aren't
too many topographical features so it's really easy to get lost out there
at 40°F below. So far we've just been venturing out a bit from home
and uni and I think I'll wait until the weather warms up before attempting to ski home. The temps have been this low almost constantly since
I've been here. People are getting sick of it. Things should warm up
pretty soon. We are stealing your sunlight at a rate of 8 minutes a day
at the moment so the days are getting pretty sunny. There's heaps of
snow around and everything is really very pretty.

William has a team of five dogs here at Hidden Hill. They just got
back from a four-day trip into the White Mountains. They experienced
temperatures down to 49°F below after a heavy snowfall in which they
had lost the trail and cabin and were forced to camp out. His mushing

27

companion had difficulty keeping her feet warm and William says it was the most difficult trip he's ever been on. He reckons the dogs fell asleep every time they stopped even briefly. There is also another dog which I'll be able to use for 'skijoring', being towed on skis by a dog or dogs. I haven't tried it yet but it sounds like a nice cruisy way to get around. I almost feel tempted to get my own dog, but maybe it's not worth it while there's a number around.

I must admit my impressions of Fairbanks are slightly biased. On the odd occasion I've been into town I am reminded of the other side of life here, the military side of town. The military personnel are not here because of any great calling or affinity with Alaska. Many tend to be associated with right-wing politics and fundamentalist churches. You see them walking around town, the guys looking tough in their big heavy jackets, boots, hats and padded pants accompanied by girls trying to be feminine wearing skimpy clothes, high-heeled shoes on icy pavements, and no hats to ruin their hairstyles. They do this in $-30°$ to $-40°F$. I just don't know how they survive.

On the work scene, I started off feeling a little abandoned as it's pretty much up to me what I do, in fact entirely so. Roger wants to buy two new FPSs (one portable), a meridional-scanning photometer and imaging spectrometer and I'm to help him choose the bits. So suddenly I'm looking at learning about imaging instruments and CCD arrays. [Charge-coupled devices are extremely sensitive detection units for use in very low light conditions.] It's interesting and all new to me. Roger is a pretty dynamite person to work with. He works very hard and is probably more familiar with most of the equipment and computer control programs than his students. There're also rocket launches going on so I'm hoping to get out to Poker Flat to catch one soon. Poker Flat is 40 miles north of Fairbanks. The FPS is in our optics laboratory on top of a hill, giving it a wide horizon. The rocket launchpads are situated on the flats below us. It's about an hour's drive from Fairbanks.

All in all, things are going pretty well. Art and I are getting along. He has been busy making himself a nice workbench and is going to be community caretaker so he has rent free. Must go, I hope the thaw stops soon and the ice smooths up for you.

Much love, Gina.

9 MARCH 1990

Dear Gina,
Hope all is well. Things here are going really well. The last ship left just over a week ago so now we're settling in for the winter. Everything is

changing very quickly. The days are shortening markedly. After each blow a bit more snow gets dumped. The cable trays are now drifted over so we can walk from aeronomy down to the mess without jumping trays the whole way. The temperature has fallen and isn't rising above −8°C day or night. It is really exciting to watch the seasons progressing.

There's not been much clear weather to do FPS obs [observations]. It has cleared up today, so I'm catching up with my small lab jobs and correspondence in between profiles. I can get a good profile in 40–45 minutes now, compared to 50–60 minutes a week or so ago.

While the ship was in Bundy had five pups. Only two, one male and one female, survived. The past week I was feeding her three times a day as well as running and keeping an eye on all the boys. In a blizz it's quite a bit extra work just to feed them and check regularly that they're all OK. Paul has taken over feeding Bundy this week. It's good to get others involved in these more routine tasks.

Four of us are heading out to Rumdoodle this weekend, weather permitting. Paul and Patrick, both diesos, and probably Scotty, our chef, and I are going. Haven't decided who's running with who yet. Have spent some time fixing up sleds and organising camping gear. Really looking forward to getting the boys out for a long run. I'm glad that the sky is clear today. At least I'll be able to get some data and not feel too guilty about taking off for the weekend if the skies are clear.

Well, Gina, I made some big decisions in the last week. I finally decided to tell Brian that our relationship is finished. I feel good that I've actually done this although I'm not sure what I'll do next year when I return, perhaps come and visit you. I just felt that the whole time we were together at Christmas was a drain on my emotional resources. We were pretending that everything was the same and Carol didn't exist. I don't understand Brian thinking we can continue our relationship while he has a serious relationship with someone else. I asked him at Christmas time and he said that even if I was living with him in Perth he would still want to pursue his relationship with Carol. Well, that's fine by me but I'm just not going to go and live with him in Perth. He doesn't seem to understand human relationships. I feel that every time in my life that he could have supported me he's chosen not to do so. He still hasn't even read my thesis! He's just not interested in something I've spent seven years of my life doing. Suggests to me he's not really interested in me and what I'm doing, just what I give to him. To me, for a relationship to work both people have to put something into it and in our case I feel that I've been the only one contributing. Every time I've tried to discuss this with him he has an emotional crisis and

I end up being supportive of him. Well, I've had enough! Carol can have him.

After exchanging faxes last week I wrote him a long telex last night. Guess it will take a while to get an answer. If I had been stronger and more realistic I would have done this at Christmas and packed up my stuff while I was there. I don't think it's good for him to be surrounded by my things or fair for Carol to be constantly reminded of Brian's past relationships. I have not got involved in any relationships here yet.

Well, Gina, I'd better go back to my profiles. You know with the lengthening nights I've been wondering if I should do any night-time green obs? What do you think would be most worthwhile, cardinal-point obs or some more zenith obs? Today the weather is just perfect; blue skies, no wind, and the wide expanses beckoning through the window. The moon is nearly full so we should have a good weekend.

Peace and happiness, love, Pene.

13 MARCH 1990

Dear Pene,
Just got your second mail message. Today is just glorious up here too. We're now getting about as much sunshine as you, so I know exactly what you were saying. It's amazing the rate at which spring is approaching. While the sun is fantastic I'm starting to worry about how much longer skiing will be OK. I have been skiing home from work. It takes 40 minutes. Starts with a big downhill, crosses one road, but apart from that winds through the woods all the way home. It's just been fantastic! My main worry is moose, crabby ones, which you should avoid at all costs particularly if you have a dog with you. There are a lot of moose around at the moment. The snow is so thick they get pissed off and move on to trails, roads and railway lines. I went mushing with William after dinner the other night, which was great. It just involves sitting in the sled and tearing through the bush at about dog-head height ducking twigs and branches. Quite different, eh?

Dogs are all the talk of the town here with the two biggest dog races, the Iditarod and the Yukon Quest, currently being run. They both go for 1000 miles and the mushers adopt the dogs' metabolism, stopping regularly for short stops but hardly getting more than an hour or so's sleep at a time for the whole race, which takes from 11 to 21 days. They travel alone and often fall asleep at the wheel (so to speak) which can be pretty dangerous if they fall off and the dogs decide not to stop. I have just read a book by Libby Riddles who, in 1985, was the first woman to win one of these races.[2] It's a great story. The Yukon Quest started in Fairbanks so it was pretty exciting watching them head out. There are two 19-year-old girls in it this year, quite a test of endurance at that age, I reckon.

Work-wise things are gradually getting more interesting as I settle in. I have been out to Poker Flat a few times to start getting to know Roger's FPS. It has some nice features, the best being that it is capable of observing two wavelengths at once by the use of a dichroic beam splitter and two photomultipliers, one of which is side-mounted. However, the instrument isn't encased and there are lenses sitting on bits of wood and it all looks a bit thrown-together. In fact last week an ice-dam around the dome melted, causing water to get on and wreck the etalon plates. So this week we've replaced the roof hatch and are now stuck with using an old set of plates suitable for green and red observations but no good for Roger's OH [hydroxyl] measurements. The upshot of this is that I'm now going to use the instrument for some vertical wind obs.

Roger is away at the moment. He left in a whirlwind and yesterday I found lots of little notes on my desk and mail messages about hints for keeping the Poker FPS running. The most recent problem has been that we were unable to see the green line and instead just a strong background. I spent last week testing the filter and all seemed to be OK. Then Friday, at last, we isolated the problem. The filter was fluorescing. Would you believe it? It has thorium in the coatings. So somewhere, sometime, it must have got a fair dose of radiation.

I enjoy going out to Poker. Roger has two students, Jo and Jim, working for him and they are really nice and good to work with. I was out there last night with Jim. It was a beautiful night, a bit moony, but some nice aurorae on the way home.

I'm amazed at the way the doctoral system works here. These guys are paid by Roger part time to do as he tells them, then they do courses, then on top of that they have to do a thesis on something. Jim has been at it for three years now yet still seems unsure about exactly what his thesis is going to be on. At least in the meantime they do have an income and are gaining experience, but all the same it's so different to our system.

Well, Pene, your decision about Brian sounds a good and positive one. I think you're right about him. He'll never put anyone else before himself and I do think there needs to be some of that in a relationship.

It would be great to see you up here next year. You'd love it. I can't stop feeling how much it suits me. In some ways I feel I could easily stay up here indefinitely but probably other things may become more important to me after a few years. Otherwise it really does have all the elements of Antarctica which I like, with the bonus of being a 'sustainable' lifestyle (that's the word which comes to mind).

I heard from Tod about the big ice-fall in East Bay. It must have been a spectacle. Were you there? Things with Tod are proceeding well. It still feels hard at times, maybe for about one day a fortnight. Generally I haven't looked back. I still feel as hooked on Art as when I first met him. He really does something to me. Life in the community with him is good. He has become community caretaker so he takes care of all the little things around the place like hand-carving new handles for the broken pot-lids. He has made a great workbench in our cabin and he's made me an aurora swing, which hangs below the skylight for aurora viewing. Next week he's going down the south-east of Alaska for two weeks to do some teaching in the Artists in Schools program. It will be nice to have a break just to digest things 'cause we haven't had a day apart since he arrived in Sydney, about four months ago now.

Well, Pene, I think I'd better get some work done now. It's a long weekend this weekend so Art and I are thinking about doing a ski trip out to some hot springs. It can still get bloody cold at night so I'm not sure that we've got enough gear. We're going to assess that tonight.

So good to hear from you. Especially since I can so easily relate to what you're feeling and feel the same high here. Take care and give Elwood a hug from me. He was one of my favourites, in fact I think I used to call him Lassie because of his classic good looks. He always looked as if he'd save the day if all else failed.

Love and thoughts, Gina.

13 MARCH 1990

Dear Gina,
Just have to tell someone about our fantastic weekend! I am hopelessly in love! Have finally managed to get things together with Paul and it's going so well! Don't know where to start and what to tell you. I am off on cloud nine and on my way over the moon.

Well, I did dawn obs on Saturday morning, then after lunch we packed up ready to go. Paul decided and told the others he was going to run with me. We got Patrick and Scott away first as they hadn't much experience running and wanted a hand to get away. As Paul and I left, on our way over the hill into West Bay the sledge turned over, smashing the new handlebars we'd just put on to smithereens. We pegged out the boys on the night-trace and just looked at each other. Why did this happen to us? I went back over the hill and got another sled and let radio know what we were doing in case the other team called up to find out why we hadn't caught up with them. We transferred everything to another sled and got going again about two hours after our first departure. About 500 m further up the track we managed to turn the sled again! Fortunately this time nothing broke. After that we had a cruisy run up the hill and on to Rumdoodle. It was cold with a 20–25 knot wind blowing into our faces and drift willy-willies dancing over the plateau. Paul and I talked the whole way. We seem to have so much in common it's almost uncanny.

Paul's actually of American origin — he emigrated to Australia in the early '80s. He's into orienteering, bushwalking and other outdoor activities. It was funny — you know, the dogs seemed to sense what was going on between us. At one spot we stopped for a cuppa from the thermos and had a hug after giving each of the boys a rub. We were at the front of the team and Arne, the lead dog, came up and leaned against both of us as if to say, 'I'm part of this too!' You had to laugh!

Well, Sunday we had a slack day. We had a visit from some of the lads on quikes. Paul and I climbed Rumdoodle (well, I think we got the right peak), although we didn't quite make it to the top. It was good just to be away from the station. There were some Russians supposed to be visiting and the Major suggested we might like to come back to see them. We all talked about it and decided not to go. The Major just wanted to have the dogs on the base to show the Russians. We decided there were enough left there and if the dogs were always on the lines when the Russians visited then they'd think they were never used. It was only a small plane stopping to refuel. They didn't end up coming until Monday and the other team was back by then, so it was just as well we didn't hurry back on Sunday.

Monday we all went for a walk with Cocoa and Kirsty down to Painted Hill and played on the windscour. Then after lunch we packed up and had a real cruisy trip back to Mawson in just perfect weather. There was no wind so we didn't even need overmitts, just gloves, while cruising along enjoying the views of the mountains and vast open spaces. We're certainly lucky to still be able to run dogs here. The sounds of the sled, a sort of clatter on ice, and on snow, a soft swish with an occasional whine as it goes over an edge, is pleasant. We stopped a couple of times to give the dogs a good drink of snow. It was so warm they were hot. Bonza loves rolling in the snow and gets a partial white covering on his black coat and looks at you with his devilish yellow eyes from a black mask and white disguise.

Well, just to bring Paul and I back to earth we managed to roll the sled again on the way down Gwamm. It is pretty damn hairy trying to ride a fully loaded sled down that slope. We negotiated the worst icy bit OK, then rolled it twice on snow banks. Actually the dogs took off as we were righting the sled the first time and got away without us. They travelled about 200 yards before the sled rolled a second time, this time ending up upside down on the handlebars. We were very wild with them by this stage and put the front brake on and they were so excited they pulled the sled all the way back over the hill with the brake on. Wow, they can work if they have to!

Well, Gina, this all feels right for me. I guess it will take a while for us to adjust and fit our relationship into the base structure and interactions. I'd better get my feet back on the ground and try and do some work.

Love always, Pene.

14 MARCH 1990

Calling off-the-planet-Pene . . .
I hope you can anchor yourself down for a minute for a transglobal link-up. Great to hear from you. Your new love sounds *good*!!

Well, I'm having a mixed day today. I was out at Poker last night so had a nice lazy morning. It's nice that Art has such a flexible lifestyle so he tends to fit in with me, waiting up for me when I go to Poker then sleeping in together. We had a fantastic weekend. After a late start on Friday and a four-hour drive we hit the trail at about 4.30 p.m. and just made it to the hot springs by nightfall. We managed to feed ourselves before collapsing in the springs; unreal. They are totally undeveloped, a little dammed pool in a stream, and we had them to ourselves. We spent the rest of the time bathing, sleeping, eating and sleeping. Now, that's what I call decadence! On Saturday night I woke a bit cold and was contemplating a bath and trying to rouse Art's enthusiasm to do the same. I got him to agree to join me if there was an aurora! At first I thought it had clouded up 'cause I couldn't see any stars, but I looked again and the sky was just plastered. I was out in the pool in a shot, and Art wasn't long behind me. There we stayed for about two hours, an auroral physicist's dream. To top it off as the main display was moving off to the south a red aurora developed in the north, solid oxygen red, but pretty unimpressive structure-wise.

The referees' reports have finally come through for my two JATP [Journal of Atmospheric and Terrestrial Physics] papers. The radar horizontal winds one is OK, but one of the referees for the vertical winds paper really ripped it to pieces. I don't know quite how to take it because apart from ripping it at the seams he said that it would make an excellent contribution to the field. The editor has basically accepted them along with his own minor suggestions, which leaves me feeling not quite sure how to tackle it. Some of the comments are reasonable; however, with others I got the distinct feeling that the referee must have felt that while he was butchering it he may as well turn it into mincemeat and do a decent job. So work-wise I'm feeling pretty pissed off today so it's nice to have someone to grizzle to.

Well, we're about to have a group meeting at 6 p.m. with Roger supplying the pizza and beer. It seems that with my arrival the group has reached some sort of critical mass so Roger has decided upon group meetings to give us a bit of an identity. There are eight of us, and quite an international bunch too as Roger is English, then we have a visiting scientist from China, Ma. The [post]graduate students comprise a fellow from the Philippines, another from India, then three Americans — Jim, Joe and a girl named Collette.

I enjoy going out to Poker. At the moment there are two rockets on standby so there's been a fair bit of action around the place: all-sky videos in each room, photometers, magnetometers and all the rest running so they can pick up the conditions. You know these papers entitled 'Rocket flown over auroral arc during a break-up event'? Well, I used to think they were lucky but I tell you, it ain't luck. These guys have been on standby since I've been here waiting for all the conditions to be right in order to fire their rocket. When I was out there last Thursday everything was looking pretty good and they got down to 3 minutes on the countdown probably 10 times throughout the night and held it there but never got any further. The atmosphere was so tense my friendly goodbye to them at the end of the night went down like a lead balloon. I think I'd hate to be involved in rocket flights with so much hinging on one event. Give me long-time-scale, ground-based experiments any time.

It's hard to believe the rate of return of the sun. It feels so invigorating. One can almost bounce out of bed and slip on skis compared to dragging yourself out in the dark, which always makes me feel like some sort of martyr.

I'll look forward to hearing from you next week. May your twilights lengthen as your daylight disappears.

Lotsa luv, Gina
(And a g'day from Art. I'll bring him in and put him on one day!)

20 MARCH 1990

Dear Gina,

Hope all is well with you and Art. Not much is happening here. I'm catching up after a couple of days' slushy. Have been doing dawn obs this morning, but we haven't been getting much clear weather. Although as the days are getting shorter, twilights are lengthening. This is good for my sodium observations as twilight data has much better time resolution than daytime data. The sea-ice is starting to form so next time we get a windless day it should be here to stay.

Have you heard that Maria has the BMR [Bureau of Mineral Resources] job so will be coming down again next year? Damian is going to come down in a similar position to mine with the Mawson Institute. It will be good to see them next summer. Looks like I'll be staying to the end of summer too.

Yesterday it was my turn at Sunday cook. I made pumpkin soup for lunch. It was a dismal failure! The curry for tea was a bit better and gulab jamuns for dessert were not my best. Guess I'm a bit out of practice at cooking. As I was cook I didn't manage to go for a dog-run. Have only been once since we got back from Rumdoodle. It's such an effort to run up Gwamm that it's hard to get anyone interested in going. Boy, if you do it two or three times a week it makes you so-oooo fit.

Things are getting better and better with Paul. We are all living up in the red shed but with only 24 people it doesn't feel too crowded. We each have two rooms to use if we want to. We were told that no one was allowed to live in the old dongas. Paul's room is two down the corridor from mine. We have been spending occasional nights in Balleny's though and often have a short siesta there after lunch. [3]

Not much news really, everything's going pretty smoothly work-wise. I've managed to get the data transfer and analysis under control again. So I'd better get back to it.

Peace and happiness, love, Pene.

29 MARCH 1990

G'day Pene,

Great to hear from you. Ain't this system *wonderful!* Did neither Maria nor Damian get the UAP position or did Maria just choose the BMR and Damian the MIAR?

Well, I'm really enjoying work at the moment. I am working on my papers, in fact that's the main thing I'm doing. My time is pretty well up to me and I need those publications. They will help me with the grant applications. I have been given some advice about how to handle the referees' reports, and now I think I may enjoy writing my response to their comments because a couple are fairly unjustified. I'm supposed to be putting in about 20 per cent of my time to the 'Poker upgrade'. I'm learning about IPDs and CCDs and later on doing some testing of these things. [4] However the upgrade money still hasn't been received. It keeps getting put further and further back and now looks like August. The good part is that this leaves me free to basically do my own research, which I now think is great although it felt a bit daunting at first.

I've been going to Poker a bit. I always get a lot out of my trips out there with Roger because we talk all the way there and all the way back. Well, after a fair bit of pushing by me every time we go, we have got the FPS looking at vertical winds. In addition I have just been given a licence to run a meridional-scanning photometer (MSP). It's a nice instrument for giving relative intensities of different auroral emissions from which energy spectra may be determined. It means I have to drive out to Poker each night to run it, but since the night-time observing season finishes in about two weeks, and since Art is away at the moment, it's OK. It is proving a bit tiring if I try to ski to work as well.

Well these things seem to take me a couple of days to write. Home is feeling a bit empty with Art away, and there's another 10 days to go. I'm looking forward to his return. I'm off to hear a woman feminist anarchist called Sonia Johnson speak tonight, with a few other women from home and about town. I'm enjoying having a good supply of really interesting women around, all doing their own thing and a lot like you and me. You know, kinda *tuff*!!!!

Better go. Take care and have fun, *miss ya!*
Love, Gina.

2 APRIL 1990

Hi, Gina,
Was good to get your message last week. I have had a couple of days observing but still no really good block of data. Last week Mal and a few others took the dogs to Fang Peak for three days. The night after they left we had a bit of a blow which dumped some snow so they had a slog on the way home. Yesterday Lloyd took the drill out on to the harbour to measure the ice-thickness, 20 cm. We did some skiing out there in the afternoon. I'm not very good at skiing but should improve with practice. Kista Strait and East Bay have only just refrozen after the

blow last week so it will be at least a few more days before we can venture beyond the harbour. The Friday before last we had a final 'swim' in the harbour for Lloyd's birthday. Eight of us went in. I managed to swim a few strokes before leaping back out. You feel warm when you do get out.

We are having the usual parties on Saturday nights. Last Saturday we had a pizza night. Mine was pretty chilli; well, I did ask for it hot. Had to wash it down with a couple of port-o-gaffs [stout and lemonade] then got into dancing with the lads. Was pretty late when I finally managed to drag Paul away from the bar. Fortunately neither of us had to get up for obs in the morning so we could sleep in for a change. Paul has to do powerhouse obs every few weeks which means getting up by 9 a.m.

Well, I've had a couple of faxes from Brian. His first reply to my long telex was remarkably cool. Now he's trying to hurt me by being angry. That's OK as I've realised I don't have to react to his emotions any more. I told him this and I'm just not going to write again. Paul has been good to talk to about these things, not that we do very much. The present is far more real and enjoyable than raking over the hurt and anger of past relationships. You know it's funny, I had a fax from Dad and Mum. It's nice for them to give me support in my decision. They have been good in treating Brian as a member of the family so ending our relationship means having the family adjust to the change as well.

Paul and I are planning on going to Hendo [Mt Henderson] for the weekend. He has to go on traverse to the PCMs soon. He'll be away four to six weeks. We want to have some time together by ourselves for a couple of days before he goes. Should be good. I'm not looking forward to Paul's absence. It'll be a bit lonely although I guess it will also be a good opportunity to get to know some of the other folk on the base a bit better. Will be good to escape the base again, having been here for a few weeks. We haven't been getting out on too many evening runs. Haven't had the best of weather and still have to face Gwamm to get away. Paul and I will take one team to Hendo when we go.

Lots of love,
Pene.

4 APRIL 1990

Dear Pene,
Good to hear ya again. I just received a real big letter from Tod so I'm feeling a bit rocked at the moment. I guess it'll be a long time before

I'm immune to such feelings. I'm glad you heard from your folks. Do you get the feeling of 'I wish they had told me what they felt before'? I guess people don't like to interfere and it's kinda life that you have to work it out for yourself. You know it's funny but I've been feeling a bit lacking in feedback re Art. Folks never really said anything one way or the other. I'm sort of assuming that if they were worried then maybe they would've let me know. Do you have anything to say on the matter? This may not be a fair question but I think I'd like to hear something from someone.

Art is due back on Saturday, which is good. The first week I really missed him. There seemed to be a big vacuous hole in the home environment which I kept falling into but this week I've been learning to avoid it and I feel a lot better. Still, it will be nice to have him back. Four to six weeks sounds like a long time. I hope you get your weekend away at Hendo and enjoy the luxury of being able to be *nooiissyy* and *caarreeffrreee*. It sounds like you've got a good group if people are into dancing at parties. My lot were pretty inhibited in this regard even with five women!

Anyway, my discovery for the week is Dipper, William's old lead dog, who is now my greatest skijoring mate. She's obedient, loves to run and has me just flying through the bush, lots of thrills and spills. On the first run she lost me at every corner and quite a few places in between as well, but last night I was a lot better and managed to get her to slow down the pace for the sharp ones. It's just such a nice feeling going out with just me and her. William's essentially going to give her to me so I think next winter I'll build her a kennel at work and skijor in because it is a bit far to ski both ways each day.

I had my first night out at Poker alone on Sunday night and I was happy that I got the MSP running (and the FPS, which runs automatically with minimal interference) without any hitches. I stayed the night, sleeping on the couch, then enjoyed the drive back in the morning with great views of Denali [or Mt McKinley, which at 6194 m is the tallest mountain in North America]. I hadn't actually done that drive in the daytime before. Meanwhile I am still working on my papers and Fred continues to fax over comments. For a change *he* is hounding *me* for a response.

Well, you missed a pretty powerful talk on the 'She-volution', as it was titled. This woman used to be a Mormon housewife with four children until she 'saw the light', dropped everything and became a radical feminist overnight. Did you realise that 'radical' means changes 'at the roots'? Anyway, her visions of a woman's world, which didn't leave much room for men at all, captured the audience for two hours.

Although it was hard to go along with everything she was saying, the feelings she was expressing were very real and there was obviously something which was striking many chords in the audience.

Well, Pen, roll on the sea-ice . . . (da, dah; da, da, dah; da, da . . . 4/4 time) . . . and av-a-good-week. By the way, I am rather surprised that you're skiing in the harbour before there's sea-ice in West or East Bays. You just take care now!!!!

So long until next week, lots of love,
Gina.

Coping with the weather in Antarctica becomes a daily routine. It is the climate which makes Antarctica different. The geographic isolation of the southern continent ensures that Mawson does not experience the warmth of summer that Fairbanks receives, thanks to its continental position and warm ocean currents. Temperatures in Fairbanks rise to 90°F (32°C) in summer and fall to −40°F (−40°C) in winter. Occasionally temperatures as low as −60°F (−55°C) are recorded.

The relatively mild temperatures of Mawson are punctuated by blizzards bringing gale-force winds and blowing snow. To qualify as a blizzard, winds greater than 35 knots and visibility less than 100 m are required for at least an hour. Few blizzards occur in summer; however, in winter an average of three days a month experience blizzard conditions. It is the wind at Mawson which gives the cold a knife-edge. Most days, about 26–28 per month, have strong winds and about half the days have gale-force winds. Mean summer maximum temperatures reach about 2°C and mean winter minimum temperatures are −21°C. Mawson's lowest recorded temperature is −36°C (recorded in 1985 when Gina was there.) Mawson's weather is tempered by the ocean, which keeps winter temperatures from becoming particularly unpleasant. Twenty kilometres inland and just behind Mawson up on the plateau near Rumdoodle the temperatures are significantly lower. Winter temperatures of −70°C and lower are felt on the plateau where the ice rises to 4 km in altitude. Vostok, a Soviet base centrally located in eastern Antarctica, has recorded temperatures as low as −89.6°C.

I became accustomed to putting on and removing several

layers of clothing. Such tasks cannot become tedious if you are to survive the Antarctic winter. Buildings have cold porches where outside clothes can be removed and stored. These areas help in the transition from the freezing outside conditions where snow is dry and pleasant to the warm rooms where snow quickly melts and becomes wet. The day's length is the hallmark of winter and routines are determined by what can be done outside in the few hours of twilight. Blizzards are that bit more difficult to cope with in the darkness of winter. Large floodlights bathe the base in a pool of light and act as beacons for people outside. You also become used to recognising regularly travelled routes by the stones, rocks and snowdrifts to be passed over. Blizz-lines, or heavy ropes, are used if necessary to connect buildings.

The world outside Antarctica is remote. Daily news reports on politics and economics seem almost irrelevant. Significance is found in life around you — the people, the dogs, the departure and return of wildlife. Antarctica is about the essences of life, distilled in this small community. They are apparent in lives being pursued and in death that comes so easily. The penguin rookeries have numerous chick carcasses strewn around. The dog-lines regularly see death for those animals unable, or too old, to cope with team life. Three graves on West Arm mark the human lives lost at Mawson. The cold and exposure make the pastels of sunlight on icebergs, the wide vistas of snow and ice seem that much more beautiful.

10 APRIL 1990

HI THERE, GINA!!!
Was that loud enough for you to hear me? Just after I last wrote we had a humungous blizz. The winds were averaging 70 knots and gusting to 96 knots for about 24 hours, and then didn't clear up properly for another 24 hours. So much snow was dropped, those who had been here before said they'd never seen so much snow fall in one blizz. We almost lost three dogs. Paul and I went over to the dog-lines after breakfast. Visibility was 1 to 2 m. We had to set up a blizz-line around the dog-lines as the chains were all buried by this stage. You couldn't see one dog from the next. It took us two hours to check them all. Blackie, Zipper and Morrie were frozen in as the snow had covered the length of their chains (i.e. more than 6 feet in the six hours overnight).

41

We hadn't organised a dog-checking roster as when we'd all gone to bed it wasn't drifting. Anyway, once we'd dug them out and shaken them a bit and they realised they were still alive they took off at 90 miles an hour, disappearing into the drift, and then came back to be tied up at the dog platform. Actually we've almost lost the dog platform, a big drift is about to encompass the entire thing. A windscour has kept the door free of snow so you drop 5 feet down from the lines on to the platform by the door. The cages have been completely covered by snow and you slide about 30 feet down another drift into Market Square.

So Saturday morning was spent with eight of us digging out the dog-chains. We dug with shovels down to the clamps on the poles and then, with the chains unclamped, Paul winched them out with a dozer (well, he calls them 'tractors'). By Saturday afternoon I was feeling really stuffed but we decided to go to Hendo, but just in the Hagglunds. Got there in time for it to blizz again and it blizzed all Sunday. The hut sort of rained inside, we couldn't get the Tilley to go, there weren't any mantles for the gaslight, there were no books in the hut and we'd not taken any with us so there was not much we could do. We both got headaches from a lack of ventilation producing carbon monoxide despite our best efforts to avoid it. (The hut is new and I think it needs another vent in one end.) Not the sort of jolly we'd have planned. If you have to stay in bed all day it's actually a lot more comfortable in the red shed and you can have a shower and meals provided if you want them. (Talk about slack!) So we were a bit dampened in enthusiasm by the time we got back.

The Hagglunds trips are funny. They are such noisy vehicles. We were sitting on either side of the engine and occasionally waved to each other. Those two little blizzes managed to blow all the sea-ice out of the harbour — well, apart from a football-field-sized stretch at one end. You can't get to Entrance Island. What a bummer! Looks like today it may refreeze again. So we may get the dogs out for a run to Gwamm this afternoon if there's any enthusiasm and the wind stays down.

What do I think of Art? Well, I liked him. Although it's hard to know what he'd be like when not surrounded by heaps of strangers and operating in an atmosphere where he's more comfortable. I think his lifestyle, from what I can gather from meeting him and talking to you both, would be very pleasant. He is a quiet person, and I sort of feel that I didn't get to see or understand the strengths in his personality although I am sure they are there. I think if you are looking for someone to spend the rest of your life with then he certainly has qualities that I like, although you will no doubt have conflicts about where to live and Australia–Alaska roots to be resolved. If you both have the same requirements from your relationship then it will probably work. It depends on where you put your priorities. Are you ready to settle down as much as he is, and is he?

Paul has been living in Perth. We've banned any talk of the future for a couple of months although once he gets back from traverse we will probably have to make some decisions about what we're going to do over the summer. Looks like I'll be staying for most of it. Paul may be going on the Lambert traverse (which is almost four months). His enthusiasm is not there though. Says he's burnt out already as he was on the Lambert traverse last summer for three months. Anyway, we'll see what happens.

The days are rapidly getting shorter now. Have to get up when it's dark. We've had eight days of cloudy weather so I haven't done any obs. I did a high-resolution order determination[5] and this morning the measurements for a low-resolution one. Do you know why most of the aurorae at Mawson seem to be green? I have seen very little red–purple yet. Or do you have to be up at the most active time? Also I haven't seen many aurorae which change rapidly, although one last week about 5 in the morning was doing so.

Well, Gina, I'm starting to feel some isolation here, just a bit. People aren't so keen to do things as they were now that I'm not available, as you might say. Paul has had some fairly negative reactions from some, although people wouldn't say anything to me. I guess as a woman down here you're isolated from personal communication with most people and Paul has joined me in my isolation in a sense. We have made an effort to interact with other people but just subtle things.

Perhaps you understand what I mean. We have to be each other's best friend and mate as well. There are others who count as friends, but have to work on it. Will be interesting to see what happens once the traverse leaves. Will sure be looking forward to when it returns. Anyway, kiddo (as Paul would say) take care.

Peace and happiness and hope your cornering in the skijoring improves, love, Pene.

11 APRIL 1990

HIYA, PENE . . . YEP, I COULD HEAR YA!

Oh dear, sounds like you're really lunging into a serious winter all of a sudden, as we have just been bolting into spring. Suddenly I do feel a world apart. Spring and the sun are just so invigorating, my energy level has gone up an order of magnitude. We now have only four hours of darkness each night. It's amazing how quickly the change has occurred and as the snow is rapidly disappearing and turning to sludge (the start of spring is *not* a pretty sight) I am at last seeing Fairbanks, the town. It's amazing what the snow hides; the roads broaden and I noticed we have some neighbours. There are a few extra cars in the carpark which were unrecognisable mounds of snow!

I've been meaning to ask you about the aurorae. On Sunday night I saw the best I've ever seen and boy, it was fantastic. Colours, rapid motions, you must get out and see some! Yes, I'm sure they must be just as good at your end but you really do have to be up around magnetic midnight, 2200 UT (0400 MBT) at Mawson. [6] The last six nights have been clear so I've been going out to Poker Flat just on dark, about 11 p.m., to start up the MSP. This makes for great aurora-observing opportunities both on the drive each way and while out there. I've been taking some photos with 1000 ASA film. When I got here in winter I hardly saw any, 'cause getting out of warm beds in the middle of the night ain't much fun, and consequently I was beginning to think they just weren't that good but the last few nights have changed that. It goes through stages, starting with a quiet homogeneous arc, gradually intensifying until at the substorm onset it bursts forth in full force, erupting across the sky, dancing, cartwheels, rippling from east to west with pink linings below fast-moving borders, then suddenly it is over, or maybe there are drifting patches of glow smeared around the sky. Pulsating shimmering light, sometimes lasting for hours, an orgasm of the skies is the only way to describe it. Anyway, the pink you will only see when they are really dynamic because this emission has a half-life much less than the green, and so it emits ahead of it when the aurora is moving quickly. The red aurorae tend to be on the poleward side and they are not real speccy in their motion, just a great blur of red. Some of the students here are keen aurora photographers and they have some nice photos of long rays, red on the top and green down the bottom.

Art got back on Saturday night and after picking him up I had to drive out to Poker. The error signals on the self-alignment unit had become pretty large and so had to be reset. At Poker resetting the parallelism means getting there and looking at fringes and tweaking some screws with an Allen key. You know, I really haven't done a lot of this, although I remember lying on the roof of Mt Torrens one day spending a number of hours trying to get the low resolution aligned and ending up totally frustrated. Anyway, I had been dreading doing this and so here I was on Saturday night, with my man just returned home and waiting for me trying to tweak these f . . . ing things. It was a real test of endurance I tell you! I was about to walk out a number of times, but somehow I got there in the end. Of course Art was still there when I got back about 4.30 a.m. and we had all Sunday to make up for lost time. It's really nice to have him back and sounds like his courses went well. He was in a small logging camp teaching the young kids, teenagers, and an adult class in the evenings. He gets them making things out of fimo (coloured plastic) as well as metals and he has some great photos of the fashion parade they had on the last day to show off their wares.

Thanks for your opinions re Art. Yes, quiet and caring is how you'd have to describe him but also very much there, even if he is quiet about it. He has a lot of nice friends and he is obviously very sincere and good to people. Sometimes he is a bit serious but he has the greatest laugh when he really gets going. He's also got a fairly quick dry wit. I do like his lifestyle and I feel we complement each other in this regard. Art's not in a hurry to settle down but I guess ready to, which is probably how I'd describe my situation as well. My maternal instincts are a worry — they're getting pretty strong and Art seems to bring them out in me.

Helen Caldicott [peace activist who has campaigned in the US and Australia since the 1970s] was in Fairbanks this week. She is on a US tour raising money. I don't know if you heard but she only narrowly missed out on getting a seat in the House of Representatives [the lower house in the Australian Federal Parliament] in the recent elections. In fact at one stage it looked like she may have held the balance of power but, alas, she lost on preferences. We actually got to have dinner with her and I think she was enjoying having a fellow Aussie to commiserate with after the loss. It's great the way you can get to meet prominent Australians OS [overseas] as you tend to get drawn together when surrounded by a foreign culture. That's what happened in Nicaragua when Tod and I met Jack Mundy.[7]

Well, Art and I are off to Chitina this weekend. I'm taking Friday and Monday off work because we don't get Easter off here. I might try and take Dipper out tonight because it may be my last chance to do some skijoring. We are going to pick up some bikes in Chitina so after this weekend I'll be into the summer mode of transport. Better get this plot done, somehow I got distracted when it wouldn't work and ended up writing to you instead.

Well, big hug, don't let the darkness get you down. I'll send you some sunny thoughts.

Lotsa love, Gina.

Art came to Alaska in 1975 at the age of 30. He drove up with his father and, while camping at Denali National Park, met a girl he was drawn to and promptly decided to stay. His father returned to Texas alone. Art had always dreamed of living in the mountains and a few years later he discovered Chitina, lying at the gateway to the Wrangell and St Elias mountains, and decided he would make it home. Located on the Copper River, Chitina had been a service town to the Kennicott coppermine, 100 km by dirt road to the east, where they had mined the purest copper in the world. The mine closed down when copper prices slumped in the 1950s and the buildings are now a tourist attraction.

As you drive into Chitina the town reveals itself by the service station, store and pub. The road then makes a hard left at the public telephone and winds past the town lake and on through a road cutting, which opens out on to the glacial waters of the junction of the Copper and Chitina Rivers. Art's gallery is just off the main road, in earshot of the public telephone and pub, in sight of the town lake and with views to Spirit Mountain in the Chugatch Range to the south.

Art acquired an old, two-storey metalworkers' shop. It sagged on its foundations, a characteristic of the permafrost below. He worked unremittingly, jacking up the building regularly to re-level the foundations while he proceeded with renovations. He turned the bottom storey into an attractive art gallery, the top into living quarters, and listed Spirit Mountain Artworks on the register of historic buildings.

The gallery stands its ground as the sober part of town and Art plays a responsible and caring role: being active with the volunteer fire service, on call with the emergency medical service, fixing tyres as tourists rattle off the rough road to McCarthy and Kennicott, directing the fishing entourages to the office that issues licences, and patiently answering the standard tourist questions with various permutations of his standard answers. As well as carrying out his own work as a jeweller he provides a sales outlet for other Alaskan artists in his gallery.

Art established himself in Chitina with gusto. He organised summer folk festivals, which brought hundreds to the small town but were finally suspended when a brawl broke out in the crowd and a fatal stabbing resulted. He became Fire Chief and organised the purchase of a modern firetruck from California. Again his father accompanied him as he proudly drove the engine up the Alkan Highway to Chitina. Later, in the hands of a subsequent Fire Chief, the engine was allowed to freeze over winter, causing untold damage.

Art became locked into a continuous cycle of confronting, accepting and losing heart with the permafrost and with the town itself. With its population of 40, isolation over the long winters and invasion by fishermen and tourists in the hectic summers, it has all the ingredients for a real-life soap opera.

The salmon run in bursts so the state of the fishing is a hot topic of conversation around town. Locals living a subsistence lifestyle can obtain licences to run a fish-wheel. Tied precariously to the banks of the powerful Copper River, the flow of the water is harnessed to turn a big paddlewheel fitted with baskets to scoop up the fish swimming upstream. There is a fine art in designing these wheels and many variations on the central theme can be seen on the river. Some, like Art's, ended up being destroyed by the river and the banks bore the scars. Residents of Alaska can apply for a dip-netting licence entitling them to 30 salmon per family. People would flock to Chitina for the dip-netting season, which commences in June. William usually obtained the community's quota so, at Hidden Hill, we enjoyed our share of salmon broiled at outside barbecues in the summer and baked in the winter.

Art maintains his sanity through regular trips all over the state. At Christmas time he takes to the road with all his wares piled in the back of his long-wheelbase orange pick-up, and sets them up in friends' living rooms in Valdez, Wasilla, Anchorage and Fairbanks. Later in the winter he works with the Artists in Schools program and spends a couple of weeks teaching jewellery making in small towns in the south-east of Alaska. Spring is time to set up shop again ready for the summer, when Alaskans and the world flock to Chitina for the salmon and for the wild mountainous regions beyond.

18 APRIL 1990

Hi there, Gina,

Hope all is well and you had an enjoyable weekend at Chitina. Do they
have any public holidays in America? We were, very generously, given
a three-day weekend for Easter by Parker. That meant we could sleep in
and not feel guilty. The atmosphere relaxed somewhat and Scotty prepared a special meal for Sunday lunch. We had sports on Saturday too.
The weekend also saw the first dog-runs on the sea-ice. These runs were
very short as we still don't have sea-ice in Kista Strait, West Bay and the
eastern half of East Bay. But we could run around Hump Island and the
next little island out and visit a cave in the ice-cliffs in East Bay. At least
we were able to give the boys a little run. Albert has been taking Pedro
and Welf skijoring. They are improving and getting used to running
with him skiing.

Well, the only other thing that happened this week is that yesterday
Jake died, from the litter of Jake, Elwood and Fanny. I went over to the
lines yesterday morning because Dave H. had said to me in the afternoon that Otis had got off and had a fight with Jake. Blackie was beaten
by Zipper when Paul took them out for a run. I had been busy doing
observations so hadn't got over to see them the night before. Well, Jake
wouldn't even walk. I ended up carrying him to the mess and, after
looking at him, Lloyd [medical officer] thought he had a bowel obstruc-
tion and was going to operate. Jake picked up a bit inside. He warmed
up and Lloyd put in a drip. He'd obviously vomited a lot out on the
line and when he drank some warm water he vomited most of it up
again. His eyes were really sad. When the anaesthetic reached his heart
it stopped beating and that was that. Poor old chap. He was known as
Gentleman Jake. He was a bit of a wimp but was always so obedient
and was the only chap who'd almost put his harness on for you. He
would sit so quietly and lift up each paw. (He did chew his harness if
you weren't looking, though.) So now we have only 22 dogs, and six
puppies, four of which have taken to running out into East Bay to
harass the seals, so they'll lose their freedom soon although they're not
big enough yet to do any damage.

Haven't got much news. I've just got up after a nightwatch.[8] Was
not too bad weather, very windy, but no drifting snow. We've not got
much daylight left now. The traverse is leaving on Saturday. Once they
go, think I'll organise a doggy trip to the Casey Range, if I can get
enough people to go. Will be the last trip up on to the plateau before
the proper sea-ice trips start. I hope to get a trip to Kloa this year.[9]
Your year had a trip to Kloa by the looks of it; any stories to tell, or
advice?

Well, Paul will be heading off on Saturday. I'll really miss him. We spend all our non-working time together, more or less, and it's so good to have someone you can talk to, someone who empathises with you. It's hard to tell you what Paul's like. I like him more and more and we're very comfortable together. When he goes I'm going to get up very early, if it's clear, to try and see some of those magnetic midnight aurorae.

Love always, Pene.

23 APRIL 1990

Dear Pene,
Thanks for your letter. I hope you haven't been wondering what happened to mine. Art and I didn't go to Chitina until Wednesday.

The weather continued to be perfect so I decided to stay and continue my data-gathering campaign: 10 successive nights of FPI and MSP data. *However* . . . On the first cloudy day Roger and I went out to Poker to change the dichroic filter, [10] which had aged terribly, when Roger wandered up on to the roof to make the terrible discovery that the periscope was pointing south instead of looking in the direction of the zenith-pointing mirror. After a bit of investigation we came to the horrible conclusion that not only has it been looking south for the whole of my so-called 'vertical winds campaign' but it hasn't looked up to the zenith since it was installed last September, so not a zenith measurement has been made since then! [11] Well, what a disaster! After all that effort! I'll probably still look at the data to get the hang of the analysis but, as Roger says, I've probably got the biggest set of the highest resolution FPS southward wind measurements ever made. Humph . . . So what? Roger also reckons that this can be the sort of error that Nobel prizes are won on but in this case I rather doubt it. I was thinking though that if I did find something publishable in them how I would word the paper, as it would look pretty funny as just '10 nights of southerly wind data'. I think we'd probably have to admit the error to justify running such an unusual campaign! Anyway the problem looks like shoddy installation, so that when the software said it was looking in the zenith it just wasn't, even though everything looked OK from the electronics below, but I guess I've learnt that it pays to check everything, and obviously no one had checked this.

With that, Art and I headed off to Chitina. Oh yes, one bit of joy that I got out of my observing campaign was that I picked up this lovely old malamute husky which I found wandering up the highway in the middle of nowhere. She was just great, real big and huggable like the Mawson huskies but a bit past skijoring so I was glad to find the owner a few days later, although she did have a great voice. She'd really talk and sing with her howls and she enjoyed coming out to Poker with me and was great company on the way home when we stopped to enjoy the aurorae together.

Speaking of which I was really sorry to hear about the sad end of Gentleman Jake. I remember him well, in fact I have a picture of coming back from Mt Henderson on a summer evening with Jake sitting on the empty sled in true Gentlemanly style. It had been fast and icy and Jake had got freaked out by the sled so we ended up having to put him on it. Needless to say he took to his new position in the team exceedingly well.

The trip to Chitina was great, a good break. The drive down is stunning: it takes six to seven hours and passes through a spectacular pass in the Alaska range, then heads down along the Wrangell mountains. We saw lots of moose, rabbits, a porcupine and the first swans. The snow is disappearing at an incredible rate; last weekend you couldn't even think about skiing. It's all gone! We were pretty busy at Chitina cleaning out the upstairs so we can get somebody in there for summer. We also pumped out the basement, which had become flooded with spring runoff. Everyone is saying that spring is pretty good this year as all the fine weather is sublimating and evaporating the snow without things going too muddy. We also watched the Copper River, which runs past Chitina, breaking up. As from yesterday the first mosquitoes are out, the Alaskan national bird as they're called — they're *huge!*

We got back on Saturday night in time for Earthday yesterday. Fairbanks is like Tasmania in that you go to an event like this and you can see almost everyone you know. I think we clocked up four dinner invitations in the afternoon with everyone suddenly coming out after the winter and being sociable again. Apart from that there was music, lots of stalls and talks and a contra dance [bush or folk dance], all outside in the sunshine, which I don't like to mention but there is such an abundance of it now it's hard not to have it creep into the conversation.

Oh yeah, we retrieved three bikes from the basement of Art's place so I rode to work this morning. It's a bit crisp so I was well awake by the time I got in. I guess Paul must have left you by now. If you're like us then it's kind of nice to have a chance to miss each other and great to catch up again afterwards. Although it'll feel pretty lonely for a while, it'll give you a chance to get to know others on the base a bit better.

Well, Pene, I really feel for you every time you mention your darkness (well, as much as I can when I'm feeling just the opposite). It definitely does slow you down and tends to make you pull back into your shell a bit, in a way that you only really appreciate when you feel yourself come out again with the sunshine. Not that I've even put in a whole winter here but I can feel it in everybody else. There's just so much excitement and enthusiasm around. The roads are just lined with joggers, walkers and bikes.

Well, lots of love and hugs, Gina.

PS: Yes, we do get public holidays but they're all funny ones: Spring break 16 March; Memorial Day 21 May; Independence Day 4 July; Thanksgiving 21 November; Christmas Day and New Year's Day. We'll probably go back to Chitina for Memorial Day.

25 APRIL 1990

Hi there, Gina,
Well, I'm purposely being antisocial today. There has been organised an Anzac Day celebration in true style like the RSL provide. It is well known by some of those here as we have about half who have had/are in military service. I'm afraid it's just another excuse for a day off and something I just can't participate in. It is a glorification of war. Service people reliving the good times they had with their mates. War is used as a justification for so many things, so people feel a diminished responsibility for their actions: they did what they did because they were told to do so and we were at war. I wish Australia would dismantle its defence forces as such. I think they are a useless waste of money. We do need to protect our coastlines, and perhaps have some sort of peacekeeping force but maintaining the traditional army, navy, and airforce and all their entrenched bureaucratic dogma and ritual is crazy. I would agree with national service in a conservation force, planting trees or physical labouring in erosion areas or things like that for young people to grow up a bit in a different environment, but putting them into military service is a farce. It exposes them to a lot of negative aggressive influences.

So I'm sitting by myself up in aeronomy while they have their dawn service and breakfast–lunch with their six dozen Fosters, spirits in the coffee, and getting ready for two-up, movies and other things in the afternoon. *Lest we forget!*

Lloyd has been quite vocally anti-Anzac in some discussion in the mess and I rang him up yesterday and asked him if he would protest with me but he reckoned it'd be taken in the wrong way and admitted he was hypocritical about it and was going to join in with everyone else. So I'm not going to demonstrate, I'll just catch up with some work and stuff like that and just not join in.

What a bummer about your observing campaign. That's the sort of thing I always worry about. I've got about 10–14 nights of green observations from Mt Torrens in which the emission intensity was very weak and I doubt if anything will ever be done with them. They took a lot of effort and energy to get.

Paul got away last Sunday, he's heading out to the PCMs with five others, none of whom have been on traverse before or ever even wintered before. He says they're like kids off on an adventure. I've had three days by myself now, really miss him but guess I'm making myself do things to fill in the time. Got into the darkroom the other night and developed a couple of rolls of black-and-white film including some good shots of the interferometer and some of the dogs.

The days are getting very short, the sun is not rising until almost 10 a.m. and setting by about 5 p.m. I can imagine what it's like in Alaska. Spring must be fantastic: all that light, and plant and animal life just booming into summer and revelling in being alive. Actually I just finished reading a book by Sheila Burnfield called *One Woman's Arctic*. She spent a couple of summers in Pond, an Eskimo community in the eastern Canadian Arctic.

Well, better get to work. Hope all's well and don't get too depressed by your southerly measurements. I guess with summer advancing you won't be able to get much more data for a while. I can get and send you some green data to analyse if you like, will probably do some night-time measurements in winter.

Peace and happiness, love, Pene.

25 APRIL 1990

Dear Pene,

Great to hear from you again. Good on your little protest! I applaud you because it ain't easy to make such protests in a small community such as Mawson. It is a pity Lloyd wouldn't join you but perhaps it is at least something that someone agrees with your motives. I guess peer pressure is one factor, but then it is always nice to have an excuse to celebrate. I remember Anzac Day our year. I know what you mean about the ritual, but I like dawn services because it's such a nice time of day and I have good memories of going to services with Dad as a kid and combining it with watching and listening to the birds. However it's also a good time to think about what the women went through too, left to just wait and take charge of the home front. On top of that I bet some of them hardly knew the men who came back to them because I'm sure army and war would've changed them, and probably not for the better either.

I'm reading a book called *Between the Lines* about the Petrov affair and the effects of McCarthyism in Australia after the Second World War. It's good. I bought a bunch of Australian books by female authors before I came over. In fact I am having quite a craze on women authors except I guess Art and I are currently reading aloud Richard Feynman's book *Surely You're Joking, Mr Feynman: Adventures of a Curious Character*. He's about as male chauvinistic as they come. That aside, he does tell a good story and he often has us in stitches. It's also quite a different insight into what it was like working on the Bomb. I don't think I had appreciated that they were still using very basic mechanical computers which were always breaking down. Sometimes they'd use a human computer with a bunch of women (of course) in a room each doing one operation and sitting in 'do loops' passing bits of paper around. [A 'do loop' is used to repeat a given operation or set of operations many times.] Also interesting to see how a mixture of military dictating to science works. Basically the scientists found it easiest not to tell them anything but then there were military outposts where people were handling the radioactive isotopes completely oblivious to the dangers! They were storing it in near-critical quantities because they knew no better!

Yes, there was a trip to Kloa my year. There were so many interested people that they had one team run the dogs out there, then another team drove the Hagglunds out and brought the dogs back. Of course the doggie folk didn't like the idea of this at all to start off with but when all was said and done I think eight people all had a tremendous trip which none of them would have wanted to miss out on. Peta Kelsey was on the outward-bound trip and they had it tough. Heaps of drifted snow, lots of real big sastrugi and they were forced to camp on sea-ice in Edward VIII Gulf. A big *no-no* but one of the dogs had frostbitten feet and ended up dying. Grant Morrison, who was on the return trip, reckoned that Peta and company were just pretty out of it through exhaustion by the time they got to them, he reckons they were beyond making sensible decisions. There was a bit of friction between the two groups even though they were good friends. Peta reckoned it was a pretty damn hard trip. She was really fit, fitter than any of the others. She is quite small so I guess she probably was a bit behind the others in sheer strength. There was some bad feeling because the others did not want to run with her for this reason and basically just because she was a woman. They ended up coping OK but I think you at least want to start out with better morale amongst your team. However, the return team then had a dream trip home, with a few weeks making the world of difference to the conditions. They also cut down on what they were carrying to the extent of depoting any unwanted toothpaste out of the tube. Team 2 had criticised Team 1 for carrying far too much gear, but then Team 1 criticised Team 2 for carrying dangerously little and so the bantering went on.

I was actually given the opportunity to go on the return trip, which I would have loved but the main thing that stopped me was work. I had only just got the FPS going and it was my last chance to get some data. In fact I was thinking the other day how that decision probably got me my PhD, so perhaps it wasn't such a bad one. I think it would be just wonderful and I guess being dogwoman you've got a fair bit of say in what will happen, so I reckon you should go for it. I'll be envious and will miss your mail messages, but don't let that hold you back.

Much love and thoughts (and don't let the Anzacs get you down!), Gina.

30 APRIL 1990

Hi there, Gina,

If this seems a bit disjointed it's because I'm writing it in between changing profiles every five minutes through dawn. Weeeelllll, things have started collapsing now that Paul's left. It's not that bad I guess, but . . . The FPS has had some problems; it's working at the moment but the periscope azimuth drive isn't working properly. The etalon plates started turbo-scanning [12] after a power failure last week (got that fixed). The 3FP computer had disk-drive problems and yesterday I hung the Kingston VAX connection so couldn't do any computing. And I've managed to get a fairly persistent urinary tract infection. (Honeymooners' disease, as Lloyd said, often contracted when you've been having more than normal sex.) It's been hanging around for about a week or so and managed to survive a mega-dose of penicillin so now am trying some other drugs. I guess it has made me feel a bit low with my body working at, say, 80 per cent normal. Hopefully it's under control now and I should be back to normal by the time Paul gets back for another honeymoon. I really miss the bugger.

We have lost most of the sea-ice again! Actually we have had some most unusual weather. Last week two weather records were broken, a record maximum temperature for April (+0.8°C), and an all-time record pressure. The maximum ever recorded pressure for Mawson was 1028 hPa, and on Saturday we got to 1032 hPa. (The pressure usually varies between 960 and 980 hPa.) It's actually been pretty good 'cause now we've had two days of very summery weather but I just hope it doesn't plummet back down to normal values. On Friday and Saturday we had a bit of snow so there'd be enough lying around on the plateau for a real nasty blizz; perhaps we'll break the maximum wind gust this year too as we hurtle down through 50 hPa.

On Sunday, with good weather and since the FPS wasn't working, I went for a short dog-run out around West Bay. We still have ice in West Bay and East Bay as far as the Jocelyn Islands but you can't get to Welch Island, and Kista Strait is open water. Actually you can only just get into West Bay through the harbour. There's a path about 10 m wide hanging on desperately to the end of West Arm then the black splashy stuff looks a bit ominous for sledging. Can you believe it? It's May and we still haven't got sea-ice.

Well, the FPS limped through the day yesterday — will try and have a look at this azimuth drive today. As the sky is lightening you can see there's quite a bit of cirrus around, not very good for daytime obs. The azimuth drive works as normal going forwards; going backwards it doesn't position itself correctly, so providing you check it and go in the forwards direction (i.e. NESW) and make sure it clears home each time, it is OK. So I suspect a little mechanical problem somewhere.

My yoga has been somewhat lacking. I'm trying to get back into it while Paul is away by bringing my mat up here to aeronomy so I can do postures between profiles. Also I am going to have some group sessions, which started last week, but they will depend a bit on the weather.

The traverse to the PCMs at this time of year is purely a support traverse. They're taking out fuel for the 1990–91 summer field operations (helicopters chew up a lot of fuel, five sleds of double layers of 44-gallon drums or, as Paul calls them, barrels; that's about 200 barrels all together). Also they're taking some food for the summer and the chippie has a lot of work to do on the huts out there. They all need roof hatches and he has made a little building for the met. blokes to do their balloon tracking in. Paul should actually get to Dovers in the next day or so and then they'll be able to see how long it will take them to do their jobs there. Of course I'm hoping they'll be back in four weeks, not six, but we'll see. I'm not feeling too bad; you know how it is when you're cruising along just below optimum and if things start to go wrong . . . but I am starting to fix them so should be apples.

With books, I do know what you mean about women authors. I find reading books by men — well, contemporary novels anyway — isn't quite satisfactory. I read *Oscar and Lucinda* by Peter Carey on the way down and it was good but I kept thinking, this is obviously a man's book. His whole style, the way he sees things and expresses them is masculine. I do much prefer women's books. I brought a few down with me and have finished two since Paul left. We do read a bit together in bed at night but not for very long.

Well, that's all for now, love, Pene.

PS: Just remembered I forgot to tell you we have a comms [communications] strike. At the moment they're just not sending any official comms. That will mean the radio techs won't get data to track the satellite in the next couple of days so we may lose the satellite for a bit. I extremely doubt that will happen but if you don't hear from me it's probably why. The comms union had an agreement with the division two years ago and they haven't come to the party, so . . .

Take care.

PART THREE

FLYING GRAVY BOATS
AND ROCKETS

*f*airbanks lies in central Alaska, 550 km north of Anchorage, Alaska's largest city, and 200 km south of the Arctic Circle. Fairbanks is a city of 60 000 people, most of whom are employed in military establishments, the public service (including the Bureau of Land Management which manages the region's recreation areas), the University of Alaska, diminishing gold-mining operations, and the service industries required for a city of this size. Shopping centres are spread around the area. The university is on one side of the town and houses, most on several acres of land, cluster around suburban and village centres through the surrounding valleys and ridges.

The Hidden Hill property was donated to the Religious Society of Friends, or Quakers, by the Hidden family in 1980. The community was intended as an extension of the Chena Ridge Friends meeting. The original cabin, now the main or common cabin, and some other cabins had been built by Nancy Hidden and Peter Hill. The mailboxes at the top of the drive were labelled with their two surnames, and so the place came to be called Hidden Hill. The community now comprises four residential cabins, the main cabin and the meeting house. The Sunday Quaker meeting is held in the bottom storey of the meeting house and above it is a fifth residential cabin.

Hidden Hill functions like the Danish concept of a co-house:

both individual and community needs are considered. The community activities usually take place in the main cabin, so our cabins were very much expressions of ourselves. Kim was immersed in an artistic chaos, surrounding herself with books, writings, poetry and a sprawl of clothes. William's cabin was highly ordered and spotless. My cabin never matched the extremes of these two but oscillated at an entropy level comfortably between them. The main cabin was maintained at a functional level. A cleaning roster ensured that it was given a good scrub once a week ready for the onslaught that occurred after meetings on Sundays, when most people would wander over for a cup of tea afterwards. Here there was an outpouring of thoughts and chatter that had been repressed in the silence of the meeting.

Quakers avoid placing expectations on people, respecting the right of individuals to discern for themselves an appropriate level of involvement. Not all the members of the community were regular attenders and many of us were uncomfortable with talk of God or Christ; not unusual among Quakers. The main visible difference to other group-living situations was that we held hands for a minute's silence before we ate. I came to appreciate this tradition; a time to savour the people gathered around the table, along with the food and the day. We'd often invite friends along on our night to cook and mealtimes were a cheerful and sometimes boisterous affair. We ate together five nights a week and one person would take responsibility for the meal: buying the food, cooking, and washing up afterwards. William usually cooked either moose he'd taken in the fall or salmon from Chitina. The rest of us chose vegetarian options.

The cabins are rented out, so the turnover of tenants is somewhat greater than in the case of a co-house, where the dwellings are often owner-built. William was the longest standing resident and he was an exception in that he had built and owned his cabin at the end of the ridge. His previous cabin had burnt down; a leak in the propane stove. It was a traumatic time for the members of the meeting, who had gathered at the site fearing that William was inside as both his dog-team and car were there. William finally returned to the sad scene and his grieving friends, having been at the movies. William never liked to post-pone a job that needed to be done and he succeeded in building a new cabin in his spare time over the following summer.

Running water is considered a luxury in Alaska, particularly on the outskirts of town. Pipes must be heated to avoid freezing in winter, and a failure in the heating system quickly results in burst waterpipes, which are very expensive to repair. At Hidden Hill only the main cabin had the luxury of running water and this housed a washing machine and shower. There was no septic system, just timber huts surrounding a hole in the ground, and a rough timber seat with the all-important polystyrene foam insulation on which you could sit comfortably at 40° below. Water evaporated up from the contents of the holes and deli-cate, flowery crystals grew down in threads from the outhouse roof. Discussion of the evolving frozen artform lightened up mealtime conversations. Water for the main cabin was pumped from a tank just outside, which was filled fortnightly by spring water brought in from out of town by the water wagon.

The water wagon also offered a snowploughing service. The driveway at Hidden Hill was about 200 metres long on an uphill gradient. After a foot of snow the four-wheel drives may make it out, but for a two-wheel-drive pick-up it was gravel bags for weight, and chains. After a more severe storm we could all be left waiting for the snowplough, although usually with a group effort cars could be extracted. Sometimes it felt as though a day's work was done in just getting there.

The cabins had double-ply walls with at least a 15 cm gap and plenty of insulation. They were cosy, kept warm by small oil-heaters that were controlled by a thermostat. Heating can be made very efficient with good insulation, to the extent that a small and well-built cabin can be kept from freezing by the waste heat produced by running the fridge. Everyday living conditions are thus very comfortable, the biggest bane of life in the Arctic being maintaining a car through winter.

All cars are fitted with engine heaters and plugged into power outlets, which line carparks at work locations and homes. Like horses tied to a hitching rail, cars are left plugged in all day while the power is cycled on a set schedule. While some cars can be started at −20°, most require at least half an hour's heating, and the time increases as temperatures get lower. In this land of cheap fuel many people have two sets of car keys, so they can leave the car locked and running to stay warm. While this is necessary for short stops it is wasteful and polluting for longer visits, like going to the movies. The more conservatively minded would run the car for a few minutes every hour or so if they were unable to plug in at 30° below. Those living in the bush without power would resort to gas-fired torches or hot coals to heat the engine from below, with a sleeping-bag placed over the bonnet for insulation. These methods require care and patience or the car can end up in flames. Once started there are additional problems in cold weather: frozen gearboxes, handbrakes and accelerator cables, and also square tyres, which make for a rough ride until they warm up.

My preferred modes of transport were bike, skis and dogs. After a heavy snowfall, bike or skis were good options. There was some danger cycling even when well lit and highly visible. The roads narrowed through winter as the snowbanks lining them swelled with each pass of the snowplough. Cars skidding out of control on icy patches were a daily sight; cyclists are exposed and vulnerable. I could keep my road bike upright in the heaviest snow conditions and was glad that the road to work was fairly quiet. Skiing conditions varied dramatically: after a warm and heavy snowfall the going could be very slow and laborious; while at 30° below there was little glide and skiing was a drudgery. No matter what the conditions, spending time outside in winter was for me necessary and invigorating.

Around Hidden Hill there was an extensive set of trails following the railway line, powerlines, survey lines and broken-out mushing trails. The area was overlooked by the Geophysical Institute up on West Ridge to the east and Ester Dome to the west. In the valley surrounding Hidden Hill there were a few small lakes, the largest of which was Ace Lake. I regularly visited this embodiment of the seasons; skiing on its buried surface in winter and swimming with the birds and beavers in summer. Like other low-lying areas in Alaska it was most accessible when frozen. In the summer sun the trails reverted to peat bogs; watercourses, lakes and rivers became barriers.

Good trails have hard-packed snow surfaces. After a heavy snowfall trails must be 'broken out' again, the soft new snow being compacted by the first person to travel over it. The trail becomes increasingly easier to use as more people travel on it. William ran his dog-team every other night in winter and spring, keeping packed many of the trails in the vicinity. There were other dog-teams along Goldhill Road, including some of the dogs removed from New Zealand's Scott Base in Antarctica. It was unusual to meet other mushers or skiers on the trial, but all contributed to trail maintenance. The valley was our backyard which could be traversed in 5–15 km loops. Crossing a railway-line and road to the north took you out to Goldstream Valley, where there were extensive trails and a considerable mushing community. Out here the O'Connor Creek Trail took you north over into the Chatanika Valley and on to either the Minto Flats or up into the White Mountains. The wilds of Alaska were accessible from my back door.

4 MAY 1990

Dear Pene,

Well, at last it's Friday and I feel justified in writing. I've been working hard to finish off those damn papers, I'm feeling so desperate to get them behind me. It's been far too long. I showed one of them to a senior colleague here. He thought I had terribly oversimplified the interpretation and that there was no physics in what I had done. His final comment was that he thought I should retitle the paper 'Why we cannot make observations using the green emission' when my whole paper is an interpretation of observations of the green line. I feel like I've been given such a hard time by these vertical winds. Starting with people totally disbelieving them to now wanting a watertight explanation. Anyway, I went home and burst into tears, and I'm still feeling pretty sensitive about it. I guess part of the reason is that in all my work I have tended to avoid qualitative descriptions involving mathematical derivations of atmospheric processes mainly because large vertical winds aren't easy to explain and they don't conform to current models.

So, Pene, they're my gripes for the week, although another is that I'm in for an Art-less weekend. He's gone down to Chitina with two prospective managers for a few days to get the shop ready. It will probably open around Memorial Day weekend, about 26 May. It's going to be hard for Art to make much money out of it this year with the costs of hiring somebody, even if it is on commission, as he needs to take out workers compensation and pay social security to the government. Art lives a pretty hand-to-mouth existence as far as finances go. It doesn't bother me really, although I find myself feeling like it's up to me to be the financially responsible one. This is different to things with Tod where we always maintained financial independence, except for one co-owned tent.

I was really sorry to hear about your UTI [urinary tract infection] because I went through all of that when Art and I first got together, and then again when he arrived in Australia. It really runs you down if it hangs on and I dare say you won't be getting much sympathy from your fellow expeditioners!!

Due to a certain happening this week when good old Dipper came on heat we are expecting a litter at Hidden Hill at the end of June. I'm really excited about this as I dare say I'll end up picking one out for myself.

Last weekend we had the quarterly meeting of the Alaska Quakers Group at Hidden Hill and a few folks came up from Anchorage. The theme of the meeting was a 'sense of place'. We had what they call 'worship sharing', with a set of writings being the focus of the workshop. We all read and thought on the topic in silence then spoke out of the silence things which came to mind. I found it pretty powerful, being one who has moved around a lot and felt different levels of affinity for many different places, along with thinking of my roots in Perth, and our old family home in the light of losing that. After feeling at a bit of a loss to be able to work out just where was sacred to me I ended up talking about growing up down the Swan River in Freshwater Bay. I'm really enjoying what the Friends offer and they're a nice bunch of I guess mainly middle-class, professional, questioning, people but of a variety of ages.

Well, I'd better go, it's now well past 6 p.m. and I have a policy of not being at work after hours.

Think healthy!
Love, Gina.

9 MAY 1990

Hi, Gina,
Another lovely, clear, sunny day at Mawson. We've continued to have good weather, i.e. not much wind and lots of sunshine, but a few cloudy days now and then, for the past week or so. With obs and trying to fit in dog-runs am starting to feel like I need a few days off. Wish I could

drive a Hagglunds out to the PCMs although they've been getting some shitty weather out there.

Paul and I have been 'talking' on the Sitor every two or three days. It's a field telex communications system. At least it means that others can't simply eavesdrop on your conversation as happens with HF voice communications down here. It is a fairly slow means of communication but it's nice to know that Paul's sitting at the keyboard somewhere out there and can respond to things I say. He's been talking about pulling out of the summer Lambert traverse. I don't think it's entirely my fault but I'd hate him to do something like that and later regret it. He was on traverse out from Casey in 1987 as well and has hundreds of days up on traverse. He's spent more hours in his tractor than he has with me so I guess there's not much novelty left in it any more. He is the only one who can make the decision but I worry a little bit. It would be great if he could pull out but still stay at Mawson until I leave too and then we could have the trip home together.

Have just had an argument with the 'dogman's offsider'. He's the sort of person I wouldn't spend any time with if I had the choice and basically that's the problem. In the normal run of things we don't talk to each other. He spends all his time up in the club drinking and smoking and then says there should be more communication. I spend the time after my meals drinking tea in the mess. Anyway Shane took a team out for a run this morning and didn't tell me. And then he says he did it just to provoke me! With great communication like that I wonder if we have any hope of organising a long dog-trip at all.

Well, not much else has happened this week. Have had a few days data gathering. Got the dayglow analysis going again so now have a few months' data to grind through. Also have managed to get out on a few dog-runs for a couple of hours around West Bay. The good weather has continued, although temperatures have dropped again. I got a bit of frostnip on my nose last night. Giggles saw it and I put my balaclava (the one you gave me last summer) up over my nose and it had unfrozen by the time we got back. It wasn't too bad. We had gone for a bit of a run down past Peak Jones Rock and I guess three-quarters of the way to Ring Rocks. Had sat on the sledge most of the way back. Wasn't much wind but it was −20°C, and I should have been running to keep warm. Looks like I've got enough people together for a run to Macey next week. Hopefully there'll be sea-ice all the way. Think I'm getting a bit run-down with all the work and lack of Paul. He at least makes me knock off as soon as I can, instead of staying up in aeronomy to get a few more things done.

Since I'm bitching about people might as well have my say about the

UAP engineer as well. If it's blizzing at all he doesn't bother coming up. He is actually quite a nice person and well liked around the base, will be in whatever he can so long as it's not work. He's probably the biggest drinker on the base, organises cocktail nights, is one of the brewers and a bit of a 'lad'. People must wonder what kept both an engineer and a physicist busy last year. I hope nothing major goes wrong with the interferometer. He has fixed a couple of things for me but I wonder if he'd be able to persevere long enough to get the interferometer going again. His lack of interest in his work really doesn't bother me except it does make it a bit more difficult to find my own motivation.

Well, Gina, I'd better stop this bitching. Sorry, probably PMT. Hope you don't mind listening to such shit. It does good to get it out of your system, though.

Cheers, Pene.

PS: Perhaps you should just ignore your colleague's comments about your paper. When I'm feeling more positive I think, 'Oh well, it's best to publish good things rather than grind out heaps of pulp' and 'I'm as good as any of the others out there who are only human' as well. And those who publish heaps and heaps are usually doing it on the backs of their postgraduate students. You can't please everyone, you know. Cold comfort perhaps . . .

9 MAY 1990

Dear Pene,

Your mail message today, though full of bitching, was very colourful bitching and seemed appropriate to my mood anyway. I've been feeling totally unenthused about work. I'm in the sort of mood where if it wasn't for riding a bike to work and getting your letters I'd feel I was totally wasting my time. Art's presence adds a refreshing sweetness when I go home but the next day and back to work always comes too quickly. I've been getting terrible urges to just drop out of the scientific scramble for firstly one-upmanship, and secondly knowledge, and go and pursue my maternal instincts instead. Oh yes, and there's also a two-week rafting trip I'd like to do as well. Oh, I wish I could find the right balance, because I know I need a certain amount of stimulation, which working occasionally provides, and I was enjoying it for quite a while there, but this last week's been such a drag. I've also been toying with the idea of doing some teaching, even though it really scares me.

The system here is so focused on a good performance in course work, and they do so many courses that it makes me feel pretty inadequate to teach one, having not taken an exam for about seven years, and never having been an A-class student.

A woman who works in glaciology just came and sat next to me on the terminals. We had a nice long rave about women in science. I've been hoping to get the chance to talk to her for a while. It just keeps confirming in my mind how it is continually women who seem to have things like work in perspective. If only we held more of the positions of influence around the place there'd be no way that people would be working themselves to the bone to achieve — what? What is all this achievement about? You work so hard to make the grade, get a PhD and then you think, what does it mean? Sometimes I worry or feel guilty that I didn't really deserve it because I don't feel any smarter, and it didn't give me any sudden or distinguishing air of confidence like sometimes one is led to believe that it should do.

This woman has been up here for eight years, and she reckons that the first four or five winters were great, but they just seem to have become too long, too dark and too cold in the last couple of years. I can understand that, and I think a lot of people start feeling that way after a while. Fairbanks has a fairly transient population, people stay for a while but then move on.

I really like the women I've met. They're just my sort and they do all sorts of good things like run dogs, build their own cabins (made easier by the fact that there are virtually no building regulations), write books, make jewellery and generally do their own thing. We had a surprise bridal shower for Anne from the community who is getting married in June. We held it at Cathy's cabin, just down the road and in walking distance of Hidden Hill. It is a typical cabin, made of logs, quaint and just oozing with character, no running water and nestled nicely into the woods (conifers). The other women were mainly from the meeting, with ages ranging from 20 to 50+. It put a good perspective on life seeing the older married ones, with and without kids, laughing along with the younger ones engrossed in heartaches and pains. All these women share some sort of affinity with Alaska because nobody lives here if it doesn't do something for them, unless they're military people posted here. I like the way, when I say what I'm doing, everyone says 'Hey, that's neat!' and they want to know all about it. In Australia more often I'm met with 'ohh . . . I never could do physics at school' or something similar, which usually ends up putting a lot of distance between us. Alaska on the other hand is very much a land of individuals whereas I think individualism is somewhat squashed in the land of the great Aussie knockers, where people take the shit out of anyone who tends to be the slightest bit different.

Your gossip brings back a lot of memories. It's funny how much people and work become such a focus and talking–bitching point in the group. I remember feeling pretty sensitive about it.

Art has returned from Chitina since I started this letter and has settled on a young art student, Larse, to run the shop this summer. Art will make regular trips down mainly to do work on the building. I will be going down with Art for a long weekend on May 28th.

Spring is just amazing. There are all sorts of interesting cranes and birds coming around. At Hidden Hill we are surrounded by a great variety of birds. Seedlings in the greenhouse are racing along, then yesterday leaves on the trees came out. I noticed them riding home, suddenly there was this green haze which hadn't been there in the morning, and today it's so much stronger. Meanwhile the semester has finished with a graduation ceremony on the last weekend. Seems so much more in the mood of things than waiting six months later for your ceremony, as happens in Australia.

Summer at Hidden Hill is a lot less ordered than winter, with lots of comings and goings. Suddenly I wish I was in a field which had summer field work like some of the other folks here. I'm feeling convinced that community living is the only way to go. We have little conflicts but I notice that when this happens Art and I go home and have a little grumble about everyone else, whereas if it was just us I'm sure we'd do our grumbling at each other. The result is that it keeps the couples or individual elements more united, with the community as a whole being the pressure valve. The other nice thing is feeling part of something bigger, the whole Quaker community, which unites the Hidden Hill residents' community within a larger group. Art and I go to meetings each Sunday, if we're in town. Meetings are a one-hour group medita-tion. I sometimes find it difficult to last the distance and usually find it difficult to focus on anything of a real 'spiritual' nature. I like the Quakers' style, they tend to be nice, strong, patient people who thrive on silence. The classic Quaker motto is 'In case of emergency . . . be quiet'. Once a month there's a business meeting after the regular meet-ing and this too starts and ends with a period of silence. I thought it was quite funny the first time I went to one. I was a bit late and I looked in to see a group of people sitting around saying nothing. I thought, how do they conduct their matters of business in silence?

I'm enjoying riding to work. I'm down to a T-shirt and vest now when only a week ago it was jacket and gloves and I was considering investing in a windproof.

Your dog-trips sound great. There's definitely a part of me which is looking forward to next winter to get out again. Hope you get your trip to Macey, don't work too hard, and feel free to bitch any time. Keep well.

With love from Gina.

In the sense that we believe in equal opportunity and treatment for women, Gina and I would call ourselves feminists. Working in a male-dominated field has kindled our awareness of women's issues. There are very few female physicists in Australia and even fewer in permanent academic appointments. There are a number of female physicists in our own generation and we have tried to keep in contact with these women. Female students tend to congregate under particular supervisors. Few women will choose to work with men who treat them differently to their male counterparts or with men who respond sexually, however subtly that may be.

A career in physics can be difficult to combine with raising a family. To obtain a permanent appointment at least one post-doctoral fellowship is required. Most physics PhDs take at least four years and a postdoctoral position, two years. Postdoctoral appointments usually involve a shift in location so physicists are usually at least 30 before they can hope to obtain stability in their lives. Only the brightest will get a permanent appointment after one fellowship and sometimes up to 10 or more years can be spent on fellowships or contract appointments. Jobs can be easily obtained if you are prepared to travel but if you decide to live in a particular place then you have to be very lucky to obtain the job you would like. Since women traditionally follow their spouses it takes a committed woman to pursue a career in physics. Time out to start a family can make re-entry into the workforce difficult. It can also exclude you from the mainstream academic career structure which is extremely competitive. Publications and presentation of conference papers are necessary to obtain the grants required for research projects. Raising a family is not an academic achievement and will not enhance your academic standing.

Internationally there are a number of well-known female

scientists in atmospheric physics. The number of women is still sufficiently small that Gina and I were always interested to hear of or meet established female atmospheric physicists. These meetings were sometimes disappointing. When the first such woman came to Adelaide to an international conference we were bitterly disappointed when she did not think two (at the time) postgraduate students worth talking to. In a sense this is discrimination on our part, expecting a successful woman to be interested in you simply because you are also female. Just because a woman works in your area doesn't necessarily imply that you'll get along well or have similar interests.

While I expected to encounter some discrimination as a woman working in Antarctica, I did not set out to change my fellow expeditioners' attitudes through argument. The large majority of expeditioners are tradespeople: carpenters, plumbers, mechanics, electricians. Such trades are one of the last male preserves in western society, although this is also slowly changing. As most expeditioners are not young, expecting non-chauvinist treatment is naive. I often tried to avoid being drawn into discussion on gender issues as I knew it would lead to conflict. At times, though, I did not succeed and we had some lively debates. I do not mind an occasional sexist remark from someone who I know respects me but I do object to constant and unending banter and innuendo. You will be guaranteed that someone will comment, 'Oh it's good to see a woman behind the sink' when you are on slushy. You just have to expect it.

What I did miss was the company of women. Men structure conversations differently to women and base their friendships on different criteria. Social interaction tends to establish and confirm the group hierarchy whereas women's conversation tends to be more supportive. Working with men we have developed the skills to deal with these differences but I tend to find conversations with men a challenge rather than something I engage in for pleasure. Not many men are aware of these differences. However, Paul provided me with easy conversation. Paul was different in that he could acknowledge the differences between men and women and could understand my perspective even if he did not always agree with it.

Gina's experiences in Antarctica were somewhat different

to my own. Each wintering group is different and this leads to very different experiences for the women involved. Gina's experiences in Fairbanks were also totally different to mine in Antarctica. She could compare her Alaskan experiences with her time in Antarctica:

Unlike Pene, I enjoyed the benefits of female company during my time in Antarctica. There was a strong level of mutual support between the five women at Mawson in 1985, which was a great comfort. Socially and professionally we were well dispersed among the men, causing a healthy female influence to pervade. Despite this we showed no open camaraderie and never found ourselves together as a group. Three of the five women had previously wintered on the sub-Antarctic Macquarie Island, but for Robyn Downey and me it was our first trip. Since Macquarie had year-round shipping access it was considered a 'soft' option at which to start the first women expeditioners before sending them to overwinter on the Antarctic continent. Enid Borschmann wintered at Macquarie in 1979, where by all accounts she got on handsomely as the only woman on base. Peta Kelsey and Judy Turner wintered there in 1983 as part of a group comprising five women, the first wintering party to include more than two women.

When Pene was forced to return from Mawson in 1983 after having an affair on her way down, the five women at Macquarie went on best behaviour, frightened that forming relationships might curtail their stay. Two years later, this air of paranoia had disappeared at Mawson and Peta and Judy enjoyed a certain new-found freedom. Peta formed a strong and open bond with 'the Bear' and they cohabited in one of the old dongas. Judy also formed a strong but less overt relationship with 'Danzo' and they were married on their return to Australia.

Although the female support was in place from the start, it wasn't until the end of the year that I attained a similar level of trust with the men. My acceptance by them was aided by the fact that I did not get involved in a serious relationship. I remained determined to return to Tod at the end of the year; as well I realised how isolating being in a relationship was when nearly everyone around you was denied such intimacy. A turning point occurred some time after midwinter when some of the men were complaining that women had it made as half of the men on base would be available to any one of them if they so chose. I reacted strongly, describing how difficult it was to be in the position of having to constantly resist open doors. Robyn and I joked that we should be locked in a pen like the bitches during our most vulnerable time of the month. The men did not realise the value of the additional physical contact they gave each other, like the friendly shake-up often given to someone looking doleful. My complaint was soon remedied as I was wrestled and jostled from then on. At last I felt I was being treated with some understanding and not as though I was on a pedestal. It was a great relief and everyone was better off.

It took some effort to become accepted in Antarctica, but this was not the case in Alaska. Arriving as a postdoctoral fellow I found I was immediately treated with a certain amount of respect by the graduate students, who were mostly male. This respect was a welcome change. In Antarctica I had virtually run the lab on my own whereas at the Geophysical Institute (GI) I was surrounded by 100 scientists working in areas from vulcanology and glaciology to space physics, with the atmospheric physics group located somewhere in the middle. Carrying out field work at the rocket range I was also surrounded by a healthy number of fellow scientists and support staff.

In Alaska I also found a strong comradeship amongst the women. I had often been envious of the apparent strength of male friendships, which were enhanced when they undertook physical challenges together. Although I had experienced such bonding in mixed groups during trips in Antarctica and Tasmania, I had never accepted these challenges without men. I was in for a feast in Alaska as most of the trips I embarked upon were with one or two other women. Here I would find a strength in my female friendships which previously I had only been exposed to in the company of men.

15 MAY 1990

Dear Gina,
Paul is having a miserable time out in the PCMs. We send telexes every

day and occasionally 'talk' on the teletypes. They have had winds, not less than 30 knots, drift, and about −30°C ever since they got there. So he's not been very happy. There are six on the traverse including the Major, which isn't helping Paul's spirits. Even talking to the PI [plant inspector] who's also 2IC, and who I get along well with, he is not very impressed with the Major's way of handling things. Paul shouldn't have gone on this traverse. He's just back from three months on the Lambert traverse and should have been given a decent break if they wanted him to go again next summer. Others were keen to go, but the Major wanted Paul to go, probably because he was the only one here with any traverse experience. He then relied entirely on Paul to organise things.

Today has been quite windy, 30–50 knots all day, and the bar is falling and temperature rising. Hopefully 24 hours will see some improvement. Has been a pretty boring week. Started really missing having some friends around. Guess Albert is probably my next-closest friend. Most of the others I get along with well enough. I don't feel as though they give me any emotional support and hence it's vice versa as well. Typical male attitude to life. Paul is not like that, and neither is Albert. I think I can trust him, he knows the Antarctic well as he's been down a couple of times. He's Paul's boss and they get along well together. Paul's pretty special and treats me so well, quite different to how any other man has made me feel.

The only story to tell was from Saturday night. We pushed all the tables together and had everyone sitting around, like a big family table, only 17 of us with one bloke over in radio. After tea Lloyd started making some sexist comments and basically just baiting me. I knew and he knew he was baiting me. He does it in a fairly gentle manner but stirs all the time. Anyway I picked up a gravy boat, full of pepper gravy, and he just kept on going, seeing how far he could push me. I don't know if people thought I wouldn't throw it but anyway eventually I did and it hit something and sprayed gravy all over one end of the mess — on the roof, whiteboard, chairs. I couldn't have done it so well if I'd tried. Everyone laughed and laughed.

It's sometimes hard to tell with Lloyd. He puts on these fronts and plays the group all the time. Good to have someone like that. If everyone was like me it would be a pretty serious, staid old world.

Otherwise have had five days of observations. Sunday it was clear but blowing 40 knots so didn't do any obs. I was going to observe today and drive the low-resolution etalon out for night-time obs tonight but it was blowing too hard this morning to do any observations, still is, but is also 8/8 cloud now as well so will give it a miss. Will enjoy my nightwatch, if it doesn't degenerate completely into a blizz; maybe watch a movie since aurora won't be visible either.

Had our monthly medical examination yesterday. I am much the same as I always was, 56.5 kg and no fat. There's one bloke down here who is more than twice my weight. Needless to say most are slowly or not so slowly increasing in weight. My Paul is a bit overweight but not too bad. Looks like my UTI has cleared up for the time being. Hope it doesn't start again when I restart my overindulgences in a week or so's time.

I know what you mean about actually having a PhD not making any difference to how you feel, and still often feeling really dumb and inadequate.

Well, just remembered I put my washing in this morning and have forgotten to hang it out in the drying room. Better do it before tea before I forget again.

Love, Pene.

15 MAY 1990

Hey, great shot, Pene!

Would have loved to see that gravy boat being hurled across the room. I'm surprised it didn't start a full-on food fight. I'm also a bit surprised about Lloyd — I thought he'd be a bit above sexist remarks. He does it a bit as an intellectual exercise. I always find that hard to respond to. I think the gravy boat was an excellent way to handle it.

On Saturday we went canoeing on a river called the Clearwater about a two-hour drive south of here. Unlike many of the glacier-fed rivers around, it has the most crystal-clear water as it is spring-fed. We could watch grayling trout swimming around underneath, and saw lots of birds: teals, sandpipers, mallard ducks, Canada geese. (Yes, I had my newly acquired bird book with us.) Best of all we climbed a small hillock and saw a bald eagle's nest with both eagles there. Also the leaves came out last week, and honestly Pene, I've not seen anything like it, the whole landscape was completely transformed within three days. They are just so green and fresh that they make you feel green. You know, we do miss out on seasons in Australia. I can't imagine what fall's going to be like.

There's a lot of people around getting allergic reactions to the birch trees. William is the worst. At this time of year he has to go on to shots of cortisone otherwise his eyes run and feel like they have glass in them.

Fortunately, for once, I'm not one of those affected. Although apparently people with allergies say they become worse the longer you live here and take a couple of years to start.

Canoeing was incredibly pleasant, we took three canoes which belong to Hidden Hill, and found enough people to fill them. Art loved it too, it was just his style. You know he's not really done a lot of outdoor things up here and usually runs his shop over summer, so it's good to do things with him. A Dutch girl who has just moved to Alaska came with us. She's living out of town working a team of dogs, so it was good to talk with her. William and I are getting pretty excited about the idea of having some pups around the place. So I hope Dipper *is* pregnant.

Driving down was a good chance for a big chat about the meaning of life. I'm starting to get a few things going at work and I'm worried about getting run-down, or swallowed up by it. I don't want this and I think after this Alaska stint I'll definitely be taking some time out. It feels good to be able to talk about kids and stuff in the light of our long-term plans, as it was almost a prohibited subject with Tod and I could feel him seize up at the mention of it. Some days I feel I'm for ever putting off the more important things in life for my career, but then I've usually been glad in the long run when I have completed things.

Sunday was a homely day around Hidden Hill, which was pleasant. Meeting in the morning followed by everyone staying for a potluck lunch, then the afternoon digesting and taking a nap, then in the evening we have sacred harp singing. We have been going along to this just because it's there. It's four-part singing without accompaniment, so is good voice and ear training. I've always wanted to be able to sing and I suddenly find myself getting a bit better at it. The words are all death, fire and brimstone, which no one pays much attention to except for a good laugh, but the harmonies are wonderful and it sounds great even though each part is fairly simple.

Today I've been looking into buying an oxygen-green lamp either from the upgrade money or a grant proposal to do some work in Greenland. They are commercially available, costing \$12 990![1] I could cut down my salary in the grant proposal to two months' worth and add on a lamp, because I think it's extremely worthwhile. Had a chat to Roger last night about winter plans, and he asked if I'd like to think about going to Svalbard, a group of islands north of Norway, in December, when he and David Rees are going to be looking at flux transfer events and movements of ions up the field lines.[2] (I'm going to have to do some reading on this stuff.) Sounds like a great place with just a Norwegian and two Soviet coal mining towns there. They can see daytime aurorae there and lots of soft polar-cap precipitation.[3] So winter may be pretty busy if I go there and also to Greenland. Roger was talking about sending me to New Zealand in November and the South Pole probably isn't impossible either. I'm not sure if he's throwing me bait to see what I bite at or if he just has more ideas than he has time to carry them out. In the meantime I feel myself positively shy away from too much responsibility. I like to feel I've got room to get out whenever I want. Unlike most people who feel insecure without some sort of permanence, I feel the opposite.

Well it's back to the grindstone, more next time. I guess you heard that Fred Bond died.[4] Lots of people I meet up here ask me about him. I think he had a pretty good reputation as a character, as much as a good physicist.

Keep happy, and keep those lads under control (you can throw 'em a gravy pot from me too if it happens again).

Lots of love, Gina.

19 MAY 1990

Hi, Gina,

To the problems of direction in life there are no real answers. Weather remains shitty, basically too windy. It has been warm though, staying around −4°C for about four days but wind has kept up a steady 50 knots for the past week.

It's really hard to know how to organise things. It's difficult to work in science and feel satisfied with what you're achieving if you don't continue to get involved with bigger and better things all the time. And if you do get involved in bigger and better things then it sucks up all your time and you've got nothing left for anyone or anything else. I don't know how to manage it. What I've done is escape back to Mawson because here so many things are looked after for you, including food, shopping, transport and socialising. So there's not much left you have to organise for yourself except your own work and jollies. But that will only last for another few months. Then I'll have to think about what I'll be doing next. I have thought of the possibility of teaching at a uni or CAE or something like that. Then I could get some more of the results I've collected written up and also it would be good to make me go back over all that basic physics I've completely forgotten. That would be good for a year or two and then start something else. I guess it depends on what happens with the other people in my life. That would fit in well with living in Perth or Townsville or Christchurch or somewhere like that. If I were completely by myself then I guess I would throw myself into work and go off somewhere like Alaska or Boulder for a couple of years. Don't know if I've got the guts to completely desert atmospheric physics at the moment — it's the only thing I know anything about. I'd have to be a dishwasher or something like that if I did.

Paul says we should go goat farming in New Zealand. That has its attractions — Paul, to start with. He does not want to have kids — looks like I always choose that sort of person. Reckons he'd be too old if he had kids now. Who wants a 20 year-old to worry about when they're 60? At the moment I have no desire to have kids but I wonder if I weren't tied up with my work if I'd be able to say that so easily. I guess there are always other things that you can do and if you have things you're trying to achieve, then not having children has its advantages. You have more energy to put into whatever else you're doing.

One thing I would like to do one day is write some books. I can feel that day is getting closer and I can well imagine doing that instead of having children. Paul doesn't seize up when we talk about it. I guess it is a pretty closed subject — he's just really laid-back, it's something he's thought about and made his mind up about. He does acknowledge that my feelings may change. We've banned conversations about the future. It's so difficult because we both realise the environment down here is so different to back home and wonder if we will get on so well in Aus, or if there is any future for us? I think both of us secretly hope there is but there's always this sort of doubt and uncertainty. Actually I think someone like Paul would be good for me if I did continue with my work because he is an outdoors-type person and he would certainly organise me to get out a lot into the bush. Would help me balance my life better.

Paul left the PCMs on Friday so should be home within the week. Boy, will that be a good thing. No doubt I will hear about all the details of the trauma of being on traverse to the PCMs in autumn. From what I've heard so far, sounds a bit torrid.

23 MAY

Well, just had three days' slushy in the kitchen. I find it pretty wearing. The cook kept me busy the last two days. Actually I find the constant company and interaction with people quite tiresome and feel like I need a couple of days by myself now. Well, Mal is slushy for three days so at least I have aeronomy more or less to myself. Bad news is that yesterday the traverse slotted a D7 and a D5 they were bringing back for maintenance! The D7 fell in sideways and will take some getting out. The cab has been smashed up but apart from some slight head injury, Patrick, the driver, is OK. Will be a cold drive back to Mawson with a busted cab. They are about 50 km south of Hendo. That route was reopened in the '89 summer and every traverse that's gone that way since has slotted a tractor. Well this time they've really damaged a vehicle and sounds like they were lucky it didn't get totally swallowed up, driver and all. The Antarctic Division may start to question whether it is worth the extra day or so they are supposed to save going that way rather than going out past Twin Tops. You know, ANARE really does have amateurish attitudes to things. There is a hangover of the feeling of Antarctica all being an adventure. It is not quite so much the bastion of the last male frontier as it was. Traverse is still, though.

This afternoon I'm developing prints for the midwinter menu. I had a nice photo of the dog-line, but the 'photographer' didn't like it because it wasn't the classic full-face husky or dog-team in front of an ice-cliff so we're using all his photos. Oh well, I can't help it if people have suburban tastes. Think I need a good kick in the pants.

We did have a good run to Ring Rocks on Sunday with Albert and Graham. Was good to get out after more than a week being cooped up inside.

Well, Gina, it's always good to hear from you. Keep the letters rolling in.

Love always, Pene.

23 MAY 1990

Dear Pene,
What a longy! Thanks. There has been a bunch of army guys around planning a huge rocket campaign to take place next winter, called Spirit II. It's a direct SDI [Strategic Defense Initiative] project and they want to make measurements of a huge auroral substorm with lots of joule heating to test out IR detectors[5], basically so they don't mistake an aurora for a nuclear attack. (Good idea, boys!!!!!) They will have a rocket window of six months, i.e. be on standby for the right event for that long. They will be doing real-time modelling of the current systems from data from five manned and more unmanned stations across Alaska and Canada. It will be the biggest campaign to have been run out of Poker and hence the excitement. Everybody wants to be in on it now because SDI spells big bucks. Roger has been selling them FPSs to give zenith winds to indicate upwelling and suddenly upwelling is all the rage, so Miss Upwelling-Price and her little projects have become quite popular. Roger now is even more sorry I didn't get any data from my vertical winds campaign. I'm feeling myself being included in on things a bit more, not that I really want to get involved in this Spirit thing.

I'm having a bit of a doubting week regarding Art. He is in Chitina this week so I guess that's got something to do with it. I'm just coming to the realisation that Art's life is fine for him but that he'd probably never be able to support anyone else on it. That leaves me as the main breadwinner, which is OK just now but suddenly doesn't feel so secure if you put kids on the scene, and what would happen if I stopped working? I remember in Perth Dad asking very early on whether Art would be able to support me and a possible family and I sort of shrugged off the question. You know, every now and again I miss Tod too. I guess I'm just coming down to earth a bit after being on quite an emotional high for nigh on nine months now!

Whenever Art goes away I get into a good book — it's nice compensation. The current one is about a woman in the 1930s who got stranded on an island in south-east Alaska for a winter, pregnant, injured and having just lost her husband. She wrote to keep her sanity and she writes with great strength yet at the same time she's not complaining of her situation or making herself a heroine, but manages to enjoy her environment despite her circumstances.

Last weekend I went cycling and hiking in Denali Park with a friend from the meeting — Cathy. The first night Art and Larse were with us and we stayed in another friend's cabin who lives at the edge of the park. Her name is also Kathy and she lives there alone with a team of dogs and is writing a book. She finds that just doing the daily chores, carting water, chopping wood, feeding and running dogs, doesn't leave her much time to write in winter. What a life, though! There's a lot of women up here like her and I have met more writers here than anywhere else. There are also writing and poetry workshops held here in summer. It's definitely a land of inspiration.

On Saturday morning Art and Larse headed off to Anchorage then Chitina, and Cathy and I drove up into the park as far as cars are allowed, then rode mountain bikes. The park is actually looking pretty barren, unlike Fairbanks which has turned completely green. In fact driving up in altitude you could see the plants regressing until just buds were showing at the park. There is still snow around and on the highest peaks it will stay there over summer. We got a number of glimpses of Denali itself, just stunning, and we got to see some grizzlies. A mother and two cubs were lounging in the sun by the river. We watched for quite a while from a safe distance.

We had forgotten the tent and I foolishly had only a summer sleeping-bag, so we ended up sleeping in one of the bear caches, which is like a sea-container used for storing food where bears can't get it. Cathy organises herself to do lots of trips, including some skiing/mountaineering in winter. Hearing about them was whetting my appetite except that I know Art isn't up to those types of trips. This thinking has added to my doubting week.

Well, better go. We're calibrating some IPDs [imaging photon detectors] this afternoon, having spent the morning chasing all the stray photons out of the room. I'm sorry I can't e-mail you a frequency-stabilised laser, there's one at Poker I'm sure no one would miss for a few weeks. As far as the land of great resources goes, yes, there are big bucks around but there's no such thing as petty cash, and every photocopy you make or pen you buy must be charged to one grant or another. It's a real pain and so it certainly doesn't feel like money is free and easy, in fact it feels like every little thing counts (especially Vax time which Roger reckons can often get up to half someone's salary!). [6]

Lots of love and Happy Paul's Return, Gina.

The Poker Flat rocket range was established by the University of Alaska in 1969 and is unique in its location under the auroral oval. It is a self-supporting institution funded by its paying customers, which include the National Aeronautics and Space Administration (NASA), the US Air Force and the National Science Foundation (NSF). Poker Flat is about 50 km to the north of Fairbanks on the Steese Highway. The Steese scales Cleary Summit, a modest ski-slope patronised by locals in the relative warmth of spring. Old gold-tailing dams line the valleys. A sense of history is preserved in the old buildings of the FE Gold Company and Chatanika Lodge.

The entrance to the range lies a convenient distance beyond the Chatanika Lodge. Regardless of the hour, the lodge opens its doors to accommodate celebrations following a long-awaited launch. The gate to the range is fitted with a security video, microphone, and large 'Danger' and 'Restricted area' signs. An old Nike-Tomahawk rocket bears over the gate in an impressive manner. The stateliness, however, stops here as old wooden buildings emerge, showing a closer resemblance to the gold camp down the road than to Cape Canaveral. The first buildings are the payload assembly building, the old accommodation quarters and the main office, where personnel and visitors must sign in on arrival. Various workshops and machinery lie scattered along the dirt roads which service the lower range. A large wind-weighting tower marks the clearing surrounding the five launchpads. The only buildings in the launch arena are low-lying cement blockhouses which provide the required shelter for lower-range personnel during the countdown. In the past, faults have caused rockets to blow up on the pad and in one instance a rocket, launched close to the vertical, landed back down on the range.

A hill overlooks the lower range. Negotiating the steep road up the hill can be a challenge in icy conditions and remaining in control during the descent even more so. A distinct white sphere near the top houses telemetry equipment. Here all-important data is received once the flight is in progress. On the side of the hill stands the optics building, which houses the science support instrumentation. Darkness surrounds this centre of activity and headlights must be turned off on approach in order to protect sensitive optical equipment. Another dilapidated structure, the optics building, leaks in the rain and was granted a reprieve after being condemned by the fire inspector. Plans are underway for a new building but the promised funding has met with inevitable delays.

In the optics building data on auroral and geomagnetic activity is made available to the principal investigator (PI) who is responsible for the final launch decision. Optical equipment designed and built by the staff of the Geophysical Institute is used to conduct ongoing research and to complement the rocket program. The sky is studied with low-light-level television cameras and photometers, and usually through a viewing dome.

The rocket scientist gets one attempt. Equipment failure or poor performance may result in a lack of publishable results and thus jeopardise further funding. During the launch window the rocket is positioned on the pad ready for flight and a full crew held on standby awaiting favourable conditions. It is an anxious and often slow period. The countdown is usually held at 10 minutes when clear skies persist and is taken down to five or three minutes if auroral conditions look promising. The aurora can change on a time-scale of minutes and in unpredictable ways. Often conditions do not develop as anticipated and the count is taken back again. It can be difficult for the PI to maintain the required air of calmness and control. Rocket scientists need experience, sound judgment and an element of good luck to accomplish a successful launch. (There also seem to be certain physical requirements for rocket scientists, given that most of them are at least 6 feet tall! A matter of perspective, perhaps?)

The US Air Force Spirit II program was aimed at determining the infra-red emissions produced during an auroral disturbance: the reason was to deduce the feasibility of using infra-red detection in identifying spaceborne threats to the nation. The state of Alaska was keen to upgrade the range to make it a viable competitor in putting commercial payloads into polar orbits. The Spirit II rocket required upgrades to the range as it was to be the largest and first steerable rocket launched from Poker Flat. Healthy funding from federal purses accompanied the campaign, which was part of the Strategic Defence Initiative (SDI, popularly known as 'Star Wars'), a relic of the Reagan era.

The initial launch window for Spirit II was an unheard-of six months, although this was later reduced to three months after delays in completion. The window was concentrated around 'moon-down' periods and many launch criteria were set. Radar surveillance was required to ensure that the area was clear of aircraft. Roadblocks would prevent traffic coming within a few kilometres of the launchpad once the count was down to 10 minutes. The launch crew would ensure that all equipment was functioning and that those instruments which required cooling, to reduce electronic noise, were at a sufficiently low temperature. Since the Spirit II rocket was self-steering it also had the potential to land on Fairbanks if things went drastically wrong. To cover this possibility a self-destruct mechanism and visible confirmation of the rocket's initial trajectory were required. It seemed ironic that the first steerable rocket appeared to be treated with more precaution than unsteerable versions.

The scientific goals of the mission were to impose the most rigorous criteria on the launch. The rocket had to fly over an intense auroral arc in an atmosphere which had received at least two hours of prior heating as a result of auroral activity. The focus of interest lay in the upwelling that such heating would produce: the greater the upwelling, the more heavy molecules would be pumped into the upper atmosphere and act as a blanket in the infra-red. Three Fabry-Perot spectrometers were incorporated into the campaign since they could measure the vertical motions directly.

Auroral activity tends to maximise in the midnight and post-midnight hours and thus follow the sun from east to west (in magnetic coordinates). A chain of magnetometers positioned across Canada to the east would therefore give prior warning of large magnetic perturbations associated with auroral substorms. These data were to be fed into a computer at Poker Flat and complex calculations carried out to estimate the amount and location of auroral heating accompanying the visible aurora.

Payload instruments were designed to look horizontally through the thickest cross-section of atmosphere. Thus although the rocket trajectory was over the sparsely populated area to the north of Poker Flat, the instruments would look south-westward to a point over Watson Lake in Canada. An array of ground-based instruments were to be installed in the vicinity of Watson Lake: all-sky cameras, photometers and two Fabry-Perot spectrometers. Auroral conditions over a large area could thus be monitored by combining this data with that from Poker Flat and the Canadian magnetometers. Computer-generated maps of Canada and Alaska would highlight regions of active heating and visible aurora. The Air Force PI would be faced with a barrage of data contained in a wall of computer screens and regularly updated. It was no surprise to find a Fussball pinball machine appear in the optics building at his request; it would be useful for alerting tired minds and maintaining a spirit of healthy competitiveness to counteract the frustrations of the launch.

The Spirit II program offered me many opportunities. Previously I had only been involved with ground-based instruments. Such instruments have the advantage of providing a large database while being limited in the information they can gather. In the case of the Fabry-Perot spectrometer, winds and temperatures can be measured with good accuracy but it is not possible to determine the height of the observed region. Rockets, on the other hand, obtain a height profile of atmospheric parameters. The disadvantage of rockets is that the data set is limited to two instantaneous samples; on the way up and on the way down.

They are also expensive and many years may be spent building and testing the instrumentation. Combining the data from different techniques provides the most unambiguous picture.

The Spirit II mission also offered me some personal challenges. I had several major concerns. The first involved the results from the model calculations of auroral heating, which would be of primary consideration in the launch decision. The model made some gross assumptions. I considered that in view of the generous funding made available to upgrade equipment, little was directed towards investigating the validity of these assumptions. A second concern involved my contribution to the program through the measurement of vertical winds. This was my major research area and experience had proved that it was difficult to make sense of the large and sporadic variations usually measured. It was unlikely that such data would be useful as a launch criterion. Finally, I was ideologically opposed to the SDI and to participation in defence research in general. In the US a surprising range of scientific research is carried out through defence funding, making it more justifiable.

Ultimately my reservations were overshadowed as the scientist in me became intrigued and involved.

29 MAY 1990

Hi, Gina,

How's it going? I had a mail message from Don last week. Sounds like they want Damian to stay for next winter but that they haven't got enough money to do it. With Dr Jacka retiring at the end of the year no one's got much faith left in the institute any more. Who blames them when the University of Adelaide doesn't seem to be interested in maintaining the Mawson Institute or replacing Dr Jacka when he retires?

Felt a bit bad about Paul's return from traverse. Dave Shaw and I went out to the big berg with the dogs in the afternoon and Lloyd was the only person who went up to meet them. I really wanted to meet Paul but no one wanted to welcome the Major back. I knew Paul would understand me getting out with the boys since we've had so much bad weather and hadn't been out all week. He pulled up to park his tractor just as we pulled up the ramp from the harbour so he helped us get the harnesses off. Wow, it was *great* to get a hug — in public on the doglines too! Although 22 dogs and Dave Shaw are not much of an audience.

Paul is definitely not going on the Lambert traverse. He's pretty depressed about the whole PCMs trip. They got the dozer out of the slot in a day and arrived here late Thursday. Paul developed some black-and-white photos of the trip last weekend. Boy, you know the D7 nearly disappeared into the crack — was only hanging on by the top of the hydraulic ram on one side and the edge of a track on the other. They had to climb all over it to attach ropes and stuff to get it out and eventually actually get into it again to drive it out when they'd pushed the crevasse in enough. Paul said it was the worst he'd seen a dozer slotted, and he's seen a few in his time on traverse. He's spent over a year on traverse now. He did quite a few at Casey in 1987. Anyway, hopefully he'll recover his spirits soon.

All the blokes from out there are really scathing about the Major. I feel sorry for him, he is not my sort of person and I think he's approached the whole OIC [officer in charge] position in the wrong way, trying to lead from in front in true military style which is totally out of place down here, where most people are happy to organise themselves into things and more than capable of doing so. I think the station leader's job should only be a part-time position and the station leader should have another job to do, e.g. a scientist with a smaller program, or the met. OIC or PI or something like that, or an electrician or plumber. Everyone's saying they need more than one plumber and electrician down here but there's not enough work for two.

Paul and I with Giggles and Dave are going on a dog-run to Macey on Thursday. If the weather is too windy to take the dogs we're going to go in the Hagglunds. I am really looking forward to getting away from the base. And I have to confess a little bit of me hopes that we go by Hagglunds because it's pretty bloody cold out there with the dogs. Well, it's not actually that it's cold with the dogs, you can always get off and run but when you get wherever you're going it's getting the dogs off the trace, setting up the night-trace and making sure that it's secure that you get cold. The last two dog-runs, while getting the dogs back on to the dog-line my hands have gone cold on me. It's pretty painful as they warm up. Have had two runs out to the big iceberg out behind Béchervaise Island. It only takes about three hours there and back and is about a 30 km return trip. On Sunday there was some sun shining on the mountains on the plateau and it was beautiful.

Have not had any weather for observations. Has been over two weeks now since I've done any. I'm starting to wonder why I'm down here because it's much easier to do computing in Australia. You don't have to fart around for hours trying to get printouts of programs.

Got a fax from Brian this morning — I should say, *another* fax from

Brian. Carol has asked him if she can move in. I guess he's written to tell me that and the whole letter he goes on about how he hopes we can get back together again and how he feels as though his life is in a vacuum now and then he says he thinks he will see how it is with Carol. I just don't know what to say! He wrote me a fax a week or so ago saying he wanted us to be back together again etc. etc. I don't want to be back with him, so I don't want to encourage him and I don't want to be negative, which would be very easy, so I just didn't reply.

Things with Paul are going well. The summer now is a bit uncertain as he doesn't know what he'll be doing. He'd like to stay here but they may send him out on changeover (which is in early December this year) if he's not going on the Lambert traverse.

I can understand your doubts about Art. You know I've always admired the way you are always self-sufficient and have had jobs all the time and supported yourself well. You have a house and all sorts of things and here am I bumbling along. This is the first job I've ever had, I've got no money and no assets and won't be that much better off when I get back from here. I've managed to only just support myself by the skin of my teeth and certainly have nothing put away for any future or old age, no house and not enough stability to even think about buying a house, let alone being able to afford to do so. I suppose if I got a contract for three or four years somewhere I'd buy a house or something.

Would you have two bods crash out on the lounge-room floor for a couple of weeks about this time next year? Paul's never been to Alaska and has promised to show me San Francisco, which he says is the most interesting city in the world. (I said I didn't like cities, and he doesn't either but he says it has so much character.) With a trip like that and buying a bomb car and paying rent, I guess my money from this year will disappear down the tube. Paul wants me to get a job so that I can support him and he will work to buy airline tickets so we can go wherever we want to go.

Anyway, better get some work done this morning. It's blowing about 50 knots, −22°C so is −65°C when you count the wind chill. Tough, eh?? Will be glad to retire to warmer climes. Hope we get some more pleasant weather soon.

Love, Pene.

4 JUNE 1990

Dear Pene,
Sorry I've got behind in the weeklies. Got busy last week and was putting off writing, then was sick on Friday so you missed out. We've

had these summer students start work and I'm supposed to be in charge of a few so that hit me with a rude shock.

The long weekend at Chitina was nice. The shop is all up and running and looks great, and Larse seems to be enjoying running it. We also took a trip down to Valdez. What a spectacular drive! We bought some watercolour paintings for the shop. This was on the Sunday night and on Monday morning we sold two of them while we were unpacking them. We also bought one ourselves as it is of Art's shop and we are going to have cards made from it to sell.

This last weekend we had a weekend at home planting the garden. It's been positively hot and the sun has become quite unrelenting. We've also been having some nice thunderstorms, which leave the air smelling so sweet. The ground cover is growing at a phenomenal rate and suddenly covering with a green carpet all the mess outside which was previously covered by the snow. On Saturday night there was an Aussie do as the Little River Band was in town, and in fact they came along to the do too. For the first time since being here I had a hangover on Sunday morning! Bloody Aussies, why do they do it to themselves? And I'd been so much enjoying the lack of alcohol in my life up here.

I find listening to the TV and radio over here unrelaxing. That American hype — I immediately associate news spoken with an American accent as propaganda. They do have some good programs but I long for the soothing voices of the ABC or BBC. Art accuses me of being 'a slave to my prejudices' — and he's right. But when you've been brought up hearing only presidential speeches and bad American comedy it's hard to undo overnight. Mind you, my previous bias against America was one of the reasons I initially wanted to come here. Figured there must be some good behind the poor image we were seeing — and there definitely is!

Of course you and Paul are welcome to stay with us any time. In fact there is a nice visitor's loft in the main cabin, or a spare room in ours, or possibly in the summer a spare cabin. So you could take your pick. I got quite excited at your mention of it.

Work-wise I'm feeling a bit up in the air and unfocused at the moment. I've been put in charge of getting the optics lab calibration facilities up to scratch so that everybody doesn't get embarrassed and shy away when visitors want to come up and use our gear. I'm having a bit of trouble getting started with that but I've also decided to try and do an absolute-wavelength calibration of the Poker FPS and resurrect my honours project. I've got two students helping me with this and I hope it will work out. Apart from that I'm having trouble finding a project I can really get my teeth into. Roger offers different enticements all the time but there is usually no follow-through. Everybody I know outside work is planning trips here, there and everywhere and some have four-day working weeks. I get very jealous, but then looking at it from the other side it would be difficult to get into things and get anything out of work. I'm having enough trouble getting anything out of my five-day, 9 to 5 weeks.

Well I'm off to CEDAR in Boulder on Sunday, back the following Sunday, so you won't hear from me next week. [7] It's time to ride home in the rain.

Lots of love, Gina.

6 JUNE 1990

Hi, Gina,

Was good to hear from you, if a bit late. Just popping down to Boulder for CEDAR, eh? Boy, you'll get to meet even more of the UAP heavies. Well, I just went out for a quickie with the dogs at lunchtime. Warmed up to −16°C today so we got two seven-dog teams out for a run. Need to get three small teams out for them all to get a run. Was great! We went to Macey on Sunday but the morning we left it was −24°C and the wind was picking up to 15–20 knots so we all eventually wimped out and took a Hagglunds. We ended up getting good weather, three days' mostly sunshine. The last morning at Macey we reckon it was about −30°C, although it wasn't that cold at Mawson. Paul reckons that was what it was because of how reluctant the Hagglunds was to start. I'll take a thermometer with me next time. All I know was, it was bloody cold. I got my nose nipped, again, while taking photos at the penguin rookery. Actually we didn't find the rookery the first day because there was a lot of rafted ice to the south and east of it and we eventually walked in and then found a route we could drive in through the icebergs. We wanted to drive in as Graham Robertson asked us to pick up a few penguin carcasses for him. A few females die each year during egg laying. We picked up six, only noticed one other. For a rookery of about 12 000 pairs that's not too high a mortality rate. The icebergs down there are just fantastic. I guess I don't really need to tell you. No chicks yet, though.

I had a run-in with the Major last night. When he got back from traverse he told me to go ahead with organising the Taylor trip for the midwinter census. Then he wanted the names as soon as possible so

Authors Gina Price and Pene Greet take a break from their studies at the Mawson Institute for Antarctic Research, University of Adelaide, in 1988. Their work at the Institute enabled them to explore one of the world's last great wildernesses, Antarctica, with Australian National Antarctic Research Expeditions (ANARE).

PHOTO: RICHARD G. FERGUSON

Mawson Base, Antarctica, viewed from the end of West Arm. Pene Greet was the only female expeditioner wintering at the base in 1990. As well as her role as the Mawson Institute's upper atmospheric physicist, she took on the job of dog handler.

PHOTO: PENE GREET

Wedell seal with twin pups at Auster, Antarctica, November 1990.

PHOTO: PENE GREET

Paul Myers and Oscar Husky take a break at Moonie Island during an expedition from Mawson Base to Kloa Point, about 300 kilometres.

PHOTO: PENE GREET

The Kloa dog runners fall in line at Ledingham's Depot, October 1990. Left to right: Albert Bruehwiler, Pene Greet, Malcolm Campbell, Paul Gigg, Scot Nichols, Craig Hunter, Paul Myers and Dave Shaw.

The Geophysical Institute, University of Alaska, Fairbanks. Gina worked for the institute as a post-doctoral research fellow from 1990 to 1992.

Repairing a sledge at Moonie Island, Antarctica, during an expedition. Due to the extent of the damage from travelling over rafted sea-ice, the sledge required almost complete relashing.

PHOTO: PENE GREET

Pausing on the trail in the Stanton group of islands during the August run to Colbeck. This was the only photo taken on this trip because it was too cold, with temperatures around -30C, for cameras to work.

PHOTO: PAUL MYERS

A lone Adelie penguin basks in the summer sunlight.

PHOTO: PAUL MYERS

The *Polar Queen* leaves Mawson Harbour on a still and sunny summer day.

PHOTO: PENE GREET

Male emporer penguins incubating eggs at Antarctica's Taylor Glacier rookery during the mid-winter census. While males incubate the eggs, females feed out at sea so each bird at the rookery is one of a pair. A permit is required to visit this specially protected area, the only known land-based emperor penguin rookery.

Jake hitches a sled ride home with Gina while on a training run during her stint in Antarctica as an upper atmospheric physicist in 1985. 'Gentleman Jake' was still in action when Pene took charge of the dog teams in 1990.

Pene and Gina are reunited at Circle Central, Alaska, October 1991.

PHOTO: CATHY WALLING

Dogs in their boxes on the back of Sue Steinacher's truck, Fairbanks, Alaska.

PHOTO: GINA PRICE

Art outside his gallery in Chitina, Alaska.

Goohaw, always the playful pup, finds a new toy.

that Tom could organise the permits required as the rookery is an SPA [Specially Protected Area] and entry without a permit, even for scientific purposes, is forbidden. Anyway, I called a gathering last night to get things organised and the Major just turned up and said he'd added his name to the list. I was really flabbergasted but didn't say anything at the time. But both Paul and Craig, the RTO [radio technical officer] on traverse, had told me they wouldn't go if Bob was going. I wouldn't choose to go out with him on a field trip either because I just don't feel particularly comfortable in his company and don't seek it out. After the meeting he went to organise something with Dave F. in the OICery [OIC's office] so I went up and rang him up and said straight out that he'd put me in a very awkward situation by doing what he had. I went down and had a little discussion with him and told him that I thought what he'd done was very presumptuous and no one else on the base would dare to do such a thing. I was particularly put out by his not saying anything to me beforehand. I said I didn't want him to go, and Paul and Craig didn't, and explained to him that I wasn't comfortable going out on a long field trip with him. If it was a matter of us being able to go or not then it might be different but there are plenty of people keen to go.

The whole thing with the Major has become quite uncomfortable. A lot of people are openly antagonistic towards him. Today he left with a group going to Macey. No one was in VLV [the radio office] so the cook answered his departing radio call in the mess. He said loudly, with the transmitter on, 'Three cheers for the OIC leaving station', and the rousing cheers from the mess were obviously plainly heard judging by the reply they got.

Saturday night was quite bizarre. Of all people, Lloyd has decided to give the Major his total support. He 'took him out on the town' and they both got really drunk together. At one point I was talking to Craig and Mal at the bar and Shane just came up and gave us this tirade about giving total support to the Major because he was the OIC and we should give respect and support to anyone in that position. We thought he was joking to start with, but he wasn't. He only wanted to argue with Craig and told me to shut up when I tried to argue with him, the chauvinist. Later I got a gutful of Lloyd and the Major in the kitchen with Lloyd saying what wonderful things Shane was doing standing up for him as OIC. Well, I guess on the station a couple of guys would support him in an argument but I doubt if many would. Later the same evening Paul and I were sitting quietly talking to Albert, and Shane comes up and wants to start fighting Paul for some totally obscure reason; it was completely unprovoked. After Saturday night (I was nightwatch so stayed to the bitter end) we were left wondering just what was going to happen. You might say things aren't exactly comfortable on the station at the moment.

I tried to ring Tom Maggs to tell him what happened last night and to discuss a few things about possible long dog-trips but he's up at Bernacci [Antarctic training centre in central Tasmania] until Friday so I won't be able to talk to him until Monday. Tom is station manager and the Major's direct superior. He's easy to talk to and fairly understanding of personal interactions. I think he should hear my side of what Bob did last night, and I think he should hear some examples of what the Major does to antagonise people.

Well, Gina, it's 6 o'clock. Time for my pre-dinner cuddle. Hope you have a good time at the CEDAR conference and get some inspiration. What I need is clear skies at the moment, not inspiration. At least since the Macey trip I have felt a bit more like working than I did before.

Love, Pene.

8 JUNE 1990

Well, Pene,

Every time I get your mail messages I feel immediately transported to my time at Mawson and it suddenly all comes back to me — bantering about who's going on what jollies and personal clashes and everything. I can also feel winter in your letters; makes me almost dread the inevitable coming of it here. Summer is just so nice and people far more loosened up. Although it is a bit exhausting too, as there suddenly seems like too much to do. Anyway, hang in there and 'Don't let the turkeys get you down', as they say.

This is just a quickie because it's Friday afternoon and I've got a few things to do before going home and getting ready to go canoeing tomorrow and then to Boulder on Saturday night. I wish you were coming too. I'm really looking forward to checking out Boulder and surrounds and maybe the conference will be fun too. This week has been hectic but good — doing stuff with some visiting scientists, as well as getting my summer student going with preparations for the absolute calibration. She's a real scream and suddenly makes me realise that I have actually learnt a few things in the 10 years since being an undergraduate.

Have a good week, and thanks for the invite to midwinter. I've been meaning to send a reply by telex but haven't got to it so please pass on my apologies to all. If there was just the slightest chance of my being able to get there I would come.

Lots of love and thoughts, Gina.

It is traditional to send invitations out for the midwinter celebrations at Mawson. Although it is not expected that anyone will turn up, the replies are eagerly awaited and pinned on the noticeboard for all to read. As well as good friends, royalty, politicians, sports stars, film stars and entertainers are asked. It would be very interesting if one day some guests did turn up. We promised a dog-ride from the ice-edge at 66° south to Mawson if anyone could make it that far.

17 JUNE 1990

Hi Gina,
Well, I hope your CEDAR conference went well. Things here are going OK. It's Sunday and I'm doing single-etalon dawn obs but it's 1130 MBT. I'm writing this in between profiles and filling in a few minutes here and there. Last night was my first whole night of green data since I changed over to single-etalon observations about 10 days ago. I am a bit pissed off as there'll be a half-hour gap in the middle where the ham gear was going flat chat. That produces variations in the voltage lines, which causes the whole thing to go crazy. The ham user will find out about it at lunchtime.

Well, things have been up and down since I last wrote. Had a little confrontation about porn in the daily newspaper. The comms guys put together the AAP news bulletin as a paper each day, adding cover and comics [Australian Associated Press compiled a news summary for Antarctic stations which was telexed to the stations]. Well, last Friday that was changed to include full-frontal pinups — genitals, breasts, open-mouth type — which by no stretch of the imagination can be called art. Greeted by this on the breakfast table, I was furious. I wrote up on the board:

'Would the fucking MCPs who put together the fucking newspaper, please distribute their pornography more discreetly.'

I thought they may understand that language. The Major said my writing comments on the board was too aggressive and the people concerned objected to being called MCPs. What a joke! At least Paul can calm me down a bit. He's right, they are deliberately provoking me and the more I react, the more they will bait me. I have requested that the practice be stopped but I haven't the Major's support despite the government regulations regarding sexual harassment.

In some ways it worries me a bit. If these blokes want to be surrounded by this sort of thing, how do they know where to draw the line between reality and fantasy and what is there to stop them treating real women the way they see these photos and stuff? I don't object to their private fantasies but when they're paraded in the morning newspapers it's a bit much. The days after the first pictures appeared, there were doctored comics about censorship and not-so-oblique comments about me complaining. I had a talk to Albert about it. He's not the only other person around who doesn't really like what they're doing but he said they were talking up in the bar the other night and some said that I was being hypocritical because, as they see it, Paul and I have our relationship so I have no right to object to their pin-ups. Also they were saying that they think I get more than 1/24th say in what goes on around the base. The way I see it, I just want government regulations enforced.

If women have to cope with this sort of extreme male behaviour then unless the blokes can control themselves and their mates they'll eventually get extremist reactions from the women. I can't be bothered. I'm not down here to fight the feminist cause with a few individual chauvinists but I'd be within my rights to request that all pin-ups in all workplaces be removed, including those ones of so-called historical interest on the roof of Weddell Hut. They were only put up in the early '80s; and should Antarctica be a museum for pornography? I just don't think explicit sex should be paraded in common areas such as the mess and club. Apparently they are having similar problems at Casey but they haven't gone past arty shots. I don't imagine Joan Russell, who is the OIC there, would put up with the shit they're dishing out here.

This is not actually very successful as I get involved with typing something and then my profiles finish and I don't realise it, so better give it away for a while.

The news as far as the MIAR is concerned is not good. Looks like the family is going to sign the collection over to the university and the university is going to put it in a university museum in the Mitchell Building. The MIAR is going to close up. The Centre for Environmental Studies is going to be renamed the Mawson Centre for Environmental Research and while there is external funding available there will be a research fellow specialising in Antarctic research (i.e. when my grant runs out that will be the end of it). I think it shows very little initiative, a lack of foresight and a lack of respect for Sir Douglas Mawson. I am convinced the bureaucracy of the university is self-motivated and has self-interest at heart. Sort of feel that the less I have to do with the University of Adelaide, the better.

So what has been happening in the great south white land? We are going on a Hagglunds trip to Taylor Glacier and Fold Island the week after midwinter — to count the penguins and to make some depots. Have been making plans for what to depot for the Kloa trip. Have not had many clear skies, a couple of twilights and few hours of green obs usually ended by cloud until last night. Have been getting a bit of analysis done and have had a few afternoon runs with the boys, which I always enjoy. Some warmer days during the week which made running more enjoyable. Today, with clear skies, it's −24°C and about the coldest we've had. Still no blizzes and no fresh snow. We had a bit of snow one day during the week. It was enough to make the sea-ice a bit slower for travelling but that was about it.

Hope all goes well. Does Alaska have midsummer celebrations?

Love, Pene.

The Mawson Institute for Antarctic Research (MIAR) was established in 1959 in honour of the late Professor Sir Douglas Mawson. Mawson had lectured in the Geology Department at the University of Adelaide from 1905. He was department head and professor from 1921 until his retirement in 1952 at the age of 70. He died in 1958. Mawson was Australia's most active and noted Antarctic explorer. He stood out in the 'heroic age' of Antarctic exploration because of his interest in science. He had declined an offer to take part in Scott's race for the South Pole, preferring to organise an Australian expedition with more scientific objectives. It had been intended that the MIAR would cultivate and perpetuate such ideals in Australian Antarctic activity, the University of Adelaide providing the necessary academic basis from which to do so.

Gina and I, although not geologists like Mawson, felt very much part of the tradition of scientific research in the Antarctic. Dr Jacka had been part of the first wintering expedition on Heard Island in 1948. He then worked in the Australian Antarctic Division, rising to the position of Assistant Director, Science, before being appointed as Director of the Mawson Institute for Antarctic Research in 1965. Don Creighton, an electronics engineer responsible for development and maintenance of the Mawson Institute experiments, had wintered at Mawson in 1963. Of the dozen or so students who passed through during our time of association with the Mawson Institute, most had wintered in Antarctica. Norm Jones, Peter Jacob and Rod Mcleod were fresh from their experiences in the winter of 1981. Paul Wardill wintered in 1983. The exchange of Antarctic folklore and the need to share our knowledge of the idiosyncrasies and technicalities of our experimental equipment forged a strong bond between all members of the institute. Our contemporaries at the time this book covers included Mark Conde, Andre Phillips, Maria de Deuge and Damian Murphy. Other staff at the institute included Richard Ferguson and Heather Duff: Richard was employed as a research assistant to study Hurley's role as Mawson's expeditionary photographer; Heather was Dr Jacka's secretary.

The Mawson Institute for Antarctic Research was a department within the Science Faculty of the University of Adelaide. Dr Jacka had been appointed as Director of the MIAR in 1965 on the understanding that he would be the Director of a multidisciplinary research institute. The university never provided any funds for the appointment of any other academics within the institute. A biological sciences group existed for some time under the supervision of a scientist seconded from the CSIRO. On this person's retirement the group was disbanded. Despite continuing efforts no further cooperation with outside organisations was achieved. Dr Jacka did maintain a research program in upper atmospheric physics and collaborated, when possible, with other departments within the university. It was through Dr Jacka's efforts that the institute survived for so long and provided a number of postgraduate students with the opportunity to work in Antarctica.

The 1980s were financially hard times within the university system in Australia and teaching positions were scrutinised carefully when they were vacated. The University of Adelaide was governed by a complex system of committees and a large bureaucracy. Forward planning of recruitment for academic positions for a period of three years and foreshadowing the following three years was made by a committee of deans of all faculties and was called the Compact. All academic positions which were becoming vacant through retirement or termination were divided between the faculties according to the Compact. In 1985 the Compact decided that when the Director of the Mawson Institute retired in 1990, the position would not be filled. Those resources would then be redirected to other areas within the university. This decision sounded the death knell for the MIAR.

At the time a succession of committees was formed to address the problem of funding for the Mawson Institute but the bureaucracy and committee structure meant they were unable to make decisions or act on any of the recommendations these committees produced. The principal problems were the self-interest of individual academics on the governing committees, inertia in the committee structure and political infighting between university departments. The Geology Department would not wholeheartedly support the Mawson Institute because its members believed that since Mawson was a geologist, they should have control of the Institute; and if the current Mawson Institute were disbanded the Geology Department would be the logical benefactors. It was difficult for other academics to allocate money to a research institute, even in honour of Sir Douglas Mawson, when their own departments were having problems maintaining their research and teaching commitments.

It is curious that the University of Adelaide bureaucracy was unable to harness the interest in Antarctica, growing throughout the 1980s, to its political advantage. It seemed to us at the time a complete lack of foresight. The MIAR could have been an excellent public relations exercise but the university never saw fit to exploit this. It completely squashed attempts to mount a public fundraising exercise in 1989 by refusing to allow professional fundraisers to be contracted for the job. It expected fundraising instead to be run on a voluntary, ad hoc basis by people with no experience in this sort of activity; hardly the way to raise hundreds of thousands of dollars.

By 1990 it seemed almost inevitable that the institute would close, despite its international reputation for atmospheric physics research. This was difficult for Gina and I to comprehend. How could the university give away such a resource? We were trying to do what we could to prevent it from happening. The experiments themselves had considerable contributions to make to upper atmospheric physics and it was worthwhile to try to ensure their future operation. Having been involved in some of the committees I was all too aware of the bureaucracy's machinations and felt despondent, doubting that anything would succeed in maintaining the existence of the MIAR.

20 JUNE 1990

Hiya, Pene,
Back again, have had a pretty good time but feel pretty exhausted too. The biggest news which awaited me when I got back is that, surprise, surprise, Tod's gunna be a dad. He says he's not real happy about it although Claire, of course, is thrilled. Apparently he had decided yet again to break up with Claire after his departure to Heard but then Claire's pregnancy was confirmed on the morning of his departure. And so there it is. My first reactions were actually fairly positive, as in some ways it is like another bridge burnt behind us, which makes me feel more sure about what I'm doing. However, today and yesterday I've felt really disappointed with Tod and kinda mad at him for not taking control of his life, which is what I thought he had wanted to do.

As far as CEDAR goes, there were a lot of postdoctoral positions going and several people asked me to let you know of these positions. FPS experience, particularly with dayglow observations, is highly sought-after.

There is to be an IAMAP [International Association of Meteorology and Atmospheric Physics] conference in Vienna in 1991 with a special session on Arctic–Antarctic comparisons. Pene, in regard to this, how about a joint project with some simultaneous observations from Poker (inv. lat. 65°) and Mawson over the equinox? I thought it might be interesting to watch the semidiurnal tide in its rapid equinoctial phase change and see how the timing compares. With the green line we could maybe do some approximate conjugate work. Have you any ideas?

[Simultaneous observations at Mawson and Poker would be approximately conjugate (i.e. similar geomagnetic longitude and opposite latitude). Such observations are important in studying the global nature of atmospheric phenomena. Tides are such a phenomenon and observations of the amplitude and phase of atmospheric tides in different hemispheres should be comparable and give information about the modes of the tidal variations, i.e. whether they are symmetrical or anti-symmetrical between hemispheres. Aurorae can occur conjugately, reflecting production mechanisms in the Earth's distant magnetosphere. There is a short period in the equinoxes when conjugate observations can be obtained; darkness is required for most types of optical experiments and both polar regions required some darkness.]

I finally got to meet Roberta Johnson. She was interested to hear of my work and would like to do some collaborative stuff. In fact I got to know many of the Uni. of Michigan folks, Tim Killeen's group, including ones doing comparisons between green line obs and incoherent scatter radar. On the final night of the conference I was thrilled to find that Midnight Oil were playing in Boulder at this natural outdoor amphitheatre nestled in the Rockies. I went with some of the Michigan folk and ended up getting a bit intoxicated on good music, good company, a bit of homesickness from seeing some fellow countryfolk, and a few drinks.

Pene, what are your feelings about the future of the MIAR instruments and whether there is anything which could or should be done from this side of the world? I know we could get at the very least letters of support from somewhere like the CEDAR community; or Roger would be interested in applying for funding for a joint US–Australian effort to run them.

Well, it's post-solstice morning and I'm stuffed. Last night after work we headed out of town about 40 miles and went canoeing with a picnic dinner. It was just great to be out in the evening light. We saw lots of beavers doing their thing, amazing animals. It was such lovely lighting, low, just hitting the trees. We also had a moment's thoughts for all you midwinterites, and your celebrations, which I hope went off well. Afterwards we went to the pub, where there was a big solstice party, and we got home about 3 a.m. Today I've been out at Poker with two summer students and it was just one of those days, computer problems, blasting photomultiplier tubes with the laser, and to cap it all off one of the students fell through the instrument dome above the MSP [meridian scanning photometer]. Poor guy felt so bad, as well as getting a horrible shock. It was all I could do to stop the incident from bringing a rapid close to his scientific career.

I hope your midwinter was good and that things are going more smoothly since your talks with Tom Maggs. Do you like the station leader set-up, with a contact in Kingston taking an interest in things? It seems like it could be good. I'm surprised to hear about your problems with the newspaper porn. I thought that sort of thing finished years ago. We certainly didn't have anything like that in my year. Perhaps having more women around and a reasonably understanding OIC makes a difference.

I'm sending you some sunny thoughts with this message as we start to send the sun back to you.

Lots of love, Gina.

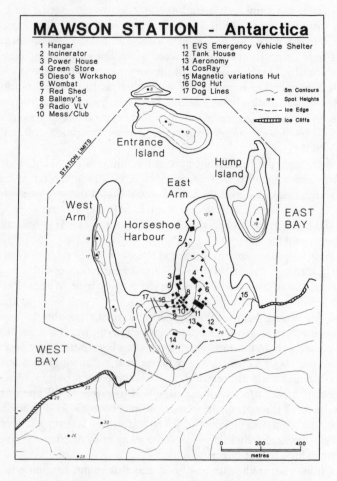

MAP: JOHN COX

PART FOUR

TURNING
WITH THE TIDE

Midwinter has always been a social festival in the Antarctic. It marks the winter solstice, the turning point in the seasons. In the northern hemisphere midwinter is a festive time, celebrations of Christmas and New Year breaking the gloom of the long cold nights. At the South (and also North) Pole the sun does not rise for several months in winter and continual darkness reigns. Mawson is just south of the Antarctic Circle and for four weeks each year the sun does not rise; it is only just below the horizon and there is a short period of twilight. Fairbanks is just south of the Arctic Circle so at this time, for Gina, the sun was only just setting in the middle of the night. She had 24 hours' light when we had almost 24 hours' darkness, and vice versa six months later.

I found it relatively easy to cope with the varying day-length providing I maintained a regular routine, rising for breakfast at 7 a.m. despite the total darkness. We often made use of the few hours' twilight by going for a dog-run after lunch. (MBT meant the sun was highest at 2 p.m. rather than 12 noon). It is possible to run dogs in the dark and stories abound of magic trips around icebergs in full moonlight. In Alaska dogs are frequently run at night, mushers wearing bright headlamps to illuminate the path. Natural light certainly makes sledging easier.

At Mawson we could make up the time we spent running after lunch by working later in the evening.

Traditionally at Australian Antarctic bases midwinter is a big celebration. Christmas and birthdays are often more subdued as they bring familial memories and responsibilities to mind. Midwinter is not a traditional Australian festival and is not usually celebrated by those without Antarctic connections. For an Antarctic midwinter celebration a sumptuous repast is prepared. The mess is cleaned and decorated to look as unusual as possible. After the meal, entertainment is provided: traditionally a pantomime and expeditioners' individual repertory and musical skills are included in the program. By the evening most participants are suitably inebriated so that any performance is likely to be entertaining. 'Cinderella' is the preferred pantomime.

At Mawson in 1990 the midwinter's celebrations were started with an explosion of a number of 44-gallon (200 L) drums part-full of fuel, about six large cylinders of LP gas, and various other 'donations' from some sections on the base, all set off with a few sticks of gelignite. This sort of explosion had, until the early 1980s, been the traditional welcome for the first ship in the harbour each year. Growing environmental awareness had caused such greetings to be banned; however, for some reason it was thought appropriate by those organising our celebrations.

Our fare for the day, all prepared and presented by our chef, included: Hors d'Oeuvres Henderson, Mawson's Own Broth, Sorbet Seismic Crush, Rumdoodle Rack of Lamb, Floating Icebergs for dessert, followed by cheeses, coffee and petit fours; the wine list included nine varieties of bottled red and white wines, six types of spirits, seven of liqueur, and various non-alcoholic drinks. More than enough to satiate 24 people.

Station food is not typically so lavish. I have been basically vegetarian for almost 15 years, although I do eat fish, seafoods, dairy products and eggs. I maintained my diet for most of my time at Mawson. Our chef would ensure there was something suitable for me at each meal. Often when I was slushy we would prepare a large quantity of vegetarian food that could be frozen and then reheated when required. Fresh fruit does not last very long after the last ship leaves, although potatoes, onions and pumpkins do keep for 12 months if stored correctly. Eggs, if waxed, turned regularly and kept in the warm store (10°–15°C) will also last for 12 months. I did not miss fresh food as much as I thought I would. I was the only vegetarian on the base although our chef did become a vegetarian for a month in an effort to control his weight.

The midwinter lunch menu is produced as a memento for the year's wintering party. Four 8 × 10 inch (20 × 25 cm) black-and-white photographs had been printed and combined as a cover for the menu. One of our photos was as usual, a group photo. This photo is also digitally scanned and sent back to Australia for distribution to families and publication in *ANARE News*, the Division's magazine. A framed copy is also made for the club wall. (Group photos, taken since the station's inception in 1956, are a source of easily accessible station history; the answer to many debates on who was there when and what their job was.)

Souvenir presentation of the midwinter menu was practised by the early explorers whose menus have been proffered as examples of the bonhomie and social life on station. For these explorers midwinter marked the start of earnest preparations for spring sledging trips when new country would be traversed and mapped and the main goals of the expedition achieved. We were also starting to think about some longer field trips, starting with a census of emperor penguin rookeries at Taylor and Fold Island.

During winter the only other living inhabitants of Antarctica are the emperor penguins. Other wildlife migrate to less extreme regions. In spring an eagle eye is kept to spot the return of the first birds of the sky. At Mawson the first returners are usually snow petrels. The graceful swoop and simple beauty of snow petrels mark them as the most stunning bird I have seen. They surely deserve the reputation of the white dove's for peace. Winter, however, is for the emperor penguins, truly the emperors of the Antarctic. These birds court, then mate, laying eggs in mid-May. The females then leave to feed in open water, walking up to 90 km across the fast ice. The males incubate the eggs, waiting 9–10 weeks for the return of their mates. The females then take over the newly hatched chicks, regurgitating food for them while the male leaves to feed and replenish the energy the

Antarctic winter has demanded of him fasting on the sea-ice.

While male birds are incubating eggs and females are at sea it is an ideal time to count the birds, each resident representing a pair. Once females start returning the rookery is in a constant state of flux; some males and females are present and you cannot be sure if each bird represents a pair or whether both birds happen to be present. Graham Robertson, a biologist I had met on my 1988–89 summer trip, is studying these birds and in particular the colonies near Mawson. Graham had spent the winter of 1988 testing counting techniques and determining the birds' eating and diving habits and watching their general behaviour. As an amateur ornithologist I was interested in penguins and had assured Graham I would help organise the midwinter census of the rookeries near Mawson. Auster rookery is the closest, 65 km to the north-east. The rookery is near a flock of grounded icebergs and can easily be visited in a day trip by Hagglunds from Mawson. This rookery is too large, approximately 12 000 pairs, to be easily or reliably counted.

By Taylor Glacier, 95 km to the west, is another rookery. Somewhat smaller, it contains only 3300 pairs and is situated on a melt-lake between some hills. From a vantage point on one of these hills the rookery can be photographed and an accurate census made. By using past censuses and following Graham's instructions for future censuses it is hoped that this Taylor rookery population can be used to monitor ecological changes in the region. Taylor rookery is therefore extremely important and has been declared a specially protected area (SPA). Further west of Taylor Glacier there is another rookery of about 1300 birds near the south-western tip of Fold Island. The next rookery of emperor penguins is at Kloa Point, 300 km west of Mawson. Graham had asked if we could do a census of the Taylor and Fold rookeries before July 10, after which time the females would start returning. This gave us a two-week window after midwinter.

Winter is always a period of relative inactivity compared to the frenzy of spring and summer, when long hours of daylight demand to be fully utilised. The penguin censuses were a high point of our winter despite having to be outside in the bitter cold. In spring, with longer daylight hours, the whole mood changes.

23 JUNE 1990

Hi Gina,

Was happy to get your letter before we headed off for the week. Your suggestions of possible jobs — boy, I just don't know what I want to do. I want to live in a non-huge city so I think that rules out most places in the US. I am not thinking about sending any letters off just at the moment.

The business with Claire is almost predictable. I don't know Tod very well but if he wasn't careful enough to prevent a pregnancy from happening then he deserves to have to cope with it. However it's hardly a good footing to start off a permanent relationship with someone, having decided yet again to end it. Perhaps that is what is required in some cases, to get people to commit themselves to any relationship. Possibly Tod would have always been in that position until he did get pregnant, so to speak. Do you ever think of what would have happened if you had got pregnant with Tod and why you made sure you didn't?

When is the IAGA [International Association of Geomagnetism and Aeronomy] conference next year? I thought it may be possible that if I have a few months' work at the MIAR then I could have four or five weeks with you in Alaska before the conference when we could finalise a presentation while I'm there. Your letter prompted a talk with Paul. He doesn't want to go back to the US to work, apart from which he probably wouldn't be able to get a working visa. (Do universities, if they employ postdocs, arrange visas or working visas for spouses?) Paul is naturalised and hence no longer an American citizen. He would be happy to travel around for a while with me next year, come and visit you and then go to Vienna and then we'd like to go to Scandinavia for a while. I'd also want to visit my sister Pam who is living in Koln and is having a baby in September. Paul may go off somewhere while we are conferencing or for part of the time. Beyond that I don't really want to plan. Think I'd prefer to work in Aust. or NZ if I could, even if it means changing areas of work.

Midwinter's went off quite well. There was an explosion to set it off. And I think we'll hear more of that as well. Casey has lost 90 000 litres of SAB[1] in a ruptured tank and that has hit the press so don't know what the press will say when they hear of an explosion at Mawson, even if it was deliberate! I went along to get documentary evidence that it

101

actually happened. Paul, being environmental officer, broached the subject one morning tea beforehand but his comments suggesting it was not an environmentally sound activity were not considered relevant.

Anyway it was too windy (30–40 knots) to get out for a morning dog-run so I spent an hour making a garish skirt from one of my bits of material. We were having a colour photo taken by video and sent back to Kingston, to test out some new gear they've got which can fax a single video frame, a 'frame-grabber'. My skirt was bright yellow with green crocodiles sporting bright pink tongues and most appropriate. Paul got dressed up too and it was just as well we did, nearly everyone else turned up in black (or dark) suits with white shirts. The most outrageous thing amongst them was red which appeared in a couple of ties and cummerbunds. Mal did manage a black cape with red lining. Waste of colour technology on that lot! I was pretty amazed at the formality of some of the others. A couple of the military blokes came with their medals and military dress uniforms on. My God!

After lunch, 2–5.30 p.m., we had enough time to change for 'Cinderella', and then I was in another skit a bit later on. I had the classic woman's role in 'Cinderella', Prince Charming. Think it went down fairly well although about half left about 10 p.m. at the end of the entertainment. A few of the dancers stayed a bit later. Managed to drag Paul off to bed about 1.30 a.m. He was quite pissed and didn't really recover until the next evening, despite getting up for lunch.

Last night and this morning have been clear. So I have another day's data for June before heading out for penguin counting. We went for a run down to Ring Rocks yesterday afternoon. Pretty cold, –25°C, but no wind and no cloud so was quite pleasant. Just got back in time for dusk observations. I had to leave the lads to put the dogs away and feed them, though. One of the boys, Welf, is sick too. Don't know what it is. He's not that old, one of Blackie's brothers. Actually I think they were born in your year, 1985. Hope he recovers as we can't really afford to lose another dog.

Won't rave on any longer. Hi to Art from me, cheers, Pene.

29 JUNE 1990

Dear Pene,

Well, good to hear from you as usual and I've got some good news on the financial front. Yes, we probably could find you some money to come as a visiting scientist for a few months next year. In fact Roger sounded quite keen about it. When he asked Gonzalo Hernandez he got all excited too and wants to be included and thought perhaps we could all meet in Seattle.

I went out to Poker with Roger this morning, always a good chance to have a chat about things. Roger is sitting on just so much data, every time I have an idea about anything his answer is he's tried it and has the data somewhere. His problem is, like many others I'm sure, getting things published from it. He needs some help so I think it's about time I got in there and took some of these projects over. I have taken my time in doing this because Roger never said, here's some data, so I got the impression that perhaps I was supposed to collect my own. Although Roger is happy for me to do that to a certain extent, I think he was starting to feel not so happy about me looking into doing this collaborative work with the Michigan folks. So today finally he said, right, you've got to start looking into how you can get something publishable out in the time you're here and there's plenty of data there and you and I could work through some with you being first author. Well, I felt pretty happy to hear this so I know where I stand and what I'm going to get out of it.

Meantime, attempts at absolute-wavelength calibrations continue. I have been out at Poker over the last two days with my two loyal students. They are both really keen. When I said we were leaving at 8 o'clock in the morning so we could get back early they were both ready on the dot. One in particular jumps in and picks up things really well, whereas the other is just not so at home with instrumentation but loves the theory and sort of goes along theorising about solutions to practical problems. I'm sure some of it is cultural. I notice many foreign students look up to you but aren't so comfortable working alongside you making mistakes.

Well, it's been pretty hot up here. We went swimming and lying on the edge of a nearby gravel pit last weekend. Dipper's puppies are due any time after this Sunday. Can't say she looks pregnant but boy, she'd better be! William has gone to the lower 48, or outside as they say, so I'm looking after the dogs. I do remember Welf. He was born in 1984 and was one of the young pups running around the station when I arrived. I hope he recovers from whatever he has got.

I heard from my youngest brother, Dunc, this week and he is coming up to visit with Leona in a few weeks, so I'm looking forward to seeing him and meeting Leona. We have had lots of nice folks staying at Hidden Hill lately. One girl could have been a Greet. She had very similar features and manner to you and your sisters. She says she has three very similar sisters, so that makes seven of you!

Now to answer some of your questions. It is not possible to arrange work permits for a visiting spouse. This is a common problem and a pretty sticky situation, but people do work illegally sometimes. I'm not sure when IAGA/IAMAP [International Association of Meteorology and Atmospheric Physics] is but it's likely to be the same time as last year, i.e. July–August. We'll have to keep thinking of joint obs possibilities. We will start observing about mid-August, but we need to have a bit of a working bee on the instrument before then so I'm not sure what wavelengths we'll be observing but my vote would go for OH and green.

Re huge American metropolises, I don't think you'd find them as bad as you imagine, compared to Australia with five major cities and 80 per cent of the population living in them. Although there are a number of huge cities here, there are also lots of smaller ones. Many of the universities are in sort of university cities which may be of the order of a couple of hundred thousand people (similar to Hobart) with many of the people associated with the uni. They thus tend to be really nice cities with a good healthy supply of culture, good food and pleasant surroundings. Boulder is like this. It is only 100 000 or so, although it is about 40 minutes from the much larger city of Denver. I think Ann Arbor, Michigan, is similar. Tim Killeen and Roberta Johnson live on six acres only 30 minutes' drive from the university there. Ann Arbor is in turn about 40 minutes from Detroit, I think. Dunc is currently in Madison, Wisconsin, another uni city. He seems to think it's really nice, pretty, bike paths everywhere, and I get an image of maybe something like Canberra.

I'm trying the big sell. Your impressions are like mine were, but I'm coming around to believe that there's lots of pretty nice places to live over here, though for me I don't feel like trying any others after Fairbanks.

Well better go, it's Friday afternoon again and I really love my weekends.

Catch ya 'ron, love, Gina.

PS. Do you know what women say about finding men in Alaska? The odds are good but the goods are odd!!

2 JULY 1990

Hi Gina,
Thanks for your letter, which I got on my return this morning. Good to get some positive input re work 'cause jollying may have come to a

somewhat wet ending. It's a long story, so I'll start at the end. On our return from Taylor to Mawson yesterday the SAR Hagglunds broke through the sea-ice. We tried for four hours to get it out but ended up all piling in the rainbow Hagglunds and returning to Mawson in the dark. Paul, Albert (PI), Patrick (dieso), Craig (Hagglund driver and RTO) and the Major have gone back out there today to try and get it out. They stand a reasonable chance if it's still afloat when they get there. If it's not then I think we will have come to an end of long jollies away from the base. We left it with the motor running, the bilge pumps going (and pumping a lot of water), and tracks slowly turning so they don't freeze up.

Paul was driving our Hagglunds. We had gone through a lot of rafted ice on the way out; obviously the blizz which broke up all the sea-ice in May did so all along the coast. In some large open areas it obviously blew right out and then refroze, leaving good ice. In areas behind islands or on the western side of ice-tongues it was smooth tracking but in some big bays out near Fold Island, Steffanson Bay and William Scoresby Sound, the eastern half of the bay was smooth but the western half, where ice must have accumulated when it broke up, was really rough. So even if we do get away to Kloa it will be a fairly rough trip. We visited and put in depots at Colbeck, Tilley Nunatak, Ledingham's Depot, Cape Wilkins and the Law Islands. We were doing ones on the way back from Colbeck when we got stuck. The clearest path to travel was always as close to the coast as possible. We went around behind Ufs Island and were hugging the ice cliffs. However, all through Alison Bay, between the end of the Jelbart Glacier and the ice tongue to the east of Ufs Island, was rafted and the bits at both ends of the bay were the worst, about 600 m of badly rafted ice.

It was going around the end of the Jelbart that the SAR Hagglunds went in. There was some newly formed ice there — perhaps some of the ice cliff had fallen recently and rafted up the sea-ice, leaving a stretch of water about 20 m wide between two bits of cliff about 500 m apart. The ice was about 20 cm thick. Paul had stopped and was turning back from the thin section when Craig went past us, tried to cross and just sunk through. Was all very simple. Then we spent four hours with duckboards trying to get it out. Fortunately it was a beautiful day. The sun rose — well, sat on the horizon for a few minutes. There was a half full moon and no wind, good for taking photographs but I found out when I got back that the last roll I took didn't wind on. Still, you get bloody cold when wet. Had to smash the ice with a sledgehammer to try and break it up to get the duckboards under the tracks. We moved it about halfway across the pool, but obviously weren't going to be able to get it out without working all night. I don't think it would have been possible or sensible to do that. So we drove back to Mawson in the dark. Fortunately we knew that was the last bit of rafted sea-ice so with the moon we were just able to find our way in the dark. It took three hours, but you can see the red shed light from almost 30 km away which makes travelling a bit easier, you only have to worry about the patch of ice you're travelling on, not the general direction. Amazing how having seen the Hagglunds go in you start wondering anew at every change in the sea-ice surface.

Well, that was the last day. We were blessed with really good weather most of the way. The first day we had got lost in some rafted ice out off the end of the Forbes Glacier and spent about two hours trying to get through. We left before it was light — an obvious mistake in retrospect. So with the rafting off the end of the Jelbart Glacier and unknown ice conditions in front of us and darkness, we had to camp on Ufs Island. The next couple of nights at Colbeck, Paul and I slept in the tent as five wouldn't fit comfortably into the hut. It was really cosy. We have found two sleeping-bags to zip together. While at Colbeck we took photographs of Taylor rookery and visited Cape Bruce where Mawson landed. At Fold Island we went out and camped at Cape Wilkins and then the next day went back to Colbeck passing through blizz conditions and navigating by radar for about 15 km from Bertha Island to Tilley Nunatak. There we picked up our outward-bound tracks and were able to follow them pretty well the whole way back to Colbeck.

We were supposed to go back the next day but Mawson was having bad weather and we were told to stay where we were, so we spent another day at Colbeck and went and climbed one of the mountains in Chapman Ridge. A fantastic view out over the islands and peaks in that area. There are some great little melt-lakes around there. It was excellent to have some real exercise. Unfortunately wasn't the best of weather so the photos aren't as speccy as they might have been but who cares about photos anyway. We had a good time. Got on well with Mal and Craig. Dave Freeman, one of the met blokes, was the fifth member of the party. He's not particularly into doing things outdoors. The day we climbed the mountain he stayed in the hut. Mind you, he may have had more than enough of our company by then and just needed the peace. Mal and Craig keep up a constant banter. Paul and I say very little. Anyway, all got along reasonably well.

Well, Gina, it's almost lunchtime so I'd better finish this off. The sky is quite clear so this afternoon I'll be getting the FPS going again. Will be good to have a bit of routine observing to get me back into the swing of work. Will write again later in the week and let you know what I'm up to. Hope to make some progress in the next couple of months and get something together for a paper.

Love, Pene.

2 JULY 1990

Dear Pene,
This is yer mite, Aht, heah. So happy birthday on you. I hope you enjoy it in style. Maybe a kangaroo steak, a little champagne, chocolate cake, lots of presents, a hefty pay rise, big job offers, or better yet, book and movie offers. Gina keeps me posted on (most of) your exploits. Sounds like you're staying warm if not dry. I hope you got all of the toys out of the water so you can still go expeditioning. And it would be great if you could get up here to visit or work(?). Gina and I are having a good time, as I'm sure she has told you. She's really blossoming here, finding a good balance of challenge and support. Gotta go. Be good, when appropriate.

Hugs, Aht.

And a happy birthday from me too. What an epic week you had. I wish I had a map of Antarctica with me because I've forgotten the geography of the coastline out west. I remember the Jelbart, Taylor and Cape Bruce.

I've got a cold at the moment so my spirits are a bit low. Had a nice quiet weekend lying low and it was nice to have the place to ourselves for a lot of it. I put a rocking chair outside on our little porch in the shade and spent most of Saturday rocking and reading.

So Maria has finished. What a good effort! I have been speaking to Gonzalo today, who was speaking with Peter Dyson (of La Trobe University) who said that the Mawson FPS is to be his and that he is thinking of sending a bod down this summer for training. Did you know about this? Anyway I am waiting for a reply from Fred re our proposal of assistance so I'm not sure how that will fit in with Peter Dyson's ideas.

Dipper hasn't dropped her pups yet and I'm getting worried that she's not pregnant. I've been told that if she goes off her food then she'll drop them between 12 and 24 hours later. Every night I've been going down there hoping she's not hungry, but always there she is, looking as hungry and pleased to see me as ever. Well must go, we're off to Chitina tonight for five days!

Love, Gina.

8 JULY 1990

Dear Gina,

Well, thought I'd leave the end of the Hagglunds saga for the next letter to have something interesting to tell you. As it turns out that little incident has paled into insignificance over the weekend. But let me continue from where I left off.

When the lads got back out to the Hagglunds it was still afloat, miracle of miracles — or should I say to the credit of the diesos for keeping it in such good condition. There were a few holes in it, from where the first set of duckboards had jackknifed up under the rear cab, but the bilge pumps managed to keep it afloat. They got it out by slicing up the thin ice with chainsaws and then winching it to the edge of the thicker ice and driving it out on duckboards. So then they drove it home and both Hagglunds are being given a complete refit in the diesos' workshop, or were until the next little incident occurred to displace them.

Well, thanks for the birthday present.[2] It came as a complete surprise. I certainly wasn't expecting a parcel from you. Had some champagne for tea that night and Scott made me satay prawns and a birthday cake with pink icing. That was Friday night.

On Saturday night Scott managed to get the frypan hot enough for a barbecue — and to almost burn down the entire kitchen. Well, not quite. The exhaust fan was on and it sucked up enough flames to set fire to the whole chimney and most of the kitchen is fairly badly burnt. The mess area is structurally unscathed but heat from the fire was enough to keep the BA[3] team out for a while and to melt everything plastic above floor level. What a mess!

Fortunately no one was hurt.

Spent today starting the clean-up. We hope to be able to refurbish the mess for use (temporarily, of a sort) in about a month but it will take quite a lot of work. We started today by removing as much stuff as possible. Have taken it down to the diesos' where it is being steam-cleaned. Looks like most of the big implements like the mixer, gas stove, electric oven and, with much dedicated enthusiasm, I'm sure the dishwasher, will be got going again. Everything has been removed, the whole place will need to be rewired and probably replumbed, there's a couple of holes in the roof where they cut through with axes to try and put the fire out and also a fairly large hole at the back where the chimney went out. The chimney and whole big fume-hood has fallen down and the kitchen has lost all its ceiling and most of the insulating polystyrene. The mess area has lost all the paint in great sheets and absolutely everything is smoked out and totally blackened.

To make it all a bit more difficult, for the past two days it's been blizzing on and off. It's still blowing 50–60 knots but there's no snow left to blow around and be a blizz. Every now and then it starts drifting again though. It's enough that the roads cleared this morning to enable the clean-up to start were, by 3 p.m. this afternoon, impassable again.

People say we were lucky the whole old station didn't go up. As the folk left the club they shut the door tightly and it is apparently more or less unscathed. It has been suggested that the fire put itself out, as with all the doors to the mess shut no air would have entered to feed the fire. My fire position is with some others in the surgery so after about half an hour of sitting around wondering what was going on we got some drinks, nuts (because all this started five minutes before tea) and started playing cards. Actually the most frightening thing about it all was that the fire alarms did not go off. What alerted us was a power blackout. Paul and I were leaving the red shed to go to tea when the lights went out. He went back up to our room to get a torch and went down to the powerhouse to see what the problem was. I went down to the mess and found it on fire. Apparently the exhaust fan in the kitchen area drew 800 amps or something and instead of closing down that feeder it shut down power to the whole station. It was at least 10 minutes before the fire alarms went off. There was no official muster and we were not kept informed of what was happening. A fire pump wasn't started as no hole had been kept open in the harbour sea-ice and the whole thing was put out with about 80 fire extinguishers. I am sure we were just very lucky because the whole thing was a complete shemozzle. I guess it is irrelevant now.

I'm up here writing this now because I have been asked to do nightwatch tonight. I can't help being cynical about it. Try and think who is considered the most useless, being both a boffin and a female, in contrast to tradesman and male, and the best you can do is nightwatch. Bit pissed off as I have only just recovered from the nightwatch I did three nights ago.

Suspect this will put a bit of a damper on outdoor activities for quite a while. All extra energy will be put into getting the mess going again. Although, judging by the revelry in the red shed corridors as I left this evening at midnight, there's heaps of energy left. Everyone knocked off at about 3.30 today, guess it is Sunday, and all keep hoping that the weather will be better tomorrow. Ho-hum, so much for all the extra allowances people down here get paid to do overtime. I can't help being cynical when the university system doesn't have enough money to pay such allowances.

Well, Gina, so that's the news from Mawson this week. I am beginning to hope that my letters will be a bit more mundane from now on. I guess for about a week work, like physics and analysis, may have to take a back seat. I may escape up here once my patience with the chauvinism runs out. It sometimes wears me down a bit.

We have been eating today in the fire-tender shelter, which was renamed this year the emergency vehicle shelter, EVS, and the Hagglunds are usually parked in there. What an expensive garage. Actually it is all a bad joke. Paul was trying to unload the fire extinguishers from the rainbow Hagglunds which was taken out of the diesos' last night to illuminate the scene. The doors to the EVS — which are multimillion-dollar jobs with special hydraulic releases to get them up in seven seconds and two backup mechanisms in case they fail — well, they wouldn't open because it was drifting and when the drift blew in between the two sensors at the bottom of the door the raising–lowering mechanism would shut off. So you can't actually operate them successfully in blizz or even semi-blizz conditions. It has been decreed that the green store is going to be the new mess until the mess is cleaned up so we'll be shifting up there tomorrow or the next day once the stoves are cleaned and set up.

Well, I'd better finish this off and send it away to you. We were planning to go for a dog-run to Low Tongue this weekend but I doubt if we'll get away now. Things will look better in 36 hours when I've recovered from this nightwatch.

Enjoy summer for me, love, Pene.

PS: All the bitches here are coming on heat for midwinter. It's a bit of a pickle with them on the blizz-lines and no one with much time to visit or look after them. Poor boys. I'll make sure they're fed and, as soon as this wind drops, I'll get them back to the main lines.

Take care, Pene.

9 JULY 1990

Dear Pene,
So it looks like becoming an epic year at Mawson. Glad you're all OK
and that things didn't turn out more seriously as there was obviously
potential for them to do.

Well, things have gone rapidly downhill for me in the last few days.
After five days at Chitina, of which three were spent with a terrible cold
and the last two in tears, it looks like Art and I are breaking up. Feel
pretty 'bummed', as they say up here. Art's staying in Chitina for the
time being while we sort things out a bit. A lot of it sounds and feels
like the Tod situation all over again. Art feels that while the here-and-
now of our relationship is good, he just doesn't feel wholehearted
enough about it to tackle anything more than the here-and-now and
particularly doesn't feel that he could move to Australia.

I'm not sure what I feel, now that he's put things like that I'm
suddenly feeling that my heart's got a lot of healing to do, both from
Art and Tod, so suddenly a break from affairs of the heart does hold
some appeal. I feel like I really didn't give myself enough time to get
over Tod and that Art allowed me to put some things on hold, which I
am grateful for, but now I feel with at least a good living situation and
job I'm grounded enough in other areas to tackle them.

So, Pene, I'm going to see a counsellor this afternoon because I can't
put my mind to work. It'll be good to hear from you. I wish love wasn't
so bloody ruthless sometimes; suddenly celibacy sounds really attractive.

Love to you, Pene — thank goodness for women, Gina.

Tod told me he wanted to end our nine year relationship while
we were in Nicaragua. We were staying with a local family and
were inspired by their strength and passion. The woman of the
house had seen the revolution come to her neighbourhood, had
suffered having her sons and daughter fighting in the mountains, had tolerated a husband who suffered serious allergies
without medication, and been humiliated by having him bring
a mistress into her own house. Nicaraguans are musical and
poetic; the Sandinistas, like then minister Omar Cabezas, were
no exception. Cabezas had fought for years in the mountains
before the revolution of 1979 which brought them to power.
In his book *Fire from the Mountains* he describes his fight for a
future, a future with his girlfriend, when he receives a letter

111

from her saying it is over. Like Cabezas I had carried a standard, a flag that I held aloft and carried to the top of all the peaks I had climbed. Tod and I had endured long separations; prised ourselves apart so that we could pursue our own paths and not hinder each other's growth. I had survived honours, a year in Antarctica, the stress of a PhD, and I had carried our flag over every rise. Now my life's standard had to be reassessed.

Weeks later I was reading *Fire from the Mountains* while hiking around the old Kennicott coppermines in Alaska. It was midsummer and I was sitting on a mountain top reading in the evening sunlight. I had tied a bell to my boot so the noise would ward off any bears as I was hiking on my own. I read the passage where Cabezas receives his crushing letter. I felt his rage, his hurt, his fury at the injustice of it all; I ran down the mountain, pack bouncing, bear-bell jingling and boots clobbering. The bottoms of my feet were blistered the next day, and that was the day I met Art.

Arriving in Chitina and finding Art was like falling into a large, comfortable, cushion. Art softened my fall as the reality of Tod and I breaking up sent me into numbed shock. There was some magic with Art during that first 10-day encounter which turned me in my tracks. As we reached the Chitina turn-off from Glennallen, a huge falling star dropped out of the twilight sky and appeared to burn out just above the front of the car. It had to be confirmation that we were heading in the right direction.

Art had picked me up and plonked me at Hidden Hill, and he could not have put me in a better place. He had set me back on track and left me to heal. When he left I started getting what I needed, some female healing.

I sought counselling with a wonderful Polish woman named Kornelia. Her therapy was based on Jungian psychology, dream analysis and sand playing. She left me alone to pick, from all the little trinkets on the shelves, suitable icons to make a sandpit creation which was to describe my current state. It was a struggle to let myself go until I found a little penguin to place on a rock in the centre of the sandpit; a good start.

By the time Kornelia returned my sandpit was complete and my pathway clearly laid out. It started with a dolphin and some fossils representing a primordial beginning (the fossils were conveniently ammonites, the symbol of St Hilda's). Further down the road was the creative side, represented by my younger brother, a boy with red hair and his double bass. He was standing beside my sacred penguin. On the other side of the road a pensive figure bowed down in thought, oblivious to all else — my studious side; and a brightly coloured skier, an outlet for excess energy which must be burnt in order to reach the tranquil scene opposite: a single swan swimming gracefully alone in the pond beside an old, droopy, willow tree. Under the tree was a park bench, waiting for some unknown person to take a seat. At the end of the path and looking back on the whole thing was a solid mother figure, a native woman with child. I had a clear sense of purpose in my life and to Kornelia it was revealing that I had chosen to do a life path.

Work with Kornelia was all new to me. In Australia counselling is not readily sought, a remnant of an English heritage which expects one to bite the bullet and carry on regardless. In the United States it was much more common for people to address their internal needs. I could talk to my close friends about it, and to some of the older women in the Quaker community. Not only were they interested but they could also provide insights and share some of their own inner experiences. I liked this liberty. My dreams were also clear and revealing. A dream image could speak clearly of how I was feeling, more than anything I could say or write.

In the first dream I shared with Kornelia I had been flying in a plane with a female instructor and Tod. The instructor abandoned us and Tod was oblivious. I tried to tell him that we had to fly the plane ourselves but my desperate attempts to communicate the situation would not get past the blank expression on his face. In fact he wasn't really there. I took control of the plane and just missed the powerlines to crash down into a brick wall. Surprisingly I was alive. Well that was something but no one was running to my rescue. Where were they? Wasn't anyone at least going to applaud me for trying?

This dream lingered with me and seemed to describe the 'reality' of my situation. Strangely there was comfort in facing up to this reality. This was a positive start to improving it.

11 JULY 1990

Dear Gina,

Wish we could sit around talking all night. I'm really sorry to hear about you and Art. It's so hard to come to terms with when you start trusting someone and sharing so much and then they hand it back to you on a plate. I've never really been in that situation because both with Darryl and Brian it has been me who's eventually said that I don't want the relationship to continue; but in both cases I've felt it's been them who've pushed things beyond what I can accept and handle. Brian just wanted so much from me that I think I sort of ran dry on being able to give him anything. And yet it doesn't make it any easier when it actually comes to splitting up. As you say, you miss the daily contact, the physical support and comfort of having someone to share things with. It's something you just can't replace and takes quite a while to come to terms with. Somehow having someone else around to share things makes life in general so much easier to handle.

It's so hard to get things in perspective. If you want to return to Australia and Art doesn't want to come with you then I guess it is probably best that you split up. I guess he also has some roots in Chitina that he's obviously not entirely relinquished.

In some ways the whole thing is a double bind. I find when this sort of thing happens to me I throw myself into my work and then you get more and more involved in your work, so then when the next relation-ship comes along there's even more at stake, more years of commitment to give up. And then men say to you, you should do your work since you've put so much into it; and then they don't want to give you the commitment needed for the relationship when they won't allow you to give it up either. Where can you get out of it? I don't ever want to get involved with anyone I work with. Anyway, at the moment I've got Paul, although I guess I don't know for how long. He's not that keen on coming to Alaska with me if I'm going to have to be working. I guess time will tell. What will happen when we return to Australia? It frightens me in a way. I guess for each relationship you get a bit more cynical that it will last. It becomes harder and harder to trust and love, harder to give up that grain of doubt.

So what can you do? You know you're right about that's where women come in, or is it just friends and also family, I guess — the people you've shared your life with, who've always been there in a sense. I don't know what it is but when a relationship becomes sexual it's hard for that good friendship to still be there once the sexual part is removed. Somehow then when anything happens, instead of the feeling of friend-ship still being there, there is a deep sense of betrayal. It can vary depending on what you expect from the relationship in the first place. Surely Art must see that you have made some commitment in that you went to Alaska to work and to be with him. Well, on the positive side you do have your job and a place to live where you have some nearby friends.

Gina, this happening to you does make me feel depressed. It sort of makes me despondent about relationships in general. Being here in Antarctica I don't know if it's a good idea to become involved in a relationship. The community here is so unbalanced and introspective. We are not having what you'd describe as a good year. It also makes me feel nervous about my own relationship. It will have a big test when we get back to Australia, and it may take a year or so to feel as secure there. In a way it will be like starting out all over again. And it is so hard to live by yourself. I know, it was great when you came to Adelaide last year and we could share Bruce's place. It did have its drawbacks but was easier knowing you were there too. Coming home to an empty house and not feeling desperately alone can be difficult. Perhaps you should look for another woman to share your flat with or is the community you're in close enough for you not to be lonely at nights?

Well, you know, I can ring you up for a chat if you like. If you think it would be worthwhile and cheer you up. You might just have me bitching about things here, which won't ease your troubles much. Paul and I and a couple of others are still hoping to get the dogs away for an overnight trip on the weekend. Won't be very far but would be good to escape the Mawson madness. So the OIC hasn't been asked yet; we did have a three-day trip plan in so we're giving up a day. It will be interesting to see what he says. It's a bit of a joke with all the clean-up and stuff that's going on and all the work that's needed and all we've been working is from 9 a.m. till 4 p.m. For all these people who get these huge overtime allowances etc, etc . . .

Well kiddo, chin up and keep your eyes open for the beauty of Alaska in summer. Go for a walk this weekend and camp out overnight and watch the moon. Crying makes your cheeks red and makes you look pretty. You'd better watch out for the 'odd goods' around too. No, you're right, I do think it's good to have a real break between relationships and feel happy about being able to stand on your own two feet again. It is hard and lonely at times but is worth the effort.

Peace and happiness, love, Pene.

11 JULY 1990

Dear Pene,

I'm feeling a bit better, not that anything has changed. Hidden Hill is just great to have, Kim has got back from Europe and just at the right time. She's been a good ear so I've been through it all with her a few times. In many ways I feel I've got all I need up here for some good healing time and time on my own. Certainly in a far better situation than when Tod and I split up. It's good to have a job, as you say, but especially good to have lots of nice women around.

Well, it would be nice to have a chat. Fairbanks is eight hours behind UT so I suggest that if you rang between, say, 9 a.m. and 1 p.m. on Friday morning that would catch me between 7 p.m. and 11 p.m. on Thursday night. Let me know if this doesn't suit, I log in every day.

Lots of love and hugs, Gina.

13 JULY 1990

Dear Pene,

Thanks for the phone call — was just great to hear you. I don't know how I sounded to you but it was so good to hear you sounding normal. Ain't technology amazing! I wonder just how many satellites we were bouncing off — must have been at least two, maybe more.

At the moment at Hidden Hill there is Kim (25), William (39) and William's girlfriend Sarah (22) who is visiting from England. It is a nice group. Kim is excellent to talk to, she's into literature, writing and all that stuff. She's been encouraging me to write when I get the urge. She has taught me to appreciate poetry when she reads me what she writes. Then last night I told William about Art and I. Good to hear how things are from the male perspective. He reckons that yes, men can have trouble in being content with what they've got while always looking for their 'dream love', but women can get into the trap of not properly questioning a relationship and whether it's really right for them. They can become in love with being in love and thus become unable to look critically at the goods. I thought this was pretty interesting as I haven't thought of it like that before and I do think that there's something in it. He also thinks that for Art, and himself as well, that they've been on their own for so long that it's really quite hard to live in a relationship and exhausting too. William's worried about how he and Sarah will be able to sort things out. Sarah met William when she was 17 or something and it's been going on for five years or so with all this long distance stuff then together during the summer while Sarah grows up and goes to college. I've become very wary of long-distance romances but I hope it works for them. Inside I'm feeling a lot better for having talked to you and William and Kim, and a lot more prepared to wait and see what happens for a while.

Meanwhile two good things have happened to me work-wise this week; I got a pay rise (now $34 400) and Roger is getting a new PC (personal computer) so I'm going to get his old one. This will be good 'cause the FPS data is on PC and so are all the analyses and plotfiles. It's been hard to get in there and even look at data with only access to a Vax.

A very delicate issue, the politics of data use. What continually gets to me is that everyone I know in the experimental field is sitting on far more data and publication potential than they are publications, while the modellers and folks trying to put together global climatologies just can't get enough basic parameters like monthly mean winds. It seems to me it would be very little out of the experimenters' data banks. In fact they have virtually nothing from the southern hemisphere. Even though there is a lot more money floating around here, everything needs the same degree of justification and bullshit as in Australia, so it's not all as easy as it may sound.

I hope you had a good dog-trip. I'm looking forward to the weekend; there are two folk festivals on in town which I may go along to. One is a women's folk festival and is just out of town, which sounds nice, and one of Art's old girlfriends, Sharon, rang up last night so I may go out with her. That would be nice as I've been hoping for the opportunity of getting to know her better.

Well, lots of love to you, Pene, thanks for your support. Oh, how much rougher the lessons of life would be without it.

Take care, love, Gina.

16 JULY 1990

Dear Gina,
Thanks for your letter of 13 July. Good to hear from you after a talk. Yeah, it is pretty amazing that we can talk over such a long distance. The conversation at this end was a bit clipped but I got to hear most of what you said. Perhaps your relationship with Art will continue but in a different way to what it's been up to now. Could you cope with it if it were on a more casual basis? Be careful how you react to that. I guess sometimes one should be more careful. It's funny how it can be hard to break those bonds that sex produces. But it does satisfy the lust and I

117

guess it's hard not to think that there's something wrong with just lust. Again, possibly a female characteristic, or a Pene characteristic.

Fred is fairly keen to see the Fabry-Perot data put into a world data centre. However, what actually goes into such data banks? Is it the raw data, i.e. Fabry-Perot profiles, or is it derived winds and temperatures? And is there room to include a description of the quality of the data? I think it is a good idea, but as you mention, there is such a grey area as far as how data is used. If it were just modellers getting long-term averages etc. then I see no problem. There are also large numbers of researchers who also have access and there could be individuals who may use the data for more detailed analysis. I object to such uses when those concerned have not got a feel for the instrument and its limitations and qualities.

Your pay rise just makes me green. You can compare your salary, US$35 000, with mine from FJ's letter, about US$24 000. I hope that the work I've been doing is worthwhile. I have to admit I've not got much analysis done in the last month and with the Kloa trip coming up and preparations for that, I don't know that I'll get a great deal (other than actual observations and transferring them on to the Vax) done in the next couple of months either.

Well, the dog-trip went fairly well. We didn't get the best of weather. Blowing 20–30 knots all weekend. There was soft snow the whole way to Paterson Islands, so one of us had to run the whole time. Coming back was better because it wasn't so much into the wind and we were able to ride most of the way. I will need to get a bit more fit before we head off to Kloa. However, it was good practice and good to see the things that can be changed to make it all a bit easier. The dogs enjoyed the run. They were pretty pooped too. They've not been on short runs around the base since the fire. Bods haven't felt as though they can nip off for a couple of hours. Oh well, hopefully things will gradually get easier. We may try and organise a trip to Taylor in the next month to see how we go negotiating the rafted ice between here and there. That was the worst section we went over in the trip to Fold.

Well, I'd best go off and do some work.
Love, Pene.

PS: Have tried for two days and haven't been able to get through on the Austpac link to Adelaide. It looks like it's up today (Wednesday). We have said we'd like to get the dogs out overnight every weekend until we go to Kloa. Will mean missing out on most other station activities unless a few others start getting involved.

19 JULY 1990

Dear Pene,

Thanks for your letter. I was gunna write yesterday before Art arrived but I didn't get to it so now I'm suddenly in the middle of things and it's harder to be clear headed. Yeah, I had been feeling like maybe a more casual relationship may suit us both, but it's kinda hard to be casual, and as for ignoring lustful feelings! That's totally impossible with him. So I went home for lunch today and we had a good talk. Art's main problem is he's just finding it hard to be wholehearted about life in general 'cause he's feeling too thinly spread between Chitina and here. He really just wants to get his building straightened out. It dips six inches across an approximately 15 foot frontage, pretty serious. That's what permafrost is all about. So basically Art is going to spend the rest of summer in Chitina. He'll be coming up for another weekend and a few days in a couple of weeks and will be coming backwards and forwards and putting a bit of time into sorting things out with us.

I feel OK about this. I feel quite welcoming towards some time on my own. I'd like to leave the relationship open 'cause I really don't feel like I could just shut the door on it completely. The only part which scares me a bit is similarities to stuff with Tod. Sometimes I have trouble working out which is Tod stuff and which is the Art stuff because the feelings are the same; it's the sources which are different. I certainly will put a stop to it if it looks like dragging out to nine years.

The other thing which has come up is that the Physics Dept is desperate for teachers this coming semester and so I have the opportunity of lecturing in first-year physics, big classes, very general, no calculus is involved, and the students assess you at the end. It scares me to death in many ways but another part of me is keen to know how teaching feels. It would write off getting any serious research done for the semester, but things are dragging so badly at the moment that I think that perhaps if I did some teaching sooner, rather than later, I could let the research opportunities get going of their own accord, then go for it next year. I feel a bit sick of struggling to get into things so this option does have some appeal. It will be a lot of work, being my first shot at teaching. I'll have to learn how to write on a blackboard and just what you can and cannot get through in a lesson. Also it feels like something discrete and challenging and peoply to get into while Art's doing his toing-and-froing.

Aside from this I am enjoying a lot of aspects of work. I'm feeling rather pleased with myself today, having just organised for us to purchase a $13 000 laboratory lamp which will be of great value. Why I'm pleased is that I've struck a deal with the company. They will give us a

5 per cent discount if we take some data on the lamp and not only that, they will give us a second lamp into the deal, which they will try to optimise for our secondary requirements, and which will make the lamps twice as valuable if they succeed. So I'm laughing to myself that they are giving us a discount while at the same time giving us two lamps more suited to our needs. Roger was most impressed!

We are going to Anchorage for the weekend for a Quaker meeting. The Quaker stuff is something I want to stay with. It has a really loose structure, you don't need to become a member. Some people here have been coming to meetings for 20 years and never officially joined so I guess I'll be like that. While I enjoy the people I'll stay with it, but if I didn't when I got back to Aus or if it wasn't convenient I guess I may fizzle out.

Must get home for dinner. Glad to hear of you getting out and about. I must do a hike soon.

Have fun. Lotsa love, Gina.

23 JULY 1990

Hi Gina,

Had a great trip away on the weekend. We had good weather, well, clear skies and no wind but hence pretty cold with about −25°C or so. Cold enough to freeze the port overnight.

We went to the western side of Forbes Glacier. There's quite a good campsite there. Had a bit of a wander around before we returned on Sunday. There's obviously a penguin rookery there over summer and quite a lot of vegetation, which was surprising to see at this time of year. Brown mosses of at least a couple of different types and lichens and green algae, all were frozen into the melt-lakes there. Had quite a good run back. It's ice all the way so we were only running to keep warm but that was quite a bit since it was so cold. Dogs are going quite well. Arne's team is the gun team and we had the other one last weekend. It's not so bad except there's five quite old dogs in it who will have to go and when you take them out it's a bit of a ragtag bunch left. At least we've got Blackie running with Welf now, so that is a good solid pair to work from.

Saturday night was fantastic, clear skies, bright stars and aurora. The aurora wasn't all that fantastic but I may have some OK photos of polar pyramids with green bands in the skies. Will be my first aurora photos if they do work out.

Got two nights' data last week before we left and Mal ran the FPS on

Saturday night, automatic obs, so he just had to start it up. Mal and three others are taking the dogs out this weekend so that'll be good for them, keep the training up. It will be my first weekend at home (so to speak) for a while. May catch up on some things. Since the weekend of the fire I haven't had much spare time. Have been doing quite a bit of work on the dog-sledging gear, making new tent bags and fixing harnesses and sledges — the nights just disappear.

Hope things are going well for you — not feeling too bad or angry after Art's most recent departure. Just let things roll by for the time being.

Peace and happiness, love, Pene.

31 JULY 1990

Well, a postscript from today. Yesterday afternoon it started blizzing and it's still at it today. Barometer dropped 20 hPa in 12 hours. We had some pretty high winds last night and a fair bit of drift. Today the wind has dropped to 40–50 knots, and this afternoon a bit less, but it's still drifting. We don't actually know what the wind is up to as the wind recorder at met. broke at 4.30 a.m. this morning. We'd had 87 knots before then. The tower up here at aeronomy with the anemometer on it fell down with the help of a ute a couple of weeks ago. It fell over again last night, needs better mousing wiring on the turnbuckles. So the weather is pretty foul. I don't mind it so much when it's light but in the dark it's harder to get around. Hopefully it will drop off tomorrow and give us enough time to get organised for the weekend.

Off down to Biscoe to do some sled repairing with Paul. Feel like I've been neglecting him a bit of late.

Love, Pene.

27 JULY 1990

Dear Pene

Well, I guess you're having computer problems since I haven't heard from you this week. Either that or you haven't made it back from your dog-run. So I hope it's the former. It's Friday arvo and I'm feeling exhausted. It's been a hectic week. Spent the first three days at Poker doing these calibrations then was up until 2.30 a.m. on Wednesday night talking to Kim about the meaning of life, men and that sort of stuff, then on Thursday Dunc and Leona arrived and today I actually organised my first meeting to keep people in touch with what is going

121

on with the calibration work. So, thank God it's Friday. Oh yes, and then today I got a message from Art saying he is going firefighting for two weeks, when I was expecting him up next week, so I feel a bit disappointed about that.

We had a nice weekend last weekend, going down to Anchorage. It's always a good time to talk while driving. The meeting was good too and it was nice to share our problems with some of the other folks. Getting back I felt a bit flat, though. Art went on to Chitina, which was OK, but I felt he was being a bit distant and unable to express his feelings. I've been talking to quite a few of his friends. He has heaps, but a lot of his old friends say that although they've known him for a long time, they really don't feel that they know him that well.

In the meantime I got a nice long letter from Tod this week. He's feeling a bit overcome with this pregnancy thing but then again he also said he's feeling like he's got more control of his life now than any time before. A big part of that is that he has definitely decided to leave the division at the end of this year and enrol for a masters in environmental studies at Tas Uni. It's great to hear him so enthusiastic about it. This makes me realise he's obviously still not quite out of my system yet, and neither me his. Boy, it takes a long time.

Well, Pene, suddenly I've just got to get out of this building and get on my bike before I feel really stressed out. I'm contemplating driving to Chitina if I can borrow a car because I'm suddenly feeling a strong urge to see Art before he goes firefighting; but then again, the way I'm feeling perhaps it's not what I really need to do and perhaps I should have a more relaxing weekend berry picking.

Hope to hear from ya next week, lots of love, Gina.

29 JULY 1990

Hi, Gina,

Things have been really hectic. I hope you eventually got the letter I sent last week. As you said, the computer was down but I thought you might have received it on Friday. We have had a week of clear skies so I've been busy collecting data. Two days I was slushy, but I tried to get obs those days as well. By the time I watched the sun rise and set for dusk and dawn measurements and set up the interferometer for night-time obs, I ended up being pretty busy. Since then I have barely managed to get the data transferred, let alone looking at any of those interesting analysis problems I have. Then last night, Saturday night, there was a power failure and no one woke me up so aeronomy was without power for four hours and I didn't find out until I got here to do dawn obs. Needless to say the FPS was as cold as a frog and still, after lunch, has not warmed up properly. Mind you it probably isn't helped by the fact that today is the coldest day we've had so far, −31°C. Yesterday I got my nose frostnipped while we were weighing the dogs. They are all in pretty good shape, most are 33–43 kg. We have three dogs 43 kg, one of them a nine-month-old puppy. Cocoa, my favourite bitch, is now 38 kg which is quite remarkable considering that in April, after raising four puppies, she was only 26 kg.

The boys are getting pretty fit with these weekend runs. Mal and three others have taken them to Forbes again. Paul and I took five to Welch Island on Friday and we got there and back in just over half an hour each way and climbed to the top of the island. The weather has been kind with bright, still, sunshiny days, although cold. The sun is starting to rise quite high in the sky so I'll have to think about changing back to daytime obs. Last night I looked out the window and thought it was cloudy so decided to get up and turn the interferometer off so I could sleep in. When I got outside I realised what I thought was cloud was in fact a great big pea-soup of aurora which was so bright in places it was obscuring the stars, really quite strange. I had difficulty convincing myself what was going on and whether it was cloud or aurora.

We have a bit to do as next weekend we're setting off for a trip to Colbeck with the dogs. We're leaving Friday and should be returning on Tuesday. Another team are going out with the Hagglunds to run the dogs back. So we all should get some good exercise and be a bit fitter and have a bit more experience of what it's like to get out for a longer run.

Well, haven't much more news at the moment. Am going to try and get a tent bag finished now before dusk obs, if the interferometer has warmed up enough by then.

Love, Pene.

2 AUGUST 1990

Dear Pene,
Art is up at the moment and we are both doing an Alternatives to Violence workshop this weekend. Art and I are still not sure where we are at. I still enjoy having him visit although it does tend to emotionally unravel me a bit, compared to when I am on my own. I hope we can continue with the part-time relationship. It seems to suit me at the moment as I am enjoying some alone time too.

We got heaps of berries. So it' s blueberry pie, blueberry charlotte, blueberry jam and tonight, blueberry cheesecake. Picking them was really fun too. I'll go again soon!

Must go as I have a lift home. Hope your dog training and preparations are going well.

Lots of love, Gina.

5 AUGUST 1990

Dear Gina,

Well, we were supposed to set off for Colbeck on Friday and it's now Sunday and we still haven't left. The weather has been marginal, blowing 25–30 knots all day. The met. people say it's just a katabatic — bloody strong consistent katabatic.[4] What makes me decide against leaving is that we had a lot of snow dropped in a blizz earlier in the week and so there is ground drift with only 15 knots of wind. It's frustrating because if you were out and had one day to run back to Mawson you'd do it without a doubt, but I just don't see any point in setting out into unpleasant conditions. And the temperature is –23°C, with 20–30 knots of wind and drift so you'd have to be crazy. Am I a wimp? I guess there's no sign of it abating either. If I knew it was going to be less windy tomorrow then I could put up with it for a day, but when it's gone on for a couple of days I'm hoping we get another blizz so the whole weather system gets a shake-up and might settle back into a more pleasant pattern.

I've got some problems with the interferometer as well. Since the power failure last week I haven't had the interferometer in temperature balance. The floor heater stopped working. Mal fixed that and since then the floor's been cold with the heater on full blast, and the rest of the instrument has been hot. Just don't know what's going on. I'll open it up again this afternoon and let it cool down. Maybe it's not fixed properly. It's hard to get stuck into anything when we keep on thinking we might be leaving for three days tomorrow. Would be good to get the FPS fixed and then go.

Well, after lunch the wind dropped a fair bit so Paul and I took five dogs out for a run: one of the puppies, Goohaw, and a few others. Was not too bad except where we had to run into the wind into a drift-stream and then it was really shitty. So might head off tomorrow morning even if the katabatic is quite strong (if it is a katabatic). I always feel better having gone out for a run. If I don't get out every few

days I get really touchy and cranky. Hopefully this time next week I'll
be able to tell you how the Colbeck trip went.

Love, Pene.

14 AUGUST 1990

Hi, Gina,

Back after a spell in the bush. We finally left for Colbeck last Monday
and ended up taking considerably longer than anticipated, mainly because
the blizz we had before we left dumped great piles of snow. What had
taken us three hours two weekends ago, the stretch from Mawson
around to Forbes, took us six hours on the first day and left us all feeling
pretty exhausted. There was soft snow 20–60 cm deep the entire way.
Both Paul and I had to run and, with the sled sinking a good 20 cm, it
was hard work for the dogs.

Well, that was the beginning and the next four days were the same.
We had two short days when we only ran 10–15 km, on the second day
from Forbes to Low Tongue, and then the last day when we took the
dogs from Ufs around to Colbeck for the others to take over and bring
them back. Paul and I had the slack team — well they aren't slack, just
light-on in dog-power. Still running Nanok and Pedro, who are eight,
and two bitches, one of whom is small. Pedro is a good worker but
Nanok is slack and would be the first to turn around when the going
slowed a bit. We managed to negotiate the rafted-ice section without
too much difficulty. It was nearly all covered in snow so it became
negotiating drifts and sastrugi 1–2 m deep and we tipped the sled three
times in one day running from Island 45[5] to Ufs Island. That is where
my weaknesses show. I don't have much strength when it comes to
sledges. So we have to try our best not to tip them over.

The night we arrived at Colbeck the others wanted to take over for
the return trip. They commandeered the polar pyramids and dogs and
gave us the hut. In normal circumstances this would have been appreciated but that night a blizz blew up and we were stuck there for 24
hours. Those in the polar pyramids migrated to the hut for the day so
there were nine in a hut meant for four. That includes Patrick, the dieso
who drove the Hagglunds out. Albert says there has to be a dieso on a
trip of that length. We had Paul for the return journey but Patrick was
needed for the outbound trip. He was sleeping in the Hagglunds.
Fortunately the blizz only lasted 24 hours. The next day the dogs took
off and Paul and I went and climbed Ufs Island and then had a look at
a melt-lake on Chapman Ridge. We had another night at Colbeck and

125

then returned to Mawson yesterday. So now planning starts for the big one. Don't know if we'll get to Kloa but will see how it goes and if we can't do that, then we'll take the dogs out to Fold Island and back. That has its attractions as we wouldn't have to organise others.

Well, it was interesting to drive back yesterday. The soft snow which we toiled over has totally disappeared. Actually the other team had it pretty easy and cruised over most of it and were able to ride the sled a lot more than we were. That team has more and stronger dogs willing to work. But anyway, I'm not complaining. On the return trip the weather was only marginal and in a couple of places we couldn't see much at all as we passed through some thick drift-streams coming off the plateau. It was nice to have a shower and sleep in a warm bed. Paul and I are pretty snug in the polar pyramid, though. The first night we were out we found out it was −32°C, the coldest night we've had so far. But you come back and nothing much has changed and the people here are still the same and still talking of the same things.

Well, I'd better get some work done. No letter from you last week. I hope all is going OK.

Love, Pene.

PS: On return the interferometer is still not working, all hot and cold.

Pene's letters brought back many memories. I could almost hear the sled clattering on the ice, a uniquely Antarctic sound, and even some of the dogs' names were familiar. I knew all the spots of which she spoke, which aroused many emotions. Through Pene's letters I was reliving my year: a year which I still had not put satisfactorily into context with where and who I was. That it had shaped me considerably was unquestionable; but as a chapter of my life it had a big introduction and a gutsy middle, but no conclusion.

Many aspects of my year at Mawson were not as I had planned or dreamed. There was no gentle farewell to loved ones as the *Icebird* heaved away from the dock because we were sailing not from Australia but from Cape Town in South Africa. The ship's construction had been delayed so we were flown to meet it on its maiden voyage.

Seven days after leaving Cape Town we hit the pack-ice — a

brilliant white sheet over ink-blue ocean. Spirits lifted as long-pondered images of Antarctica began to materialise. Three days later we were at the edge of the fast ice, 90 km and a 30-minute chopper ride to Mawson, and close enough to make out the mountains I had heard so much about. We arrived in a drawn-out dribble to a none-too-excited reception by the 84 crew, making us feel like the intruders we were. I found Mark Conde working in the aeronomy lab and after a quick tour he mentioned the dogs and we were off. The weather was perfect, not a breath of wind, and running along the ice-cliffs with the pups and a training sled I was dumbfounded. With a big grin on my face I adopted the nonchalance of these old hands, who were discussing station gossip, rather than upset the scene by gasping in endless amazement.

The 1984 winterers were not a happy bunch. Frictions had developed between many people, and the three occupants of the aeronomy building were no exception. Mark Conde and Andre Phillips were both students with the Mawson Institute. They were thus motivated by the pursuit of their PhDs and not by the healthy salaries that everyone else on base enjoyed. Mark had upgraded the FPS and obtained an extensive data set of both night-time and daytime observations. Andre built aerials and installed a 2 MHz radar for measuring winds in the middle atmosphere (60–110 km altitude). Alistair Urie was employed by the Antarctic Division as an electronics engineer and he maintained and operated the routine equipment. My work over-lapped the three; I was employed to run the Antarctic Division equipment but I was also to carry out research using both the radar, about which I was rapidly learning, and the FPS, which I had operated during my honours year. Due to funding restrictions only one engineer was appointed and sent to support the physicist at Macquarie Island, leaving me on my own in the aeronomy laboratory at Mawson. It thus appeared to the rest of the base that one woman was replacing three men. This did not improve morale in the lab on top of the hill.

It took some time for me to settle in over the summer. Andre and Alistair took me under their wing in an intense training program and at times I felt torn between them. Alistair worked a regular daytime schedule but Andre chose rather erratic hours.

I was also undergoing intense social training. There had been only one woman on base during 1984, a doctor who was married to one of the scientists. The general attitude was not particularly amiable towards having women on base, and as the youngest and one of the first three to arrive, I felt pressure to set a good example as I was scrutinised from head to toe. Amidst these distractions I struggled to become acquainted with this strange new land, a combination of rock, ice and seasonal wildlife — a land with a cold heart and untouched soul.

The summer building program was moving ahead at a frantic pace. I was not the only one led to question what the 'r' in ANARE really stood for: Australian National Antarctic Research, or was it Rebuilding, Expeditions? Many of the construction party were down for summer and brought with them a working-holiday mentality. They were out to maximise their short-term gains while looking to home for their longer term needs. This differed from the attitude of those anticipating making the base their home for a year. Inevitable frictions developed between those returning and those remaining. In addition those from the previous winter began to question the abilities of their replacements. The aeronomy lab was no exception, with doubts circulating as to my competence.

Boffins are unappreciated on base as they do not perform any 'essential' function and generally their work is invisible to everyone else. As a group they are often ostracised. There were times when, as both a woman and a boffin, I felt everything was against me. Work-wise I was in over my head and the Antarctic Division accepted they were taking a risk. An engineer is well trained in maintaining and building equipment but cannot be expected to carry through a research project. On the other hand a physicist pursuing a higher degree is more likely to produce scientific publications, the desired end result, but may have trouble maintaining the broad range of equipment involved. In the past the division generally opted for an engineer if they could only afford to send one person. I thus felt like somewhat of an experiment on two counts and, as my boss put it: 'Well, kid, you'll either sink or you'll swim'.

My tool of trade became communication, and a willingness to ask for assistance and advice. Women tend to be better at seeking what they need than men, who must constantly manoeuvre extended and delicate egos while interacting and negotiating. My three colleagues in the lab were barely talking and rarely sought each other's advice, while I freely accessed their net wealth of knowledge. All that year I continued seeking advice and assistance wherever I could find it. Among the 28 people in the wintering party there was expertise in almost any area one cared to name, and the facilities required to put that expertise to work. This nurtured a sense of fulfilment, transforming the group of individuals into a secure community able to survive in an isolating landscape.

Socially the year was testing. Sometimes I even plucked up enough courage to wear a skirt. The attention this invited was formidable (despite my skirts being safely below the knees) and I needed to mentally prepare myself on such occasions. Rewards came with always a few people thanking you for baring both some femininity and some ankle. The eyes on the base kept a constant watch on where the attentions of the women were allocated. If I spent one-on-one time with other women, that was fine; with my work colleagues, acceptable but only just; and with anyone else, it evoked a wave of suspicion. The male involved would be designated 'a sniffer' and be hounded and ostracised.

One incident brought the situation into the open and became known as 'not the nine o'clock obs'.

It was my first time as nightwatch. A party atmosphere was developing in the club, it being Friday night, as I strolled over to the 'blue box'. On the way I met one of the summering electricians (whom I had become close to, with the inevitable rumours resulting), and he decided to accompany me. The generators roared continuously as I meticulously set about the observations, carefully recording everything in the large, hard-covered log. Amid the panel of gauges protruded a red button and while I was concentrating on the gauges that logbook went for the button. I hardly knew what had happened as the emergency stop button brought the numbing ruckus to a halt, and we stood in darkened silence. Within minutes every diesel mechanic and electrician and a few extras had arrived to investigate, finding us painted with guilt and embarrassment. Stories of what we had been up to emanated in all directions and the humour of the situation assisted in turning it into a huge release valve for some of the built-up resentment towards women. It was most refreshing to be directly confronted by accusations and suspicions rather than only sensing a hidden groundswell or murky gossip.

There are certain strategic personnel in a wintering party and the personalities of those who fill these positions can make or break a year. High up on the list is the cook, whose work environment forms the central hub of base life, and who must work with every expeditioner in turn as they perform their one-week round of duties as kitchen hand or 'slushy'. The older woman in this position quickly became a motherly figure. This had both positive and negative aspects. The OIC possessed good humour, a sharp wit and a bigger dose of wisdom and smaller dose of ego than many in such an office. The doctor maintained a low profile and with the two designated nurses being respectively a carpenter and a radio technician I was determined not to become seriously ill. The foreman of the construction team was amiable and able but despite these qualities the usual rift formed between the task-orientated construction crew and the more casual approach of the maintenance team. The latter, a group of fresh young first-timers, were bright enough to quickly learn the ropes and would outwardly challenge the more rigid approach of some of the more experienced voices.

Midwinter was an exuberant time as we rehearsed feverishly for the first public appearance of the Mawson Bush Band and the usual performance of 'Cinderella'. The band was a one-hit wonder with 'Ode to a Husky' played until there was no excuse for not singing along. Not long after the celebrations the base went quiet. There are few entries in my diary from this time: reports of radar aerials blowing down, the aerosol counter dying, and the ionospheric conditions which were causing poor radio communications with the outside world. A satellite link had been installed the previous year but the temptation to use it for calls to Australia was generally avoided due to the prohibitive cost, $19 a minute. Occasionally radio communication was excellent during the two daily one-hour skeds allotted for private communications. Although two-way dialogues were often hampered by radio noise, there was comfort in just hearing a familiar voice. I would reply 'yeah, yeah' just to keep the conversation moving; needless to say this led to misunderstandings. In the worst cases communication was reduced to a mutual sharing of radio static when voices were swamped by what sounded like the roar of the elements blowing between you.

Trips with the dogs offered the chance to explore Antarctica on more equal terms. In a land where there are no native peoples and all are visitors, the dogs provide an element of continuity. There was a certain security in travelling with them and I trusted their sixth sense. If the dogs wouldn't venture into an ice-cave, then I wouldn't either. They were wary when travelling over crevassed areas and at such times could be relied upon to take heed of a certain urgency in your calls.

In October four of us made plans for a last trip to Mt Hordern. In 12 days we encountered two major blizzards. We spent three nights weathering it out in a polar pyramid tent and another three in a hut with foodstuffs being shaken off the shelves. In the tent I was the only one who slept while the others lay awake reading their field manuals, particularly the chapter on 'emergency shelters'. I had also considered the possibility of losing the tent; my strategy for survival would put me on the dog-line, curled up between my most trusted friends.

We returned to base knowing that something was wrong. In trying to radio Mawson the previous day we heard plans being made for an evacuation; the Americans were offering to land an aircraft on the sea-ice at Davis. However, we heard no names or details until we returned to Mawson. There were no helping hands to greet us as we pulled up to the dog-line; even the mess was quiet. Finally we were told that Steve Bunning, an expeditioner with the construction team at Davis, had been severely burnt when the interior of a tank he was painting spontaneously ignited. All hearts at Mawson had turned towards his young family, waiting at home, and to those at Davis dealing with the emergency. A reflective mood prevailed and most people had quietly retreated, suddenly mindful of their own vulnerability. In the following days a US Hercules evacuated our fellow expeditioner but sadly he died on the flight back to New Zealand.

Meanwhile the *Nella Dan* was making the earliest ever trip

into the Antarctic pack-ice in order to study, among other things, crab-eater seals. Tod was on board running an echosounder in search of krill. I was looking forward to speaking with him over the ship's radio. Late in the evening of our return, as if the news from Davis wasn't bad enough, I learned of the death of the *Nella*'s Danish pastry cook, who had apparently fallen down the galley stairs while on duty. His body was being stored in the meat freezer. I was hoping it was a poor joke but that was not the case. Things then seemed to go from bad to worse: days later the *Nella* became stuck in the pack-ice, 500 km west of Mawson. The *Icebird* was due to leave Hobart with the new expeditioners and rumours circulated that it would divert to the assistance of the *Nella*, despite the fact that it was not an ice-breaking ship.

Emotionally I was on a seesaw. One day it looked as if I would get home before Tod, and the next that he might in fact be on the *Icebird* with me. Either way he would not be on the wharf in Hobart. The end-of-year tensions were mounting and many were almost foaming at the mouth with excitement. At the same time our approaching departure brought us even closer as a group. A depth of trust and support had developed between us and saying goodbye was going to be harder than any of us realised. I was receiving a lot of brotherly support, and when the scientific personnel were transferred from the *Nella* to the *Icebird*, I was put on the first chopper out to meet Tod and the ship.

I felt like a million dollars lifting off from the chopper pad. Half the base were out to farewell me. Many were staying for a second summer but for them, too, the splitting of the winter group would be difficult. They would have to adjust to seeing new faces in their familiar places. I felt I had achieved my goals; I had learnt a lot and gained the respect of many on the base as both a woman and a scientist. I had kept the lab alive over winter and obtained some good data.

The chopper flight to the ship was too short and I was in Tod's arms before I knew it. It was all very strange trying to talk; the water, and the presence of other women chatting and giggling. Tod and the others off the *Nella* were feeling resentful at being forced to abandon their ship. Their attitudes would soften, however, as the *Nella* remained stuck in the ice for nearly two months until broken out by the Japanese ice-breaker, the *Shirase*.

Recovering from our feelings of loss and reviving our relationship would be a long process. The trip home was just the beginning.

14 AUGUST 1990

Dear Pene,

It was great to hear of your trip to Colbeck. Sometimes I really live your letters and that one brought back memories of a similar trip I did to Low Tongue in heavy snow, pushing the sled all the way and losing our voices yelling encouragement to keep the dogs going and then, to top it off, when we got there they managed a huge fight! In fact I think we might have even had Nanok in the lead too. That trip was with Grant Morrison and always comes back to mind as the hardest day's mushing I can remember. It's great that you're getting the dogs out so much, I know that some of the folks my year were pretty damn green and unfit when they headed out to Kloa. So sounds like you should be in good form.

Well, last week got a bit hectic with the trip to Tangle Lakes, hence no letter. We had a nice trip away but unfortunately Leona and Dunc didn't make it. They got stuck trying to hitch across a gravel road to meet us. Just no lifts, so they had to go back to Fairbanks. Anyway, Art and I had a nice time. The Alternatives to Violence workshop was pretty amazing. Got a lot out of it and was good doing it with Art and it resulted in us feeling a lot closer.

I've been feeling pretty emotionally confused since. Somehow, since things got unsettled with Art, I've been turning back to old Tod feelings. It got to the stage where I sent him a fax last night and this morning he replied that he's having trouble getting me out of his system too, but that he has decided to pursue a continuing relationship with Claire and is starting to get excited about the fatherhood business. Surprise, surprise. Sometimes I feel mad the way Claire just waltzed in and had the guts to just nail him like that, as I just couldn't. Last night I rang Tod. After feeling pretty pissed off with him we had a nice chat, talking like old friends and being supportive of each other and feeling pretty genuine about it. One good thing was that it didn't bring back feelings of wanting to get back together. It's just nice to feel that there's someone who knows you, cares about you, and who you can ring up when all else fails.

On the work side of things, I'm going to teach. I'm feeling excited about this and feel like all other things being equal then if I like it I'll be looking pretty seriously at going back to WA after here and trying to get a teaching position.

On the other side of things this Spirit II project (SDI-funded) is becoming all too real. In typical defence department style they seem to feel the need to invent these sick words for what they're doing and suddenly the jargon is that in wanting to measure the response of the atmosphere to heating, it is not the upwelling we are measuring but the *heave* of the atmosphere. Yuk, eh? It sounds like something you do when you're constipated and is certainly unscientific. Ethically I can justify this work as it's obviously important. I've always felt that our biggest threat is of an accidental nuclear war but on the other hand I'm sure that this is not the whole story and I'm unlikely to know exactly what it's all about. Given this, am I encouraging them by going along with it? I find it hard to take it too seriously, seeing these lead-headed military types trying to play their games when they have very little appreciation of the science behind it all. I'm sort of fascinated to know how it all fits together and just who does design these experiments because I'm sure it's not scientists.

Next week, Wednesday to Friday, we are having a meeting of the upgrade aeronomy advisory committee. It will really be something. I stand to learn an awful lot just listening to the bigwigs discussing the pluses and minuses of different systems. The wives are being forced to entertain the group in the evenings. Makes you realise just how it's perhaps impossible to get too high up the ladder without a wife. However, it's good to have a set-up like Hidden Hill because I'm sure they'd all pitch in and help me out if it became necessary. That would be novel for everyone too.

I've ordered the oxygen lamp and a heap of 10 nm–filters to help us look at lots of different spectral lines so I'm hoping that with this I may be able to do an absolute-wavelength calibration of the interferometer and possibly improve the current estimates of wavelength of these emissions so that we may in future be able to calibrate our obs without the lamp. The work we've done so far is looking promising. I calculated the order to within 10 orders with all the numbers looking consistent and also producing an estimate of the phase change. Observing should start within two weeks, and until we get our other set of plates back we'll be looking at red and green. When we do get them back we'll be looking at green and OH during the time you'll still be observing.

Must go, I've got someone who has just returned from sabbatical moving into my room. Apparently his wife is rather upset that he is sharing a room with a woman. I must admit that hurt me a little bit.

Well, pass on a stern word from me to the FPS to get its shit together, 'cause it really would be nice to have some data to present at Vienna together.

Lots of love and hugs, Gina.

17 AUGUST 1990

Hi, Gina,

Good to hear from you. Am doing my first obs for a while this morning, and today will probably be my last time doing high-resolution twilight obs. It's about time I changed back to daytime obs, days are now getting pretty long. If you are looking at green then it would make some sense if I did some green obs as well. As for timing, I will be going away probably the second week in September for my long trip so we are not going to get very much data before then. I should be back about the beginning of October, depending on just what we end up doing, and will be doing observing from then on.

I had a chat to Rich Collins a day or two ago. Boy, am I glad I'm not at the South Pole. He didn't actually say he was getting sick of it but you could tell from what he said and how he said it that the novelty had well and truly worn off. I felt bad in a way that I had all these exciting tales of trips here and there to go off counting penguins and/or running the dogs. Must try and have a few more chats to him too.

Also had another long chat with Tom Maggs about life in general for me at Mawson. Others are also doing the same, so think they may be getting the picture. On the return of the dog trip from Colbeck, the two runners who took over our team put their tent up in a depression at their second campsite. It was on a different island to where we had camped at Island 45, which had some pretty nasty tidecracks to negotiate before the campsite. Anyway the spot they chose suddenly filled up with water on the rising of the tide at 7.30 a.m. So the Hagglunds had to go out taking another tent and rescue gear. Their air-mattresses, cook boxes and all the gear in the tent had been floating in centimetres of water. So they unloaded the sleds and packed everything into the Hagglunds and then the Hagglunds came back in two days along with the dogs. Actually one Hagglunds came back for the night and only two stayed out in the second Hagglunds for the last night. Bit of a joke and a bit of a fuck-up.

Also I have fucked-up; our really good bitch who we were hoping to use as lead for the long trip is pregnant and probably due to pup in three or four weeks. Not sure what we'll do.

Not sure what to say about your Tod feelings. I must admit I have no desire to talk to Brian at the moment. I could just feel some long silences if I tried.

Hope your weekend is enjoyable, Love always, Pene.

PS: Well, didn't send this on Friday because the mail link to USA was out. Have had five days of shitty weather, wind and blowing snow. All the dogs are getting off the dog-line, sick of being cooped up after a couple of weeks of running. Spent four hours this morning in the surgery doing a desexing operation on one of the bitches. Looks like it's been successful. Quite an ordeal. Lloyd was keen to do the operation and he thinks it's good practice for the people who've done the anaesthetics and theatre sister training. Got some good photos of aurorae last week. Probably have a few more opportunities to get some more. I'll have to mount them and have a look at them on the wall in the next couple of days. Tried some 1600 ASA ones but think they might be a bit grainy.

27 AUGUST 1990

Hi Gina,
Hope all is well with you, I didn't hear from you last week. Hope you have been able to rationalise and accept your Tod feelings. It is really hard to accustom yourself to being by yourself and not be planning your future with someone else. In some ways it is silly but living with someone else I always tend to be much more extroverted in my outlook on life and when I am by myself I easily become very introverted and inward-looking. Things which when I am with someone else I take totally for granted and never even think about. Like as though having someone else around, you don't think about the burdens of living and the blankness of the future. It is probably just a reflection of general contentedness but when you are by yourself it can be hard to cope with those things. I guess I always go back to my family for support and a framework or base from which to view the world. Don't know what I'd do without that.

Well, we have had two days good enough to get the dogs out for a run in the past 10 days. August seems to have particularly bad weather. Today is another blizz. Last week we had four days' drift and wind, two of which were blizz days, and two which were just cold, $-26°$ to $-28°C$, and windy, 30 knots. On the two days with no wind and falling snow we managed to get the dogs out. The bad weather seems endless. All that means no more data. Work-wise I have been trying to catch up with analysis. I still have several months to grind through.

We have been making preparations for Kloa. Paul and I have been rebuilding sledges, making harnesses, new tent bags, fixing up choofers [stoves]. The list of things to do is almost endless. Also, we need to get the dogs out as much as possible. We are going to try and take two puppies with us and they need as much work as they can get beforehand. The first run we went on last week was an absolute fiasco. There was an all-in brawl as we were getting ready to go. The sledge turned over as we took off, the lead dogs wouldn't lead and the team just wouldn't pull. We couldn't even get as far as Departure Rocks. My God! On the return to Colbeck they apparently had to run out in front of the team the whole way. I don't know why! At least the next day things went a bit better.

Cocoa is looking decidedly pregnant. We will keep any dogs that she has. Almost hoping she just has bitches so she can lead us to Kloa but we do need some good new boys to take over from the crones in that team too so I guess either way will have its advantages. [6]

Hope all is well. Love always, Pene.

29 AUGUST 1990

Dear Pene,
Well, I'm in the midst of the optics advisory committee meeting. Today, the first day, was spent 'brainstorming' on the scientific value of what we are trying to do. Boy, it was fascinating for me — makes me feel that all I really know about is my tiny little field of experience. It is with an accumulation of years working in the field that you get an overview of what it's all about.

That was last Wednesday, then I wrote some more on Friday but that got lost. Last week was really full-on, with the three day-long committee meetings along with lunches and dinners. I was exhausted by the end of it and thought I'd come in over the weekend and write you a nice longy, but alas I couldn't face it. The weekend was quiet, I slept and planned lessons while the sky just poured down. My neck and back have been stiff since the stresses and strains of the meeting. I must get back into some yoga.

There were seven bigwigs visiting aeronomy, supposedly to advise us on how to spend all this money that's come our way. We ended up with a $4 million budget covering the purchase of, wait for it . . . eight imagers of different forms (all-sky, narrow and wide field etc.), four spectrographs, a UV Michelson, two observatory FPSs and two portable. In reality this will probably be cut in half, but it's still a hell of a lot. We also stressed that it was essential that they employ at least five personnel dedicated to making it all happen, i.e. a manager, technicians and engineers. If it is only Roger and I we don't stand a hope in hell. Someone up top thinks that money can buy good science but on its own it ain't gonna do anything and there's already enough unanalysed data around the place. I ended up feeling pretty cynical about the whole thing, and I guess also feeling pretty confused about whether I really want to stay in this business. Roger has told me I can stay as long as I like.

And so, Pene, I just don't know. In some ways I'm enjoying being a female in the field, particularly when it comes to group dynamics, and I can't wait until there's more of us, but I don't much like the stress of it all. I'm starting to work too hard and feel caught up, which I don't want. What is the answer to all this? My summer student has finished up having handed in a most impressive report. That made me feel good, as I know that she's thrived on working for a woman, so I do find this role-model stuff fairly important and extremely satisfying. Meanwhile, teaching at this stage is just a bunch of lesson plans and notes, and more lesson plans and notes hanging over me. I'm looking forward to getting started in two weeks now.

This coming weekend is a long weekend so I'm off to Chitina. Art and I have had lots of phone calls and I'm looking forward to seeing him. A few hugs and a bit of TLC won't go astray at the moment. Dunc spent a week down with Art and it sounds like they had a good and productive time.

My other real worry at the moment is for the world with this Middle East crisis. Don't know how much you're hearing about it, but the US is recruiting people and to all intents and purposes preparing for war, with a rather worrying enthusiasm. Makes me wonder how long I want to stay in this country. They've upped the surveillance on the Alaska oil pipeline so suddenly things are feeling just a bit too close to home for my liking. I have a growing feeling that the only hope for the world is with women. Speaking of women, did you know that Australia now has two female premiers, in WA and in Victoria?

As for cooperative experiments, our instrument is in pieces at the moment having some machining done, and it's going to be two weeks before we get it back together as Roger is away. Our recoated OH-red plates haven't arrived yet so to start off with we will be observing red-green until they arrive. For us it's going to be quite a slow start unfortunately. Our most promising time is going to be when you return from Kloa.

Dipper never did produce any pups, she just got fatter with all the extra titbits. Winter is on its way. The winds have been getting quite chilly and change is in the air. The dogs are starting to hype up — they know it won't be long.

With love and hugs, Gina.

30 AUGUST 1990

Dear Pene,

I've got the use of a car for as long as I want it, so now I feel nicely independent and ready to cope with the winter with or without Art around. I'm also feeling very tempted to get a young pup. A mushing friend of William's, Sue, recently returned after participating in a joint Soviet–American dog-sled trip along the Soviet far eastern coast. They began in Provideniya, crossing a coastal mountain range and pack-ice, to finish in the small village of Uelen, 250 miles away. They were being flown out of the village, dogs and all, when their biplane crashed soon after take-off. A Soviet musher and a total of four dogs (two of Sue's) died in the crash while two other dogs fled from the crash site. Sue suffered four broken ribs and bruising and was flown out, with two of her dogs still missing. Two months later one of the dogs, Vixen, was found by a friend of Sue's back in Provideniya. Vixen was living in a buried pipe, having survived and retraced the full length of their trip. She is a chronically shy dog and it took some coaxing to retrieve her. Eventually she was returned to Sue, pregnant, so now there are seven Glasnost puppies needing homes. There's no saying what sort of a mongrel the father was, but I can't help feeling some sort of a pull towards these pups. Now would be a good time for me to get one as it could run along with Dipper to get the hang of it, then take over from her next year.

Work-wise I've done sweet F.A. this week. I've had bad period pains and now a lower-back problem, and Roger is away, which has all led to me having a lot of trouble motivating myself. I'm playing with ideas for teaching still, but next week I've got to knuckle down and get a bit more serious about it. So, first thing tomorrow morning (Friday) I'll be hitting the road. It's a wonderful drive and I do enjoy driving on my own, and I am looking forward to seeing Art. It's been three weeks, and lots more thinking things over for us both, so we'll see how things feel. We are going up to McCarthy for a dance on Sunday night. It is the final fling of the summer, so that should be fun.

So catch ya next Tuesday, love and thoughts, Gina.

PS: The night-times are getting dark, particularly with no snow around, and it feels like winter is already closing in. There is a flock of sandhill cranes, hundreds of them, feeding up in a paddock I ride past each day. They have stopped over on their way south. They've been there over a week now. I'm gradually rugging up more to ride my bike in the morning. Oh help! Hope you're enjoying your sunshine!

1 SEPTEMBER 1990

Hi Gina,

Well, first day of spring for us and first day of autumn or, dare I say it, fall for you. The days are almost normal length but changing very rapidly. We still haven't had very much good weather, had a couple of twilights data this week, should probably have done daytime obs today but it's Saturday and had a lot of things to get done with the dogs this afternoon. Actually it was about 5/8 cirrus this morning so wouldn't have been too good. This afternoon I dug out the pupping cage for Cocoa as she'll probably drop her pups this week. She's my favourite bitch, has lots of character and is a good lead dog. Our departure for Kloa may be delayed a bit as the traverse that's out dumping fuel for the Lambert traverse in summer is taking longer than planned. Not that it matters much; the later in September it is, the more likely we are to get nice weather. We'll be gone three or four weeks. No doubt the first thing I'll do when we get back is write you a mail message.

Don't worry about your letters sounding down. It's just good to hear from you, no matter what, and I realise that if I didn't have one set of problems I'd be having another. I have been doing a bit of stuff on the 3FP. It's been slowly getting to the stage where it needs quite a bit of attention, keyboard cleaning, a couple of problems with disk drives, the storage tank for the refrigerant has started crumbling and needs to be replaced. I guess this summer I'll have to calibrate all the filters too. Oh well. Actually it's a pity but that experiment hasn't been done proper justice. The fundamental papers describing the instrument have never been published, so where do you start when you have a small contribution to make?

Non-work-wise the only run we've been on was today. Paul and I took seven boys out. The seven we had I could imagine going somewhere, which is an improvement over last week, but we need to get them out as often as possible. We went for a quick trip over to Welch Island. It's been windy all this week and there's not much snow left on the sea-ice. We put a rope around one of the runners to slow the sled down as we just couldn't keep up with them when both of us weren't on the sled, it was −27°C this afternoon and blowing about 15–20 knots, so it was bloody cold and we needed to keep running.

Oh, I nearly forgot — on Thursday after dawn obs four of us Hagglundsed to Auster rookery for the day. I got back in time for dusk obs. We went to check out the penguins. Had a reminder that the sea-ice is over the ocean because a route we'd been going in by was through an alley, about 500 m wide, between a few bergs. Well, one of the bergs had turned over which had caused the landmark, a jade berg with Sphinx-like legs, to tilt by about 30° and all the ice in the alley was totally smashed up. All this had happened since another party were out there last Saturday. Boy, you wouldn't want to be anywhere near a berg when something like that happened. Needless to say, you couldn't drive a Hagglunds over that ice now. Piles of it 20–30 feet high all over the place and there'd be thick and thin bits and could be mushy in places; there was a seal nearby, so had to be open water somewhere.

We found another path in to the rookery. All this destruction was a couple of kilometres from the rookery so it wasn't like in your year when a berg at the rookery turned over.[7] The chicks were really cute, little balls of fluff and white eye-patches. They make fantastic noises, the whole rookery sort of babbles like an alien choir. Took a few photos, although I don't have a long lens to get good close-up shots. Was bloody cold though, nice clear skies, −20°-odd, and about 15–20 knots of wind. Not nice weather to stand around outside taking photos. I got my nose nipped again and one of my fingers is nipped. I had only just recovered from the last nipping. Once you've been nipped the skin is more tender and nips more easily. The biggest problem is that if I try and wear a face mask my glasses fog up. I can tell you there's many times I've wished I had the contact lenses I so nearly bought last year. They make it so much easier. Paul wears contact lenses. I sometimes try to wear my glasses and avoid putting my face mask on and then I get nipped. On the run to Colbeck I just didn't wear any glasses for a couple of days. Below about −20°C you need to wear a face mask, especially if there's any wind.

Paul and I have been overhauling a sledge to take on the trip with us. Putting new runners on, new handlebars, a new longitudinal. It's nearly a whole new sled. Has been quite a lot of work but hopefully we'll get it finished tomorrow.

My daily calibrations are nearly finished so I can set up for night-time green obs now and go and have some tea. It's almost 9 p.m. Although your work may be more consuming than you'd like it to be, you'll probably feel good about achieving things with it in the long run.

Guess I've turned off to the world. I'd sort of gathered from the newspapers down here that there was a female premier in Victoria, but not WA, and the Gulf troubles I just want to forget about. Seems like it could be the scene of the next major conflict in the world. When will money stop turning people's heads? What can we do? Living down here you get back in touch with how some more normal — or should I say more pedestrian, or non-academic, or non-intellectual, or non-peaceful — anyway, you see how other people think, those who you wouldn't usually see or choose to be with. It is a bit depressing at times but there is hope, I think. I believe. I sure hope so anyway.

Peace and happiness. Love, Pene.

5 SEPTEMBER 1990

Dear Pene,

It's Wednesday and I just returned from Chitina late last night, having taken an extra day just being real slack. It was a great weekend in many ways. We went out to McCarthy where the fall seems to be more advanced than in the rest of the state, and it was just spectacular. The dance was great — I danced with Art all night. Then we stayed with some friends of his who live in a yurt, a circular construction, where we caught a bad case of yurt disease, i.e. we just hung out and sheltered from the rain all day and spent most of it in bed, rather than returning to the real world. The next day the sun came out and we enjoyed riding our bikes out in the beautiful fall colours. I felt like I was in a book.

The realities of the weekend were a bit harder to take. Art and I are breaking up. He's going to come up to Fairbanks soon and pack up his stuff. Some of me feels really bummed, although not as bad as before as I've been sort of preparing myself for it, but then again on Monday I just found myself with no energy or motivation to continue with anything at all. I guess one hurtful part about it is that Art wants to pursue things with this other woman. Things got pretty hot for a while there as we talked through all that. Art was pretty defensive and me pretty pissed off at him, but once that was out we were able to enjoy the rest of the weekend. I guess that if you're going to break up then sooner or later the issue of one or the other getting involved with someone else comes up, and has to be faced. Anyway, we still feel like good friends at this stage so I hope we can maintain that. I think I do really need some time on my own. That does feel right although a bit daunting and scary at the same time. Then again I couldn't think of a better set-up than here to go through that. The main thing is that neither of us has regrets. I think we've been good for each other, so now I just need to learn how to be good for me for a while.

Teaching is getting real close now. First lecture is at UT 0210, Tuesday (your time–day) 11 September. So maybe you can think of me as you sit down for breakfast. It is an evening class, 5.10 to 6.10, Monday, Wednesday and Friday so I should get some of the mature-age students. Today I've been sussing out what teaching support there is. There is an orientation course for new staff over the next two days. I have lots of ideas and have produced a summary of the course to hand out, but I haven't actually worked out the content of any lectures yet.

I'm going to miss you when you go to Kloa. It must be fun getting everything ready and being able to share it with Paul. I take it he is going too? Who else is going and are you happy with the company?

Lots of love, Gina

For me it went without saying that I would be running the Kloa trip with Paul. By this time our relationship was very solid. In these circumstances a relationship either thrives or becomes increasingly difficult. Paul and I shared everything. We shared our passion for working with the dogs and we both handled them in a similar manner. When working with dogs a balance between dominance and understanding is required. Some people are more aggressive in their handling than others. Paul and I naturally used the same techniques with the teams and this made running together with a team a pleasure. Although we hadn't formalised our relationship we both respected each other and knew we were committed to and could trust each other. We were not openly affectionate but we were rarely apart and were always considered as a couple by others on the base.

A staunch friendship is not unusual in Antarctica. Often two people quickly become good friends and spend most of their time together. Friends often plan trips away from the base together; this gives them common experiences and in 12 months strong bonds are formed. For Paul and me such a friendship was heightened by our physical relationship. Although our relationship set us at some distance to others on the base, we did have other friends.

Paul and I usually had half an hour together before tea to talk the day's events through and hence we were some of the last in the mess for tea. We'd end up together with one or two others at the last half-empty table. This became known as 'Paul and Pene's table'. After tea we would work on the sledges or make harnesses, read together or go to the 16 mm movies, depending on our projects at the time. The old 16 mm movies were shown on Wednesday and Sunday nights. Videos were available at any time in the video room but we seldom had the time or inclination to watch them. Because we were able to spend so much time together and work together to achieve things we got to know each other very well, very quickly, much more quickly than one does in Australia, where seeing someone two or three times a week requires an effort. The rapport that Paul and I had built up over a month or two usually comes only after years of friendship.

Maybe this commitment hadn't come through in my letters to Gina. Paul and I did not have any problems in our relationship so I didn't need to talk about difficulties or problems. It was hard to describe to her what sort of person Paul was, his dry sense of humour, how he lightened my day or just what it was that made us 'click'. We shared a somewhat cynical approach to many things but in general had similar attitudes and approaches to problems. We had enough things in common and enough things to offer each other — Paul was good at doing some things I was not and vice versa — that our relationship really did thrive. When things are going well they don't need to be discussed and it's only when things start being difficult that they need to be shared.

9 SEPTEMBER 1990

Hi, Gina,
Hope you have found some enthusiasm to do some living and working-type things and that Art's final decision hasn't had too many negative

effects on you. Was thinking of you 0210 UT on Friday, hope the lectures are going well. Must admit I would find it a bit of a daunting prospect.

Well, things are really getting under way for our trip. Yes, Paul and I are going together. That was unsaid I guess. Would need a lot of rethinking if it was any other way. The other team is Craig Hunter (SRTO) and Dave Shaw (met. tech.). Paul and I are just about packed up ready to go. Craig and Dave will be ready by Wednesday. We will be a happy group, I think. We hope to head off Wednesday. It's quite exciting. I do feel ready for it now. This has been helped by a few days of nice weather. A quick blizz yesterday and back to balmy sunshine and no wind this afternoon. Hopefully that means the bad August weather is over.

Cocoa has had her first pup this afternoon. (No more yet.) Think it's a boy. So that's pretty exciting. Paul and I were walking past the pupping cage all day going back and forth to pack up the sled, which is over at the dog-hut. There's an enormous drift, actually two enormous drifts to go over. The dog-hut has formed a windscour around it otherwise it would be several feet under the drifts by now, and that's the roof not the floor. Most of the old station is completely buried. The electrician and chippie say the puppies run over the roofs and make quite a racket. Anyway, Cocoa was racing out and barking at us all afternoon and we reckon she had the first pup in about five minutes. We could hear it wailing and still she rushed out to bark at us again but when we went in the cage she dropped to protect the pup and hasn't got up again. Looks like she's a pretty good mother. It's her second litter. However, it's still pretty cold here, in the high minus 20s most days, so she'll have to watch the pups in the cold.

Well, the only other news is that Parker is out to put the RTOs through the wringer for what he has described as phone tapping. He has it in for these guys. Says he's going to charge them under Commonwealth Acts or something like that. I think he's crazy. I don't think he's got enough support from other people on the station to do this. I also think it will just divide the station even further and make the station group more uncomfortable. Anyway, doesn't really bother me as we're leaving for a few weeks and we'll soon talk it out in the field.

The other news I have for you is that Mal is going to run the FPS doing automatic green obs while I'm away. So if you are running we may be able to do some comparisons. We'll be doing green obs in the cardinal points. I thought it would be worthwhile doing it because by the time I get back, nights will be getting fairly short. So I hope you can get your FPS going too.

Well, think that's about it. I'm writing this while doing dusk observations. We had two good days last Thursday and Friday. I was tuning up in the morning and we had a power failure. The power was off to aeronomy for seven hours because the PLC[8] has totally chucked it in. We've had five power failures since then but hopefully it's OK now. So that was Thursday. Paul and I ended up taking five dogs for a quick run around Welch Island Thursday afternoon. So I didn't totally waste the good observing weather. I got set up again on Friday morning after the temperature had stabilised, only to find I had to spend the morning fixing the white light source and that the view switch wasn't working properly. On Saturday morning I got up at seven for dawn and there was no wind but 7/8 cirrus and by 11 a.m. we were into a blizz. I fed the dogs at 4 p.m. which was probably the worst time of the day weather-wise and by 9 p.m. there was almost no drift and only about 40 knots of wind. When I was feeding the dogs, a tin with 12 blocks of pemm in it just blew away — must have weighed at least 10 kg. So that's how things are going at Mawson. I must get some pictures of the station now with all the drifts around. May wander around with a camera for a while tomorrow.

Peace and happiness, love, Pene.

I was envious of Pene's trip to Kloa; she was embarking on the ultimate trip in Antarctica with a tried and trusted companion and a well-trained team. She was fit; she was confident and had every reason to be. During my year at Mawson, Peta and Bear had formed a strong relationship centred around the dogs, like Pene and Paul. Bear had previous experience with the dogs and was nominated dogman; the two of them soon took charge. Peta and Bear adopted a rigorous training schedule for the three pups, two of which, Blackie and Welf, would now be on Pene's team. Training the dogs requires consistency and dedication and they would take a small team out whenever possible.

I had been keen to be involved with the dogs at Mawson in 1985 but I did not have the experience, confidence or work schedule to take on full responsibility for them. Neither did I have a regular running partner. I had made a point of spreading myself around at Mawson as the social aspects of a year in isolation were as important to me as exploring the place itself.

The tight partnership of Peta and Bear was resented at times by others on base. A couple can become a self-sufficient unit, not reaching out to the rest of the group to the same extent as everyone else. I felt a sense of responsibility to the group and tried to remain sensitive to its needs. I enjoyed the diversity of people and would be happy sitting next to anyone at meals.

The trips I undertook were varied and with a different party each time. New and deeper insights on personalities were obtained and tighter friendships formed. After the intimacy of a tent or field hut, the base would feel hustled and anonymous on return. I do not carry regrets; if I had the year again I would make the same choices. However, I still mourn the lost opportunity of doing such a trip and of working closely with the dogs on a regular and consistent basis. In my mind Pene and Paul had the right approach and even compared to other years they were poised for an enviable journey.

12 SEPTEMBER 1990

Dear Gina,

Well, we're still here although plan to get away tomorrow. We had a blizz on Saturday, clear Sunday, blizzed Monday, blowing snow on Tuesday and now it's Wednesday. We are just about ready to go and although it has been a fairly unrushed business packing, we put off going today because the other team weren't quite ready. I can't help feeling we may have forgotten something.

One unpleasant part of the preparations was proving to Parker that the .38 could be used effectively to put a dog down. Shane had tried to put a dog down with it earlier in the year and he had ended up getting Parker to finish the job with the .303, the only other firearm on station. We put down D-Day, who has been pretty useless of late in the team and at an age where he's not likely to improve. Paul and I had talked about it with Lloyd and worked out how it should be done. Paul did the actual deed, he's a bit more familiar with firearms than I am. D-Day dropped on the first shot and was definitely dead. Parker wasn't satisfied with that and after agreeing that he was dead proceeded to pump two shots into him with the rifle. It was a strange thing for him to do. I was not very happy about having to kill D-Day but that's how it goes. It's just one of the jobs of being a dog-handler. At least now we can take the pistol with us and put down any dogs if they collapse on the trip without resorting to ice-axes. Paul had to sign for each bullet that we take. I sure hope we don't have to do that sort of thing but it's best to be prepared if you do have to face the situation.

Feel quite ready to set out and then it's just day after day. I do hope that we will actually make it to Kloa. Andrew put up a seismograph chart last week with tremors from a large ice-fall 170–250 km from Mawson. He cannot say whether it's east or west though, so there may be some interesting ice to negotiate. We will just do whatever we can. I think it may most likely be from the Amery ice-shelf, which would be that distance off but to the east, so not in the direction of our travel.

It will only be a couple of weeks from when we get back to the first ship arriving. If Paul is going home early I will probably try to come out before the last ship, so may be back in Australia about end February, early March. If I don't come out until the last ship it may be end March, early April before I return. The Mawson Institute still only has money to pay me until the end of April.

All this business with the RTOs has fallen in a heap. Parker had the radio operators monitoring how much time the RTOs were spending in the Anaresat building. Once the division people talked to a few other people down here, they dropped the whole thing like a hot cake. The RTOs' union threatened to go out on strike. Craig, the SRTO, is coming with us and needless to say is looking forward to getting away from the place.

Take care and look after yourself and I'll write on my return.

Love, Pene.

12 SEPTEMBER 1990

Dear Pene,

Hope you get this before you leave. I've been thinking about you heading off and hoping I wouldn't miss wishing you well on your trip. I started teaching on Monday and have been in somewhat of a panic since then. Next class is today. The first class went OK, although half the time had gone before I got into any physics, and then there was one almighty sigh from the whole class. I then hit them with calculating the height of the aurora from two altitude measurements to revise their trigonometry, but I think I lost half of them. So today we're doing some basic maths. Then yesterday spent the day at Poker. It was wonderful driving out in the fall colours. I was at work till about 10.30 last night writing out a summary of the course, then when I got home Art had arrived. So there's a lot going on. I'm enjoying having the teaching to get my teeth into so I don't dwell on the other stuff too much. Teaching is very absorbing and so far feels good.

On running the FPS, if the periscope has trouble when it's windy, then some nights of zenith-only obs in such conditions wouldn't go astray! We should be up and running in a few days. Principally we'll be observing in the green — I've *lost* the red filter. How embarrassing! I hope it turns up soon.

Pene, please take care and be safe, I'll be thinking of you lots. I hope that the ice-fall isn't in your direction, and I wish you good judgment if it is and for all the other situations you'll be evaluating. Keep your wits about you, and most of all have a wonderful time. (I'll send you some nourishing thoughts whenever I sit down to a big hot meal.) My thoughts are with you, Pene, and some for Paul too.

With love always, Gina.

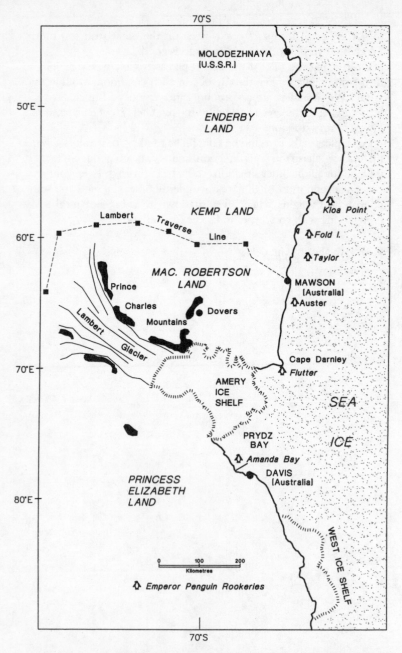

Lambert Glacier Basin. Officially Pene's expedition to Kloa had two main aims: observing emperor penguins at Fold Island and Kloa Point and training the dog teams. MAP: JOHN COX

PART FIVE

PURPLE POLAR
KNICKERS

Armed with hot thermoses and toasted sandwiches, we left for Kloa about 12.30 on Saturday 15 September. Snow showers played over the islands to the west. The two teams set off down the snow ramp on to the harbour. The first few days we'd be travelling over familiar territory and camping on islands we'd visited before. Officially the trip had two main aims: emperor penguin observations at Fold Island and Kloa Point rookeries, and training of the dog teams. We also intended to thoroughly check the depots — some had been set out specifically for survival; others had been created when passing dog-teams unloaded unnecessary gear and rations. For all of us on the trip it was a chance to immerse ourselves in the Antarctic environment — a real adventure. Such an opportunity was a rare privilege and we had worked hard to avail ourselves of it. I was confident that we all had experience working with the dogs and surviving in tents with what we could carry on our sledges. The weekend runs and earlier trips ensured that both dogs and people were fit for what lay ahead.

Our companions for the trip had been chosen after a meeting in June for all those potentially interested in participating. Those who thought they might want to go on the long leg of the trip were left to see if they could organise their work schedules to accommodate the three-week absence. For most, such a long trip would preclude other extended absences from the base. As it eventuated, the three others were the people I would have chosen. Paul and I would travel in one team, Dave Shaw and Craig Hunter in the other. Although travelling together, the two teams would also require a sense of independence.

As trip leaders Paul and I had agreed with the station leader that whatever happened we would turn and head back for Mawson on 1 October. If all went according to plan we would do that some days earlier. We did not have to set a fast pace so we were determined to enjoy ourselves and make the most of our freedom to travel unhindered into what was, to us, unknown country. When we reached Ledingham's Depot after a week's travel we amused ourselves with the idea of being the only people in Kemp Land. We could make the rules and when the return party were expected to join us we made a sign: 'Welcome to Kemp Land. Population, 4; no OICs; no pets; no meetings; no Madness'. (*Mawson Madness* was the name of the daily news-sheet and to us symbolised the inanity of bureaucracy.)

Although enjoyable, the trip was still hard physical work. Paul and I worked together as part of our team. We got to know each of the 11 dogs as individuals: Pedro in the lead followed by the 'Cocoa Mafia': Cocoa and her brother Merlin and Cocoa's pups from the year before, Oscar, Goohaw and Jedda. Jedda was usually at the back of the team. If given a chance these five animals would lie together preening each other but most frequently preening Cocoa. (Only three of Cocoa's pups had survived and as they were all bitches they were put down.) Kamik and Choofa followed the mafia. Choofa and Oscar were our hardest, strongest workers; they would start the sledge running and always pulled when in the trace. The other three were old dogs, kept near the back so we could easily reach them if they weren't working. Despite this, Blackie, Welf and Otis were lovable and part of the team. Our travelling routines became less of a chore and more just the necessities for life, like going to the grocery store or buying petrol for the car.

Mornings we would awake and, being a morning person, I was usually awake first. It is hard to make a break from the warmth of a sleeping-bag. Paul would light the choofer and Tilley lamp and lie back down again for 10–15 minutes while the tent warmed up. I was next to the outside wall of the tent and couldn't do anything until Paul had decided to start the day. We'd get up, pack the sleeping-bags away and get dressed. Quite a few layers are required for temperatures from 15° to 25° below zero. During the morning routine the dogs would be greeted and given a few moments' individual attention; then we would breakfast and pack the sledge. Paul was the inside person and I, the outside person. This meant I packed and arranged the gear on the sledge and laid out the trace ready for hitching up. Paul looked after the cooking gear, lamps and all the bits and pieces inside the tent. Once the contents of the tent were packed on to the sledge we'd both go into the tent and warm our fingers on the Tilley lamp and put on our instep crampons. The lamp was the last thing to be packed away before the tent was dropped and packed, a task most efficiently done together. The tent would be lashed on top of the sledge and later if we were lucky enough we'd perch atop the green canvas bag, riding side-saddle. The load was spread along the sledge for the best performance when gliding through snow — not too much weight at the front, not too much weight too high.

Once the sledge was packed we'd prepare the dogs. They knew the routine and as we were packing they'd arouse themselves for the day. We usually left harnesses on all bar Jedda. (She'd eaten two harnesses in the first few days but by the last days of the trip we were able to leave her harness on as well.) We'd take five or six selected dogs to the trace and then Paul would keep them sitting while I fetched the last dogs — usually the troublemakers or excitable animals. With the dogs in place the night-trace had to be fastened around karabiners on one side of the sledge. The heavy steel pegs and deadmen used to anchor the night-trace would be stowed in a peg-bag on the handlebars. The front peg anchoring the lead dog would be removed and, with a foot firmly planted on the brake, the peg anchoring the rear of the sledge was then removed and stowed in the peg-bag. This was always a tense moment. If the dogs took off before we were ready — and they were always keen to leave as soon as possible — it could mean one or both of us would be left behind, the sledge could easily turn over on tide-cracks surrounding most of the camp sites and the whole team have an all-in battle. With a firm hold on the brake I would don my sledging overmitts and give Paul the thumbs-up — we were away again. If we survived the first half-hour with no dramas we'd start relaxing and smiling. Another day opening before us with new vistas and promises.

So the hours and kilometres would pass — sometimes with hazards, blowing snow and wind trying to whip maps from your gloved hands, other times with blue skies, beauty and splendour, or snow-baths in warm spring weather for the hot dogs. Ice, islands, snow and clouds drifted past. We were travelling at a speed which enabled the scenery to be imprinted on our minds and absorbed into our souls.

The end of the day was another routine; somewhat easier as the dogs were always keen to rest and did not absorb as much of our attention. We'd approach a campsite, often coaxing the boys to haul the sledge up on to an island over 1 m or 2 m drops — an extra effort at the end of the day. Pegs secured the back of the sledge and the lead dog. (Yes, give him a pat for a good day's work and a few moments' special attention.) The night-trace would be laid out and secured — a stainless steel wire with 70 cm lengths of chain for each dog. The dogs would be placed to minimise disturbance — Blackie at one end, Pedro at the other; Oscar and Goohaw together, the bitches Kamik, Jedda and Cocoa separating Merlin and Pedro, Blackie and Oscar, Choofa and Goohaw. This would mean a quiet night's sleep for us all.

Next we'd put up the polar pyramid tent. Paul and I worked together then: as I shovelled snow on the valance, Paul would unload the sledge, unpack the inside gear and get the choofers going to melt snow or ice for a cuppa. As this was progressing one of us would feed the dogs. With the sledge three-quarters empty we'd turn it ready for the morning's take-off and firmly lash the remaining items together in case a blizzard blew up overnight.

One night as we unpacked the food and started feeding the dogs they all pulled simultaneously in the same direction on the night-trace. Eleven dogs rushed for the one pemm block that had been given to Pedro, first on the line. In 10 seconds we had one writhing ball of fur, gnashing teeth, steel wire and chain. Snarling, snapping and howling rent the air. Jedda got the pemm block, Goohaw managed to wind the night-trace around his paws and howled in increasing panic as the fight pulled it tighter and tighter. Paul and I went to work peeling dogs away from the edges and securing them so they couldn't rejoin the melee. We could secure three with their harnesses over the handlebars. Others could be pegged down until we were left with the hard-core fighters, separated carefully to avoid teeth sinking into human flesh. Eventually we had them all out and could start to untangle the knots and tangles in the wire and chain. Goohaw was not badly damaged, his pride probably hurt more than his body. Another half an hour and the line was back out, secured in a different position, and the dogs were licking their wounds.

We collapsed into the tent — this was not the sort of episode you need after a long day. After reviving ourselves with tea and sledgies and a few moments' rest, we tried again to feed the dogs, this time successfully. Jedda got a second pemm block, not because she was being praised but because you couldn't leave her out when all the others were being fed!

Not every day held so much excitement. Our activities depended on how long we had been travelling. Often after soup and a small meal we'd explore the islands where we'd camped. A more extensive meal and a drink was followed at 8 p.m. by the nightly sked with Mawson, assurance for them that we were surviving and in no difficulty. We'd talk through the day's events and retire, never too late, for travelling meant continued exertion and required plenty of sleep.

This trip was the highlight of my year at Mawson. I was glad we had persevered with preparations and achieved what has since become impossible. Other than our nightly skeds with Mawson, Craig and Dave would set up an Icom radio, powered by batteries recharged with a solar cell. We could listen to the BBC or ABC world news and Craig occasionally managed to contact fellow ham-radio operators. We had no other communication; correspondence with Gina had to wait until I returned to Mawson in October.

27 SEPTEMBER 1990

Hi Pene,

Just a hello to an empty aeronomy lab to let you know I'm thinking of you and looking forward to your return. I wonder often about how you're going. We had a women's circle meeting on Sunday — we meet at the solstices, equinoxes and one time in between each. This was the equinox meeting. It was nice because it was focusing on the coming of winter, slowing down, going inside yourself. It's a time of reflection. In fact I think it's all the things I feel like I need right now. So at least I'm in phase with the seasons. We always open and close the circle with a prayer to each direction, and whenever we look and send our thoughts south, I think of you, although it's always in the wrong context as to everyone here the south stands for the sun and the warmth, and the north for the chill winds. We also have a women's music–singing group going. We've been meeting about once a fortnight and we sing some rounds, blues, spirituals with lots of good harmonies. I hope I can learn to sing better harmonies. Some of the women are really good and they have excellent voices.

And so, Art has moved out of my life as it was. He's now *all* back down in Chitina and by the sounds of it really thriving on having all of himself in one spot rather than being spread out between Chitina and Fairbanks. As life's fine sense of timing would have it, the week Art was up moving his stuff out, Scott from Hidden Hill announced his engagement (I think it must be the law of conservation of couples) and promptly moved out. After deliberating about it for a morning I moved into his old cabin. Art and I were able to clear out of the old one together.

I'm really happy in my new space. In fact it feels so good I want to put a big sign up saying 'Gina's Place' to celebrate the fact that I've never had my own place before. It's still quite a mess with stuff spread everywhere waiting to get drawn into its place. It's smaller than the old one, has an upstairs loft, downstairs kitchen facility but no running water, so at least I can entertain in my own cabin. Also don't have to worry about feeling like I have to go to meetings on Sunday mornings, as we did in the old one, because the meeting house was directly below. It has a nice open view of the valley, giving a light and airy feeling. So I feel like in the last month or so I've suddenly got really established, getting a car, a cabin, a computer at work, and starting teaching. All this has helped a lot with losing Art.

In hindsight I feel like I did jump into things with Art, to hide from my feelings of loss with Tod, and it's only now that I'm feeling set and secure in the other areas that I feel I can start to go through that grief, although now I've got Art grief to go through as well. Pene, I want to stay single for 12 months (at least). OK? I really feel the need for this, so can you subtly remind me if you hear me questioning this conviction?

Teaching is going pretty well. Some days I just love it and others it doesn't go so well. It's taking up a lot of my time, in fact nearly all my time, as I find myself having to think deeply about things like Newton's laws, and just what a force and mass are, before I can teach it. It is fun to ponder these things, and of course each week I have to do the homework questions like everyone else for when they ask me about them. Some say the difference between giving and taking a class is one week. For me it's about half a day at the moment. Hopefully I'll be able to bring this up to one day soon.

I don't think that I'm really high up on the popularity stakes. I gave them a quiz the other day which almost half of them failed. In the other class they were given a homework problem to do in class as a quiz and half of them got full marks. But anyway, I think my 'kids' would have got far more out of doing this quiz than they would have got out of redoing a homework problem. Two women topped the grades in my class. They are a pretty nice bunch all in all. There are a few military guys. It's quite nice to have a chance to mix with them, the 'other side of town' and I really like them. They are cooperative and respectful.

Well, better do some work. It's nice to write to you even if you're not there and at least you'll have something waiting for your return. I hope you're safe and snug and warm, the dogs are working well for you and that you're all having a wonderful trip.

And I guess *welcome home*, for when you do get this.

Love and hugs and thoughts, Gina.

My cabin came to define my sacred space. Within it I felt full and complete, with all my requirements for high-quality living within reach. I slept in the loft; just big enough for a built-in bed and a small landing. A metre-square hole was cut in the landing through which a ladder poked for access. Surrounded by tall spruce trees, I slept in their midst and viewed the world from the same vantage through a flattened window. It was a safe shelter which always revived me. I could smell the first fall of snow and absorb the transformed scene, looking out across the valley from my bed. It had the cosiness of a cubbyhouse and I could feel a glow of self-sufficiency.

The downstairs was dominated by a large octagonal window, lined with a bench seat. The southern aspect made this an ideal place to lie and absorb the delicate rays of the winter sun during its brief traverse. A balcony formed the entrance to the cabin. Adorned with flowers in summer, it became an extension to the living space; while in winter the railings and seats were draped in snow. In the dark nights I'd retreat back into a large arm chair situated in the warmer depths of my cabin between the base of the ladder and the stove. The kitchen area included a small fridge, cupboards, sink and water container. A well-stocked coat-rack lined the wall by the door, and a high shelf built on to the loft contained an array of boots. The small monitor heater formed a central hub around which life revolved; I would often plant myself right in front of it to dry out sweat-soaked clothes after a good ski.

8 OCTOBER 1990

Hi Gina,

Well, I haven't been able to log in to Adelaide as their Austpac connection is out of order so I haven't received any news from you. This is just to let you know I am back at Mawson.

We had a fantastic trip, away 22 days, but we didn't get to Kloa as Edward VIII Gulf was too badly rafted. We got about a quarter of the way across the gulf so we were about 20 km from Kloa. It was a bit disappointing that we didn't get to our final destination but all of us had a good trip so it didn't matter that much. It's hard to know where to start telling the story and how much detail to put in.

Paul and I and Craig Hunter (SRTO) and Dave Shaw (met. tech.) ran out to Kloa and then back again to Ledingham's Depot. That was stopping at Low Tongue, Island 45, Colbeck (three nights, one for bad weather), Tilley Nunatak and Ledingham's Depot, which is near Fold Island. At Ledingham's Depot we had a blizzard and we were there for three nights, one day totally blizzed in and then a day of blowing snow during which we walked to the emperor rookery. There and back was an afternoon stroll of 20 km slogging through soft snow. What a rest day!!! We loaded up the sleds with extra pemm and had a long hard day's slog through more soft snow for 42 km to Havstein Island. East Stack next night (just east of the Hoseason Glacier), Crooked Island, Moonie Island, one day going out into the gulf, one day fixing the sleds, so three nights all together at Moonie Island. The view from there out into Edward VIII Gulf is just fantastic. Seven glaciers pour into the gulf and there's several different levels in the

Chena Ridge Friends Meeting, Hidden Hill, Alaska: Sunday morning gathering outside the Quaker meeting house with the first snow fall in September (Gina is eighth from right, standing).

Gina's cabin at Hidden Hill, Alaska, after a light fall of snow in September.

Pene Greet and Paul Myers 'blizzed in' at Ledingham's Depot, Antarctica. The book is not a prop—field trips were one of the few occasions when Pene had time to read about the sledging experiences of past explorers.

PHOTO: PAUL MYERS

Gina shelters in a wind scour overlooking West Bay, Mawson 1985.

Moon over the aeronomy roof at Mawson, Antarctica. An all-sky camera is in the front dome and the FPS periscope behind. These instruments are used to observe optical emissions, aurora and airglow, from the sky. At times through the year the moon did not set, skimming the horizon to the south.

PHOTO: PENE GREET

Paul Gigg, Dave Shaw and Pene Greet with an emperor penguin carcase at Auster rookery, Antarctica. Australian Antarctic Division biologist Graham Robertson had asked them to collect as many carcases as possible for use in research. About 6 to 8 females, out of approximately 12000, die during egg laying.

PHOTO: PAUL MYERS

Tent lights glow under an aurora during a dog sled trip in the White Mountains, north of Fairbanks, Alaska.

An aurora lights up the optics building and viewing domes at Poker Flat Research Range, Alaska, where Gina and her colleagues made their observations. The building is lit by red lights which do not interfere with the optical equipment.

Moonrise over the Kloa expedition camp at Ledingham's Depot, Antarctica.

Sharon, Gina and Cathy in front of Grewingk Glacier during a kayaking trip in Kachemak Bay, Alaska.

Nestled in a spruce grove half-way between Hidden Hill and the Geophysical Institute, Cathy's cabin was a natural place of congregation.

Mid-winter camp on an overnight run to Forbes Glacier, Antarctica. Pene managed to capture the green final arcs of a spectacular aurora against the night sky.

A Hagglunds, one of the tracked all-terrain vehicles used on Antarctic bases, after breaking through the sea-ice near the end of the Jelbart Glacier at midday during mid-winter. Made in Sweden by the Hagglunds company, the vehicles are designed to float. This one was eventually retrieved the next day.

Reunited at last. Pene and Gina on the porch of Gina's cabin at Hidden Hill, Alaska.

Gina, Tucker, Simon, William and team on the trail in the White Mountains, Alaska.

Sue Steinacher and Gina surrounded by Sue's dog Tucker, Maimi, Dune and others in the White Mountains, Alaska.

Edward VIII ice-shelf. The mountains of Enderby Land, I think they are, poke up out of the plateau behind. And then to the north, Kloa Point and Cape Gotley. Truly a vast vista of wilderness, icebergs, sea-ice, rafted ice, the continent, plateau and nearby islands. It was worth the trip just for the view. We had one nice sunny afternoon while we were at Moonie Island.

Once you're out and travelling the days merge into weeks and time just disappears. On the return trip we went back the same way, staying at Crooked Island, Broka Island, Law Island. Blowing and falling snow held us at Law Island for a day, then had a relatively easy day back to Ledingham's Depot. The return runners were a bit disorganised. They could have been there earlier and even after the bad-weather day at Law Island we still had to wait a day for them to get to Ledingham's Depot. So we had three nights there and then a night at Colbeck on the way home. So we did sort of one and a half legs of the trip. Albert and Mal took over our team, and Giggles and Scotty took over Craig and Dave's team. It was hard to give them up. Most of the return runners were not all that keen on spending the extra time out and only wanted a shorter trip.

I was glad of a shower when we got back. Washes every other night with a flannel aren't exactly refreshing, and after three weeks my hair was somewhat greasy. But I have scrubbed up pretty well. Have a liberal coating of freckles and almost a tan on my face. However, I lost a few layers of skin on my nose from sunburn or/and nipping. One morning, early on, I got the end of one of my fingers quite badly nipped and it is about to start coming off. [It takes quite a while, in this case three to four weeks, for frost-nipped skin to die and separate from the live skin.] But I'd go again tomorrow morning if I could and we're already thinking of what other trips we can do. With the boys really fit, it will be good to keep them running as much as possible.

Weather-wise we had our share of everything, a blizz and a few days of blowing snow. Trying to cross the Hoseason Glacier the weather turned bad on us, so you could only see 200–500 m. That is the worst glacier to pass this year. It must be moving more quickly than the others and there were big waves in the sea-ice out from the front of it, crests 2–3 m high and about 100 m between crests. All the tide-cracks in the area are mounded up into big pressure waves. The best description I can think of is, you get a kid's plastic jigsaw puzzle, push the edges together, and the cracks between the pieces where they bulge up are tide-cracks and the pieces, bits of sea-ice. At least we were able to pass through the area without too many problems.

On the way back through there the other team bolted for a seal and flung the sledge sideways into a tide-crack. That cracked two bridges and delaminated the back half of one of the runners. They stopped for a couple of hours to fix it up. We didn't realise at the time and we ended up camping at different spots that night. From a vantage point on the island we were heading for, we'd spotted them moving again early in the afternoon. So fortunately at least we knew they must have been OK and there was no need for us to backtrack and find out what had happened. We talked by radio before the evening sked so were able to coordinate our movements and meet up next day.

Paul and I had our own sledge problems. With the depots we had put in at midwinter we were able to travel fairly lightly until Ledingham's Depot. Once we left there the sledges were heavily laden. One of our longitudinals broke, which caused the runner to twist out from the bridges. We patched it up but then a couple of days later, going through all the rafting in the gulf, the runner started twisting again. It took us the best part of two days to fix it. Had to replace the longitudinal. The back bridge had totally broken after cracking when the longitudinal first broke. The runner had been twisting in the rafted ice and that had stretched all the bridge–runner lashings, so they all had to be replaced. We ended up with a sled held together for the most part with met. string. We had used up all the spare hide very quickly. Anyway, after that we had no more problems and the sledge went well.

We all got along together, the dogs pulled well. We usually travelled within sight of each other and generally the following team caught up and travelled just behind the leading team, but sufficiently far behind that the dogs didn't acknowledge the presence of the team following. It can be a real pain if they're constantly trying to turn around and see who's behind them. So we didn't talk to the blokes in the other team very often while we travelled. I guess Paul and I didn't talk to each other all that much either, but we don't need to talk much. The two teams would set up and cook tea in separate tents but then after tea we'd get together before the sked for a drink and a talk about the day's travel and tomorrow's plans. It didn't take us long to exhaust the exchange of station gossip, despite the problems with the RTOs when we set out. We did eat together when we'd had a shorter day and had extra energy or time to put together the meal. We ate freeze-drieds, except when we were at Colbeck hut and for the two meals of frozen satay prawns I'd taken. They were our special treats the night we turned around at Moonie Island.

Craig told us some good stories that people on the base say about Paul and I, the sort of stories you don't usually get to hear. It makes me laugh. Not hard to see how embellishment of the facts occurs. One that

I had no idea about ... I dropped a pair of purple knickers in the laundry one day and someone purloined them for posterity. Well, apparently it's a great joke to put these purple knickers under someone's pillow, supposedly to sweeten their dreaming, and just to see how long it takes them to find them. I made sure I had plenty of knickers before I came down and had bought a number of different plain-coloured ones. I had wondered what had happened to that particular purple pair but I certainly wasn't aware of their migration through the red shed until Craig asked, was I missing a pair of purple knickers?

He and Dave Shaw are good-value companions, and both very capable in the field. Craig had set up a radio with solar panels and they looked after the communications. We didn't have any arguments about anything. When we were going out into the gulf I was becoming uneasy about continuing and we pulled up the teams together and had a good look at what lay ahead and discussed it for about half an hour and then made a unanimous decision not to continue. You know it was all just jolly good and there was a remarkable lack of tension in the group.

Our team were the old men, bitches and pups. We had four old men, three bitches, and three pups; with Merlin there were eleven dogs altogether. The old men were Pedro, in the lead, Otis, Blackie and Welf, all of whom were cunning and I don't know just how much work they did. Old dogs have a knack of keeping their traces tight without pulling. The pups worked well and one of them, Oscar, ended up being the best puller and has obvious potential as a lead dog. Oscar and Choofa were favourites, Choofa being a dedicated worker too. We got to know all their foibles pretty well and I think the team was fit and working quite well by the end of it. Unfortunately the morning Mal and Albert took over, Pedro damaged his paw and ended up coming home with us in the Hagglunds. I think this may have partly been because Mal and Albert didn't understand him. He has bad arthritis and limps about as you saddle them up and takes a while to warm up but after the first 20 minutes he works well. Poor old bloke, it's pretty amazing that he got as far as he did as he's eight years old and will not be with us that much longer. I hope we may get some more puppies from him before he goes.

While we were out Kirsty had her pups. Four boys. It was her first litter and unfortunately all of them died as she didn't feed them. Wish we'd been back on the base as Paul's had some experience with pups and may have been able to get the pups to feed. So we still have no pups. It is a bit of a problem as we could do with some more dogs. This time next year they could be scratching to put together nine dog teams. The next couple of bitches who come on heat will be mated.

This may mean a rush of puppies all at once. We could easily handle another five or six dogs, especially once the old ones are culled.

We are now trying to readjust to being back at Mawson. It's a bit of a let-down. The first voyage sails from Hobart tomorrow. Everyone here is all agog as to who's coming and going and I couldn't care less. I guess once I settle back down to work I'll get back into the hang of things. It sure is hard to get motivated. I miss having Paul around for 24 hours of the day. Unfortunately it looks like Paul may have to go home on voyage 4, which leaves in early December as the new 1991 diesos come in then. So we may have a couple of months apart. I'm not looking forward to the ships coming and going as I'll lose him soon. Feel like I have to stay until either the last or second-last ship, leaving in February or March, since Damian and the person from La Trobe are coming down to learn as much as they can about the FPS. As far as my own work is concerned it would probably be better to go home on voyage 4 and spend some more time analysing and writing stuff up but don't think I'll be able to do that.

It's starting to feel like summer is here now. On the bare rocky spots the snow is starting to melt. We climbed Ufs Island again on our way home and there were some icicles forming in sheltered spots on the northern faces of the rocks. Also we saw half a dozen seal pups as well, such tiny, skinny, newly born things. The last couple of days had clear skies, that endless penetrating blue which goes on for ever and ever. It clouded over last night so I didn't do any obs but it's clearing again this afternoon so I'm doing some calibrations and I'll do twilight dusk and green night-time then change over to sodium daytime obs tomorrow. The nights are getting fairly short now, will only be about five hours. I will do green obs at night for a couple of weeks and we may get something worthwhile comparing. Mal didn't actually run the FPS while I was away. He said there was only one clear night when he could have and that was a Saturday night and he didn't want to have to get up the next morning to turn it off. That's a bit slack but at least nothing broke down.

If the Austpac link is not up by tomorrow I'll give the institute a ring to see what is happening.

Peace and happiness, love, Pene.

9 OCTOBER 1990

Hi again,
I rang Don this morning and told him the Austpac link was down. It's up again now so just got your letter. Sounds like a good thing that

you've got your own cabin, and lots of women's meetings and things. I do so envy you that.

Oh, I didn't lose any weight. The lads all lost a few kg. I am 56 kg which if I remember rightly is about 0.5 kg heavier than when I left. No, I didn't sit on the sled all the way. Most of the time at least one of us was running. On some days, like the day from Ledingham's Depot to Havstein Island, we both had to run most of the way. So, must be muscle!

Take care, love, Pene.

15 OCTOBER 1990

Dear Pene,

Well, great to hear from you, what a trip it must have been, and glad it all went relatively smoothly. We had our second decent snowfall last Thursday and this time I think that it's here to stay. The roads are now pretty treacherous for biking, so I'm looking forward to there being enough snow to ski to work. Last week was hectic. The class had their first mid-term exam so we had to set the damn thing and of course suddenly everyone was taking interest in the course and coming to see us with questions.

Gonzalo, Roger's main collaborator, is up along with Cathy Price, who is on her way to the South Pole for the winter. She has summered before so has a pretty good idea of what she's in for, although still has the normal amount of apprehensions. If you're interested in a radio-pal over summer, I've mentioned you to her so she wouldn't mind that. She was given six full days of intensive FPS training, with Roger and Gonzalo's undivided attention. They were out to Poker every night putting faults in the system and doing bulk order-changes and the lot. To tell you the truth, me and the grad. students are a bit jealous. It sounded like a thorough and worthwhile exercise done in good spirit. I went out there with them one night but teaching kept me from doing more. Besides, I got a bit fed up with Gonzalo telling me I should be writing five papers a year. Honestly I'm just not prepared to buckle under that sort of pressure, and if it's buckle or get out, then I'd have no difficulty choosing the latter.

So it's nearly the silly season for you.[1] Hard to believe, especially with winter settling down here. It seems that suddenly everything I hear from Australia mentions spring at the moment; not surprising, I'm sure I'll be mentioning it when it comes up here again. We have a new person moved into our old cabin at Hidden Hill. His name is David and he's young, bright-eyed, bushy-tailed and keen. He is working at the environmental centre. It's nice to have some new blood around the place.

Claire wrote to me recently about how she's finding things with Tod. She is struggling with the same things I had to struggle with: Tod being able to be quite loving but just not being able to commit himself. It occurred to me recently that Tod and I have gone on to play exactly the same roles in our subsequent relationships as we were playing in ours. There must be something in the saying 'you get what you ask for' and it makes me realise that perhaps we've each got to do the changing within ourselves rather than try to find it in someone else. Maybe my 12 months off will help me with this.

I haven't spoken to Art for over two weeks now. I'm feeling pretty cross and angry and hurt still, so I'm going to wait until that's died down a bit — however long that may take. Sometimes I feel that Art never really gave of himself. He did a lot on the outside, probably to cover this fact, was always there physically and all the househusband bit. Underneath he didn't reveal his inner needs. The first and only time he did this was in expressing his need to break up. I can't see how he's going to find a meaningful relationship until he can overcome this barrier.

Well, Pene, better go and prepare my lesson. Oh yeah, with all this training program I'm not sure how much good data we got over the last week, and besides we haven't had that much clear weather. But we will continue to try. Looks like this comparison may not amount to much.

Much love and hugs, Gina.

17 OCTOBER 1990

Hi, Gina,

Good to get your letter. Things here have been pretty hectic for the last few days. I had two clear days, doing obs for 20 hours per day and then on Monday and Tuesday I was slushy so I'm catching up with things again. Paul and I are planning to go to Macey on the weekend with the dogs so have some sled repairs to do before then, and packing. The dogs are fit and healthy. We went out on a short run yesterday and had four dogs who had been on the run and three who hadn't and the three who hadn't could barely keep up with the pace. We were really zipping along. All the snow has blown off from the ice by the coast so it's slick sledging country, you've got to sprint to keep up with the unloaded sled.

All the bitches back from the run have come on heat so we may have some puppies soon.

Paul has tried and he's not going to be able to stay past voyage 4, which arrives on 10 December. So I am going to see if I can go home then as well. There's a lot of pros and cons either way. Paul has asked me to; means I won't have much overlap with the bod coming down from La Trobe, or Maria with the dogs; but would also mean I would have more time to write up my own stuff. Mawson Institute keeps saying they still only have money to pay me until April and then undefined murmuring about other possible grants but nothing definite.

In some ways I'll be glad to get out of this rat-race. The place is run along crazy lines and things just aren't logical. Like the diesos don't have enough money to employ Paul over summer yet the division would send Parker out to the PCMs on twice the salary. Did I tell you the last story about Parker? It happened while we were out with the dogs. There was a party and the station leader, having taken the position behind the bar, was requested to fill the doctor's glass while he went out for a piss. Well, Parker pissed in the glass and added whisky etc., and then wouldn't apologise for doing so. Lloyd hit the roof and has made an official complaint.

Well, enough of this bullshit. Sort of feeling a bit drained and tired. Have sat at a computer too long today. Plotting out data and writing field trip reports. Better finish this off and go and do some sled repairs before tea.

Hope all's well, I agree with you about Hernandez's comments re papers. I think one or two good ones a year is enough. Fuck the push-push-push system. Life's not all work.

Peace and happiness, love, Pene.

23 OCTOBER 1990

Hi there, Gina,
Hope things going well for you. We got back yesterday from our trip to Macey. It was excellent sledging, blue ice all along the coast then a bit of soft slushy snow out to Macey. Coming back yesterday it was overcast so even the snow was quite firm. We did it in — must almost be record time for dog-teams by themselves — about six hours for almost 50 km. Rode the sled most of the time except in the snow. Actually I am more stiff from this run than probably any other trip

because every time you got off the sled you had to sprint along just to keep up. On the lay day in the middle we took one 9-dog team out to the rookery. That must have been a good 15 km round trip as well. We pulled up at a nearby berg and one of us stayed by the dogs while the others went out and took photos. I took some of a seal with twin pups just born plus more of the emperor chicks. The usual Auster stuff [Emperor penguins and stranded icebergs] I guess.

John Colley, a radio tech. — we have three this year — and the electrician, Bill Collins, came with us on the trip. Neither of them had run with the dogs before so on the trip out Paul and I split up to run a team each. Yesterday we let them take the team by themselves. Bill is fairly interested. I hope he may go for some runs over summer as he's been a bit too dedicated to his work over winter and hasn't had many jollies. John I doubt will run again. He's had his dog-trip and I think he enjoyed it. At least they'll both have some idea what sledging's all about.

We got back to find the ship is catching up and now due here on Friday morning. Of course they do have to see what the ice is like off Mawson but looks like things are winding up fairly quickly. I am looking forward to new faces and more bods around but as always it's hard to make the changes involved. Why do humans resent change so much?

MIAR wants me to stay at least until voyage 7, of course, so at the moment trying to see if I can pull any strings to get Paul to stay here longer. He's prepared to stay as a voluntary dog-man type person but have to wait a few days to see what the division's reaction to that is.

I have to shift my room tonight. I'm going to shift into the room next to Paul's so we can maintain a bit of our privacy. Will be a few extra bods around for a while and then the traverses will be leaving. The Lambert traverse is going out with six people for three to four months and the mini-traverse is going out to open up the camp at Dovers in the PCMs. They'll be leaving together about 10 days after the ship departs.

Well, one of the bitches, Jedda, has been served. Another, Bundy, is very ripe so hopefully we can convince Bonza to do his thing as well and we'll have some pups around Christmas time (64 days, it's supposed to take).

Peace and happiness, love, Pene.

23 OCTOBER 1990

Dear Pene,
You must be sooooo fit, I don't know that I can take hearing about much more dog stuff. No, not really. It's great that you're getting so much mileage out of them.

Things up here are good and bad, winter's closing in. Saturday was a beautiful day and the lakes have just frozen up so I spent the afternoon ski-skating around, it was great. William has taken his dogs out but there really ain't enough snow yet. The temperatures haven't plummeted, haven't gone below 0°F, but they could do any day. Hidden Hill is pretty lively and full of good spirit at the moment. Our new resident and caretaker — David — met a hitchhiker from New Zealand named Simon at some stage, so when Simon broke his ankle up in Coldfoot, at the truckies' stop, he decided he should hitch the 300 miles to Fairbanks for some medical treatment. It must have been a hell of a trip down. The doctor said he was lucky he was wearing good hiking boots, which helped hold the ankle in place.

Simon is a doer. He's into climbing, hiking and skiing and has also spent a year in Antarctica as a caterer on the New Zealand base. He's also pretty mellow and has accepted his current disability with grace and taken the opportunity to learn guitar and read, although he was seen hobbling down the university ski-trails at midnight one night when he couldn't get a lift.

Work, apart from teaching, ain't going nowhere, fast. I'm a bit concerned that there are too many opportunities here and there just isn't the follow-through. Roger is very overcommitted. I find this frustrating. I'd rather do fewer things well. I'm at the stage where I think I'll scream if I hear the word 'opportunity' again.

About you being so eager to return home with Paul, I can imagine that you may regret it in the long run if you rushed home just for that. It sounds like you've got some good potential coming in for a summer and it sounds like the base could do with this new blood. I couldn't believe your story of what the SL did to Lloyd, what a whacker! It sounds like he's getting pretty desperate for some sort of recognition.

Yesterday I got a fax from Tod saying that he and Claire are now living together and he's actually finding this decision isn't feeling too bad. I think I needed to see/hear this in black and white. I was thinking about going home for Christmas but now there doesn't seem much point in going to see Tod at any rate. It still rattles me, but I'm glad to be feeling things more finalised. So I'm almost feeling 'free' with two relationships in the gash, although I think it may be some time before I'm ready for another. A few of us at Hidden Hill are going through some heavy emotional stuff. We're doing our best to help each other.

This Thursday night is the last night for the Howling Dog, a pub just out of town, which is closing for the winter. I haven't been to the pub or drunk for ages and suddenly I'm feeling a great need to do it. Kim is feeling the same need and there's a few other takers, so I think I'm going to indulge myself in some escapism and drown my sorrows for a night.

Good luck with the onslaught of new faces. Yes, humans do resist change, but then again they adapt pretty quickly. By the way, I got a peek at Damian's thesis the other day, as one of the principal investigators in atmospheric physics is examining it, and it's grey! (Doesn't look too bad, actually.)

Much love, Gina

24 OCTOBER 1990

Dear Pene,

Just a quickie as I have to tell someone of the disaster that happened last night. It was our new $13 000 oxygen-green line lamp, which at the moment feels like my only contribution to this place. Roger and I took it out to Poker last night to check it out. We had it running for about half an hour, balanced on top of the instrument. When I went to pick up the power supply, without even touching it, the thing fell off and shattered. What a horrible feeling it was! I couldn't believe it! Roger was really comforting, but shit, it sort of felt like the last straw for me. I mean, my life has felt like one blow after another recently, and work on the research side has been rather similar. So it's dead! All we managed was to record three profiles before it fell.

So I just had to tell you all this. Pene, surely my rough time of late must come to an end soon don't you reckon? I feel like since finishing my thesis and turning 30, I have been really tested. I was thinking of asking you if you've ever felt times in your life when that was the case, and then I thought that the years '83 and '84 were pretty rough on you, with your aborted trip to Mawson and all that entailed, and then you had lots of bad luck and disorientating times at the start of your thesis work, and you were stuffed around a lot. So I guess you have some insight as to how it feels. The only good thing is that surely things can only get better!!!

I got a letter from Art yesterday and he told me that he's not rushing into anything with his other woman and that they've decided to just be friends for a while, which felt like a token effort to make me feel better. It was meant well, but I've got more steam to let off yet. I rode my bike home yesterday and today. It's just great getting out in the blustery weather. It's about −5 to −10°C but actually nice to have a bit of wind for a change. I enjoyed having the wind to battle against on the ride. Think I needed that. Then Kim and I went for a quick ski before dinner and we got out there and had a good scream. Boy, that felt good — although it brought a panicked William running to see what was wrong. Actually William's going through an emotional, long-distance crisis at the moment, so we're sort of all limping along together.

26 OCTOBER 1990

Well, the good news this morning is that the people who made the lamp are amazed it broke because it's made to be flown in rockets, and it sounds like there is a chance they will replace it for us, although not sure at the moment. They are a small Canadian company. They got Roger to tell me not to worry about it and that they've dropped quite a few themselves.

And so, I guess I'd better plod on. Life continues and I have a class to prepare. Thank goodness for teaching. It's really holding my life together at the moment by just forcing me to be there and 'perform' three days a week, no matter what. I always feel better afterwards. It's very therapeutic.

See ya, Pene, thanks for being there.

Lots of love, Gina.

27 OCTOBER 1990

Hi Gina,
I am writing this doing obs into twilight. It's getting cloudy, a cirrus bank from north-west and stratus to east so I don't think it will be clear for dawn in a few hours' time. However, I am persevering with dusk as I haven't had any twilight data for about a week although I ran nearly all day yesterday and today but clouds came in last night too.

I can understand your not wanting to come to Aus. While you are in Alaska you should have some time to spend doing the things and seeing the places you want to see there and not spend your time dashing back to Australia to tie up ends of old relationships.

29 OCTOBER 1990

Well, it's Monday now and it's obs again today after being cloudy yesterday. Took the opportunity to go for a bit of a longer run out to the big iceberg which is grounded out near Azimuth Island. I guess it's about 15 km out, was a good day and despite the cloud there was no wind. Felt positively warm at about −10°C. The melt has started in a big way over the last week or so. You can see little puddles of water here and there around the base. Wind feels quite warm after the chill breezes of winter. I took a few photos yesterday, hopefully some of them will work out, the Adelies have arrived in hordes as well so there won't be any more dog-trips to Macey now. [2]

Lloyd was thinking about sending Paul home on this ship because he's got this infected gland in his neck. The infection has broken out a couple of times during the year. The swelling in his neck increases and then he gets really lethargic as a reaction to the toxins it produces. He may have to get the gland removed or something like that. He's had mega-doses of antibiotics a couple of times and looks like it's under control again at the moment. If the swelling got much worse it could block off the airway or something like that in the throat. Anyway, Lloyd rang the specialist last week and the specialist, whom Paul had seen before he left Hobart last year because it was swollen then, wasn't particularly worried so Lloyd decided to let him stay.

The first choppers are due in a couple of hours. The ship has been delayed because one of the engine couplings has broken and they can't fix it. They're progressing very slowly on one of its two engines. I guess that will take a few days to fix when they get back to Hobart, I don't actually know but it will probably mean some rearrangement of the shipping schedule. Electronic mail and faxes and telephones have surely changed the communications scene from the days when the first ship brought the first real news for months.

So the summer starts. Damian may be in later tonight, they'll have a few chopper flights but the flight will be fairly long as they're about 200 nautical miles from Mawson. They have special dispensation to fly in from beyond 80 nm. (That's nautical miles, not nanometres!)

Peace and happiness, love, Pene.

Well, just logged on to Hermes and found your last message. I started making a resolution not to log in every day and the very week I do that, I miss getting a letter. Shit! Well, not to worry. By now you won't feel so bad about the lamp. Actually I was hoping to get another sodium lamp this summer because we need a reference to determine the temperature of the hollow cathode lamp. It would make all this work so much more valuable. So at least you had your lamp. I probably won't even get to see mine. Although I guess that doesn't make you feel much better.

Yeah, you're right about '83 and '84 for me. (Although I still think that the last two years of high school were probably the worst two in my life so far, going through puberty and all that.) When I was returned from Mawson in '83 it certainly was a blow and dramatically changed my plans but the things I then did in '83 have given a new dimension to my life. On returning to work I did have to overcome a lack of self-confidence as far as work was concerned, and dealing with people in general and bureaucracy in particular. It took me a couple of years to get over it. Anyway, that's all past now. At the moment I think I've got into a bit of a rut with work and I need to make an effort to get some more stuff finalised and published. I have produced nothing for over 18 months now.

Have you heard that Dr Jacka is quite ill? Don has a job starting next month as the science faculty computing officer. The new dean of science is Roger Clay and sounds like he's going to be fairly sympathetic towards Don and Heather spending time on Mawson Institute stuff to tie up things next year and keep Damian in touch. I'm dreading going back to Adelaide with all the Mawson Institute dispersed. I'm thinking about the possibility of finishing off at the Antarctic Division and spending a couple of months there if there's money somewhere to pay me. Would be nice to spend some time in Hobart/Tassie.

I hope the next 12 months goes smoothly for me and I don't end up feeling like you did last week.

Cheers, kid, and hope you're feeling better by now. Things must start looking up soon.

Love, Pene.

31 OCTOBER 1990

Dear Pene,

Well, good to hear from ya as usual. I'm a bit recovered from last week although it took a rather wild weekend to do it. Went to the pub on Thursday night and danced until about 3 a.m. On Saturday night at a Halloween party did the same thing, then on Sunday I came down with a cold, probably a fitting end. It was good. Good to get into dancing more than drowning my sorrows.

Meanwhile, William's heavy-duty week came to a quite different ending. He ended up proposing to his girlfriend in the UK over the phone on Saturday morning after a three-hour conversation. What's more, she accepted! William is over the moon. It's quite an achievement when you've been a highly successful bachelor for 39 years. Sarah is only 23, but they've been going out with lots of long-distance stuff for five years now. Oh, the ins and outs of Hidden Hill, a never-ending saga.

After deciding not to go to Oz, suddenly at a meeting I find that I am down to go to Svalbard from 10 December to 17 January, about six weeks. I think this will be good. It means Roger and David Rees will be there for the first two weeks, then I'll stay on with one other grad. student, Joe, whom I get on well with. He has spent a fair bit of time up there and loves it and knows some of the local Norwegians. By staying on after Roger leaves I should get a chance to get out and about a bit. Norwegians celebrate Xmas and New Year in a big way so that should be fun. We will be staying in the town of Longyearbyen, one of three coalmining towns, and we will commute to the field station each day. This way I'll get a break from here without using up my holidays, leaving lots of time for some trips back here in spring and summer when I return. I'm going to try and make the time in Svalbard a productive time scientifically. I'm looking forward to working with David Rees. He will have his Doppler imaging system there, so I'd better read up on it before I go.

I spoke to Tod the other night and although I feel a lot of love for him I know it can't be realised in practice. I'm gradually accepting this more, although I don't know that I'm much closer to understanding it. Having a baby involved certainly does help define things. So I guess I will find somebody who suits me just as well, or hopefully better, when I'm right and ready. Single-hood is going pretty well for now, its kinda nice to feel free to do as I please.

Love and hugs, Gina.

5 NOVEMBER 1990

Hi, Gina,

Things here are revving up for the summer. All the new folks arrived last Tuesday so aeronomy is fairly busy now. Damian has come in with so much to do, he's not quite sure where to start. I got him observing on Wednesday but it clouded over early on Thursday morning so wasn't exactly a long observing period. Andrew Klucky and the new engineer have their two photometers to install and we have the carpenter here working for them. So, with a chippie at our disposal, some other long-lost jobs in aeronomy should finally be finished or done. The place is really buzzing and the computer is in great demand.

Paul and I took a heap of summer arrivals out to Auster yesterday. It was a bit of a flop because although it was a perfect day when we left, by the time we got out there there were heavy snow showers and it looked horribly as though it might clag in and start blizzing, so we quickly turned tail and headed back for home. The Hagglunds are going out to the PCMs in a week. They have to have an overhaul in the workshop first, so will probably be the last chance we get to use them.

Hopefully we'll get the word this week whether or not Paul can stay for the summer. He's keen to work with the dogs and keep me company too. I am sort of getting back into work, also been thinking a bit about what to do when we get back. The new OIC for 1991 is Louise Crossley. She's coming in on voyage 4, has a PhD in history and philosophy of science. Will be interesting to get to know her. She plans to work on Davis's diaries while she's here.

Peace and happiness, love, Pene.

5 NOVEMBER 1990

Dear Pene,
Good to hear from you in the midst of all that activity, sounds like things have come alive. Up here it snowed all weekend. I was out on my bike in it yesterday, skinny tyres and all; worked quite well. (Have you read Tom Robbins' book, *Skinny Legs and All?*) Certainly was easier than trying to extract the car. This morning I did manage to get my car out. Quite an achievement! At least it's still warm, rose up to nearly 0°C with all the snow, although it is forecast to drop down to 20°C below as soon as the snow clears up.

This morning I was thinking that if I pushed for it I could arrange to work a four-day week, since it's all soft money. Boy, that's tempting; quite a few of my women friends in the health-care profession work four day weeks, and I always feel jealous. It would mean that on top of your normal weekend, which always goes too quickly, I could have an extra day for housework, making bread, tending the garden in summer and all those little things which I love to do but which I don't get time for. Maybe I'll think about it for next year, after Svalbard.

Good news on the work front. It turned out that the lamp was not broken after all. One resistor had popped out of the circuit board in the fall, which was why it wouldn't run, and what looked like shattered glass when we looked in the front window was just the glue. So I was pretty relieved to hear that. In fact I read a saying yesterday, 'If you haven't made a mistake lately, your life is too safe.'

Well, that's about it for news. Louise certainly sounds interesting. Say g'day to Damian and Andrew for me.

Love and hugs from Gina.

12 NOVEMBER 1990

Hi Gina,

Well, don't know when you'll actually get this because Austpac out of Adelaide has kicked the bucket and we had a message from Don that it may take a few days to restore. It has been going very slowly the last few weeks.

Will be glad to see the last of the traverse. They are supposed to be leaving tomorrow, both the Lambert traverse and the PCM mini-traverse. They are travelling together as far as Turners Turnoff where the PCM mini-traverse heads south-east and the Lambert keeps on going south. The wonderful new route reopened in 1988–89 through Mt Henderson has been deemed too slotty — as it was when it was no longer used in the '60s. I managed to draw slushy for the farewell dinner on Saturday night and then cook yesterday. So once these bods leave we'll be back to 19 people until the ship comes in again in three weeks' time (or so). It's been too busy, lots of people running around and being busy or trying to be busy. After two busy days in the kitchen I was hoping for a rest but the sky cleared so had to come up and spend half the night getting obs. At least Damian is here so I can get a reasonable night's sleep as he's been getting up in the mornings to do obs and we do a short automatic sodium run while the sun is a fair way below the horizon. There is Fraunhofer[3] contamination in sky profiles all through the night, so the sun is not setting at 20 km altitude. This means it is quite light all night. It has changed really quickly. Last week the emission was against a dark background one day and the next there's the sunlight starting to creep in.

I have done quite a lot of observing in the last week, Wednesday, Thursday and Friday and then on Sunday, as I finished slushy, the sky started clearing so I had to stay up till 1 a.m. doing obs. No wonder I'm feeling tired today. Feel like I need a few days of quiet and rest to catch up with things. We've had just over 24 hours in this run. It's starting to cloud up now and getting pretty windy outside, there's a bit of drift because we had a good snowfall on Saturday night and Sunday. (Well maybe half a centimetre, it's hard to tell because with the wind it all blows away again.) Paul and I went out for a short run on Sunday afternoon and there was a real snowshow, big flakes falling, Mt Henderson totally disappeared from view and you could barely see Gwamm. I'm expecting, if we get any decent winds in the next couple of days, we might have a blizz. The cirrus is streaming in from the west.

Snow petrels have started nesting around here too. They are beautiful. You hear them calling from the rocks and swooping around the islands and around the base. Ahhh snow petrels, one of the things I love about Antarctica.

Andrew K. and the '91 chippie Stu, have been making a mezzanine floor in aeronomy so you can walk around underneath all the hatches in the western end of the building. The place is positively buzzing. Andrew is also cleaning up the UAP side of things, so the lab looks like it might be organised by the end of summer. Stu is showing enthusiasm for the dogs and I think will make a good dog-handler.

Hugs from Pene.

14 NOVEMBER 1990

Hiya Pene,
Up here we've just had our first cold spell as, out of the blue, the temperature plummeted to 40°C below over the weekend. It's back up again now.

The community has been pretty lively of late, in fact so much so that I think tonight I might just have a night off and eat dinner on my own. I've been struggling to find any quiet time. I've been going to a yoga class on Wednesday mornings for an hour, which has been good. This weekend I am planning on going to a women's yoga retreat.

Work is depressing me at the moment. I'm just not getting anywhere apart from teaching. Fortunately there's only three more weeks of semester then maybe I'll get back into it. Hopefully Svalbard will be a good environment to improve my enthusiasm. The campaigns I'll be part of are all new and different for me. We will be looking at the Hydrogen emission, H alpha, from the geocorona. It has an intensity of a couple of Rayleighs[4] so it's quite a challenge. Also we will be looking at the O+ emission at 732 nanometres which is supposed to stream up the fieldlines during active aurora and get pumped into the magnetosphere. We are looking for 'flux transfer events' when the field-lines on the day-side actually snap and then reconnect, breaking all the currently accepted laws of field-line behaviour. I'm not sure how we'll recognise the signature of a flux transfer event when we see one — feels a bit like Winnie the Pooh looking for the North Pole!

Back at Hidden Hill, Kim has just broken up with her boyfriend so I've been returning the favour of being an ear for her. Oh, the comings and goings at that place! Our New Zealand visitor Simon is still there. He's a nice addition. He would like to go back to the great white hell in maybe a scientific capacity. He has either a degree or part of a degree in science. I took him out to Poker yesterday. He's about six foot tall and reminds me of a friend in Australia. I do have a soft spot for people like him, but this six foot tall Alaskan mushing friend of William's has her eyes on him and I daren't stand in her way.

Next week is Thanksgiving. Nothing short of just a huge pig-out. Lots of people say it's their favourite holiday 'cause it hasn't got the added stresses of presents and family get-together which Christmas has, but rather just a big shared feast. We get a two-day holiday, so after dinner on Thursday I'm going down to Anchorage on the Friday night for a Quaker meeting. Art will be there so I guess it will mark the breaking of the silence with him.

Lots of love and hugs, Gina.

17 NOVEMBER 1990

Well, Gina, lots has happened. Firstly you need to know that I can only log in to Hermes in Adelaide in a very circuitous manner via an account at Hobart Uni. I can send mail from there and I can read mail at Hermes. Adelaide computer centre had a couple of lightning strikes and they are not going to fix up the cards that were damaged as they are not covered by maintenance contracts. So there will be no mail for a couple of weeks until they get a new computer on line.

The other thing that has happened is that Paul's lump on his neck has flared right up again. One night this week he woke up in the middle of the night and was really dizzy and ended up collapsing on the floor. Lloyd was on nightwatch and came up straight away and it ended up that other than the pain, most of the problem was from hyperventilating, but the lump on his neck is now of a size that it's putting pressure on the nerves in his throat. Lloyd has said he has to go home on the next ship so I am going to go with him. He will probably have to have the thing cut out once the inflammation has died down, which hopefully it will do before we get back.

It's a bit disappointing that I won't be able to stay for the summer but I think it will be best in the long run.

Otherwise things have settled back down a bit here. The traverse got away on Thursday after a couple of days' blizz and blowing snow. After Paul's problems in the night Lloyd put him in the surgery and he has been getting his mega-doses of antibiotics through a drip. So he's had a few days of enforced rest. Hopefully he'll be up and about from tomorrow. He's not been too bad and we just have to hope that the infection stabilises and this thing doesn't grow any more. He's been spending today in the darkroom. Sooo . . .

Hope things are going well at your end of the world.

Love and hugs, Pene.

22 NOVEMBER 1990

Hi Gina,

Just a quick note to let you know the Adelaide connection is back in use. So if you were thinking about sending a letter send it the 'normal' way to Hermes.

The ship left Hobart today, so Paul and I will be heading back home before we know it. Paul oscillates in health. I think he's improving a bit at the moment although he still has a constant headache. I'm going to stay in Tassie for a while until Paul gets fixed up. Will take a week or so off and then work at the division. I'll write a longer letter soon. Have to nip down to the dog-line to get the boys away on an overnight trip. No, unfortunately, not going myself. Paul hasn't been well enough to take off. Maybe late next week we'll get away again.

Hope you've got lots of snow and good winter things, not just cold. It's positively tropical here, between −5°C and zero most days. Getting around in a sweatshirt like Mark used to do. Never thought I would have been warm enough. Amazing what winter does to you.

Peace and happiness, love, Pene.

27 NOVEMBER 1990

Dear Pene,

Sorry to hear of Paul's health, sounds really unpleasant. I hope the trip back isn't too uncomfortable for him with a constant headache in the rolling seas. Tod is on voyage 4 so you'll get to catch up with him. Meanwhile things are getting busy for me too as I go to Svalbard in two weeks, and finish teaching. So it's back to science and boy, I hope I can get into it this time. I'm sort of worried that I won't and will continue on at my uninspired pace.

We had a great and huge Thanksgiving dinner at Hidden Hill with 25 guests and just heaps of food. We still have a fridge full of turkey and desserts. I also caught up with a friend from Anchorage who did a number of cruises with Tod. I first met him at Mawson in 1985. It was rather nice to see him, a fellow Australian and all, and to talk about mutual friends back home. I am feeling rather vulnerable when it comes to Aussies at the moment, especially when they've shared Antarctica and Alaska as well. On the Friday I went to Anchorage, drove down with William and Carl in the front and Kim and I in the back, singing, laughing and talking all the way there. Kim gets me going, which is good most times, but then it's also nice to have male company — more grounding.

In Anchorage we stayed in this huge house with an indoor pool, and a bunch of the Anchorage Friends, or Quakers, were there. Art came round for the Saturday afternoon and evening. I had spent the morning wondering where he was and why he hadn't turned up and getting all anxious. After a long walk and a swim in the indoor pool the anxiety had gone so by the time he did show up it was nice to see him. We both had tears streaming down our faces and couldn't stop hugging. I think I had almost convinced myself that Art probably wasn't even missing me but that obviously has not been the case. So it was nice to catch up on news while not having time to get into gory details. Art is coming to Fairbanks with his Christmas show on Thursday so I guess more might come out then.

Back at work and I've just had to move offices. Twice, what a drag! I do now have a better view, as I'm gradually creeping around towards the Alaska Range and the south, i.e. the *sun*. We have heaps of snow and the skiing is great. In fact we drove back from Anchorage in a snowstorm. It was a pretty slow trip. I'm getting used to skiing and getting around in the dark. You have to. I enjoyed skiing to work yesterday and will ski home today. I took Dipper out the other day and we met a moose on the trail who just wouldn't move until a train came along, which scared it off the track when it blew its horn.

Enjoy your last few weeks, and I hope Paul manages at least one more dog-trip with you too.

Lots of love and hugs too, Gina.

1 DECEMBER 1990

Hi Gina,

Was good to hear from you this week. Things here are not going all that well. Paul is not much better. He only managed to get out on a run once this week. His headaches, well, he has one all the time and then he has a bad one which comes and goes. Will be a bit of a drag until he can get this thing removed. And while Damian and I were doing a bulk separation change on the FPS, the microprocessor section bit the dust. It won't scan or anything!

I'll be leaving in a week. The new engineer hasn't really got any idea how it all works, so he and Damian are having a look around to see if they can work out what's wrong. It's now at the stage of checking every wire on the backplane of the two chassis with the microprocessor bits in them. And there's so many there, it's like a maze. Oh, shit! I'm glad this has happened now and not during the year.

The ship is a bit late as they've had rough weather since leaving Hobart.

On Tuesday 18 December Heather has organised a retirement function for Dr Jacka. She asked if we could send a message up from here. Thought you may want to send him a message as well. He is going to continue to work on the lidar.

Io, one of the puppies earlier this year, has come on heat and she should be pregnant now. So that will be at least two litters for the summer. We could really do with having three here as a good bunch of young dogs is needed. A couple of the other bitches looked like they were on heat but although we put dogs with them they weren't seen mating and I wonder if they were cycling properly. Will be a pity not to see some new pups born.

Peace and happiness, love, Pene.

PS: Well, it's now Sunday. It's windy today. Paul and I went out for a run yesterday afternoon, around Welch Island. Was good. But it started blowing last night and it's a bit too windy to run today. Tony and Damian fixed the FPS and they have very red faces. The main problem ended up being that when they first took the cards out to clean them, they swapped two when they put them back in. So things are looking a bit rosier. At least the FPS should be running when I leave. In some ways looking forward to going back home but there's too many things to be sorted out. Just hope Paul gets better quickly.

3 DECEMBER 1990

Dear Pene,
I hope Paul can hang in there until he gets fixed up and I hope you can too, as it must be quite draining on you.

Well, I'm feeling really miserable today. I leave for Svalbard in a week today (that's Monday 10th) and I've got a fairly hectic week between now and then with teaching, setting the exams and organising things for the trip. On top of that Art is up and my period a day late (although there isn't any biological reason why I shouldn't get it). So today I feel a bit like an emotional wreck. It is nice to see Art but of course it is kind of taxing too. Things haven't happened with this other woman he was interested in and the stupid thing is that here am I feeling sorry for him. Goodness me, we women can be pathetic with our always wanting to make people feel better when they're down. So part of me thinks that the sooner he goes the better while the other part is becoming quickly addicted to having that closeness again.

One really good thing is that Art won, in a raffle, a 12-week-old chocolate labrador. He is the most hilarious thing. You've never seen so much excess skin on a puppy. He is just so laid-back and completely lovable that he can't help but make you feel good. He's not at all hyper, in fact completely the opposite. If you want him to go for a walk you have to chuck him outside for about five minutes before you go and then the cold tends to energise him. Sleeping in front of the heaters certainly doesn't.

We have a full moon at the moment and it is so bright, unbelievable and I have enjoyed skiing home under the moonlight a few times. It's great skiing home after work. I prefer it to skiing to work. Last week it hit 50°F below. It wasn't bad to ski in, in fact the ironic thing is that you have to dress much more warmly to drive. Boy, driving on frozen square tyres with frozen gears and iced-up windows is such a pain! The only times I've really been cold have been in the car. My heater doesn't work well so that doesn't help.

I hope to hear from you once more, and I certainly hope to see you up here. Roger responded pretty positively before when I asked him about getting you some visiting scientist stuff.

Well, I guess you've got more sunlight than you know what to do with at the moment. Enjoy your last week. Getting back to the division can't help but be a rude shock and terrible downer, but then having a healthy Paul should cheer you up.

Take care, love and thoughts from Gina

7 DECEMBER 1990

Hi, Gina,
Well, the ship is procrastinating about getting in. Yesterday, according to Parker, they were going to be in the harbour by 9 a.m. What a joke!!! They arrived at the fast-ice edge at 6 a.m., 45 nautical miles out. But they were still going to get in to the harbour to pump fuel, which is not

needed until the end of the season. To impress the pollies on board, no doubt. Well, it took them six hours to break about two nautical miles so they've given up and decided not to bring the ship in after all. I'm still laughing. It seems like the division people just never learn. Parker's been running around like a plucked chook. As Paul describes it, 'panic, panic, panic, panic, wait . . . panic, panic, panic, wait'. They were going to be here yesterday but as yet we haven't seen a chopper because there's a bit of snow around the ridges, although not a breath of wind here, but they haven't been flying. So we're waiting.

Have managed to get out on a few more afternoon runs. Yesterday we took out a 13-dog team. One of those things you're always going to do. Four of us rocked up for a run yesterday, Dave Shaw, Paul, Stu and myself. Dave, Paul and I had all been on the long leg of the Kloa trip; Stu is showing the most interest of the 1991 crew. He's their chippie. So decided instead of taking two teams we'd take 13 dogs in one. What a laugh. After trying all the lead dogs in front we ended up with Oscar, the 12-month-old puppy. The other leads all just wanted to run back with a gaggle of dogs up the front. At the start only the rear four or six dogs were working and the front mob looked like Brown's cows out for an afternoon stroll. However, once we got Oscar out in front he was pleased as Punch to be there and then we went a bit faster and got them all working a couple of times. I'm sure they thought it was as much a laugh as we did. The remaining doggy feat I want to accomplish before I go is to take out a team of bitches, with Maria.

Well, not much has changed since I last wrote. We had a blizz the night I was on nightwatch, and a few days of pretty shitty weather last week. Am a bit bored the last few days. Paul isn't too keen to do things like sled repairing and that sort of stuff, like we used to. Leave it for the next crew, he reckons; we had to do it all when we arrived. I don't entirely agree with that attitude but that's how it goes. There's a couple of sleds that need some attention but they're not too bad.

Paul is not that well in general. Spends about every second day in bed with a headache, so I guess that doesn't help his overall frame of mind.

Well, Merry Christmas and all that stuff. Have fun and be careful of tall dark handsome bods, or blond and blue-eyed ones too, around Svalbard. Just don't do anything I wouldn't do . . .

Peace and happiness, love, Pene.

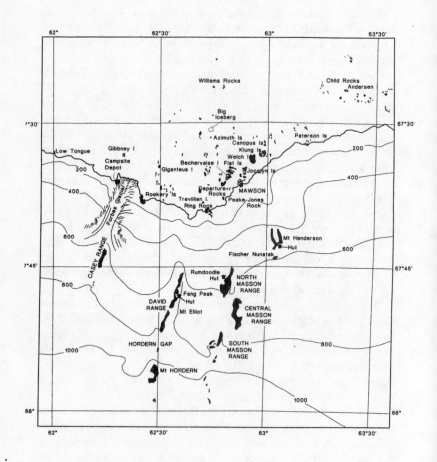

Mawson Coast and Framnes Mountains   MAP: JOHN COX

PART SIX

WHEN LETTERS
ARE NOT ENOUGH

aul and I left Mawson on 11 December; Lloyd accompanied us to the ship to inform the ship's doctor of Paul's condition. Five of our fellow expeditioners were returning to Australia with us. Being a mid-season voyage there were many empty cabins and several politicians and journalists on board for the round trip. The *Aurora Australis* was newly commissioned and although she had been unable to break into Mawson, due to snow cover over metre-thick ice, she sailed impressively through heavy pack-ice en route to Davis. She was spacious and, being expressly designed as an Antarctic research and resupply vessel, provided comfortable and congenial facilities.

The trip to Davis base took two and a half days and we had four days there unloading cargo and delivering and retrieving expeditioners. We were able to spend some time ashore but our activity was curbed by Paul's health. The trip from Davis to Hobart took 11 days. Our return voyage was subdued despite Christmas celebrations. Paul was unwell and spent a lot of time in bed. I spent a few hours most days working on data analysis as the ship had computing facilities. Paul and I kept pretty much to ourselves as we were not in the mood for socialising. We were both looking forward to his recovery and tried to make the days pass. On our arrival in Hobart, Paul was immediately admitted to hospital. He was given intravenous antibiotics and discharged after a week. When after three weeks the infection showed insufficient improvement, he was re-admitted to hospital.

As we left Mawson, Gina was leaving Fairbanks for Svalbard, a group of islands about 1000 km north of Norway. Norway maintains a research station there near the township of Long-yearbyen. Most of the town's population work in or serve the local coalmines. A Russian coalmine also operates some distance away. At 78° north Svalbard had, at this time of year, 24 hours' darkness. This allows for continuous optical observations of atmospheric emissions, including observations of daytime aurorae, which reflect different magnetospheric phenomena to night-time aurorae.

The total darkness also reflected Gina's mood. Her teaching, which had provided direction during the period of her break-up with Art, had finished and she hoped that in this trip she would find new enthusiasm for her research. Gina was also dragged down by her correspondence with Tod, who was at sea with us. It seemed appropriate that while she was in the depths of a Svalbard winter, Tod, at the height of the southern summer, was returning home for the birth of his daughter Sophie. They shared the news over the telephone and subsequently Tod and Claire asked Gina to be Sophie's godmother.

Gina wrote at this time:

Svalbard is totally dark. The first days I felt like I was in purgatory with a pervading feeling of 'Boy, if I don't come out of this feeling cleansed and renewed and ready to enjoy sunlight, home and friends then there is something wrong'. The company of a bunch of male scientists offers no relief. Life seems to lose its form when there is no differentiation between night and day, work and home, weekdays and weekends. Life simplifies itself into a single strand of beads; into an arithmetic progression of eat-work-eat-work-eat-work-sleep.

This time also marked the closing of the Mawson Institute for Antarctic Research at the University of Adelaide. We both felt saddened and appalled by this. Gina wrote to Dr Jacka:

Dear Fred,

I would like to wish you well on your retirement and thank you for all that you have given, through the Mawson Institute, to upper atmospheric physics in Australia. Sitting here in Svalbard trying to stabilise the temperature of a Fabry-Perot Spectrometer, which is wrapped in a sleeping-bag, I miss the ways of the Mawson Institute. And this isn't the first time. It is with the benefit of hindsight that I appreciate what the trademark of the Mawson Institute has meant: well-thought-out equipment design, good performance and a world of opportunities for students who pass through. I am only extremely sorry that this opportunity will not be available for future students like myself.

Thank-you, Mawson Institute, and thank-you, Fred.

Kindest regards, Gina Price.

Gina spent six weeks in Svalbard. At any one time there were six scientists present but the individuals changed. When Joe, a colleague from Fairbanks arrived, things improved as he had spent time in Svalbard before and knew people and places to visit. Christmas celebrations also helped the atmosphere. Gina sent the following fax to her parents before Christmas:

23 DECEMBER 1990

Dear Ma & Pa

We had some big winds last night and arriving at the station early this morning we found we had lost a dome and a small hut had blown over and was blocking the door. Oh so many memories of Mawson here; however, the big difference is that there is a bunch of scientists with me and some of them even seem to know what they're doing.

The landscape is stark, no trees, but polar bears and a funny short-legged reindeer (which looks more like a pig than a reindeer). The station is in a long valley like a dried-out fiord with quite steep mountains on either side. The town of Longyearbyen (named after Mr Longyear) is up the next valley which I am told has a glacier at the top of it, but in darkness I ain't seen it yet. I am looking forward to the full moon (the moon is two weeks up, two weeks down) when I may really see where I am. Up until now about all one can do is make out the silhouettes of the mountains. There will be six of us here over Christmas, two Norwegians, one Scot and the rest from the US, of whom half are graduate students. Half the group has changed since I've been here, so it has been nice to have a flow-through of different faces. Most of us are staying in town and we usually eat in town at one of the two choices of places to eat.

Town is interesting, with a population of 1200, and is essentially owned by the coalmining company, Store Norske. Everyone knows each other, or at least knows whom they do and don't want to know. Actually Joe was just telling me that he doesn't think that there is the claimed population, suggesting that half the houses — all of which have all the lights on all the time — are actually empty and only there to fool the Russians. I'm starting to get to know some of the townsfolk but I think you have to be here a couple of weeks to show that you're serious about being here before they'll open up to you.

The weather swings from blowing snow to blowing clear skies and very occasionally the wind drops. When the weather has been clear the aurorae have been fantastic, going all day and all night when they really fire up. The daytime aurorae are quite different to the night-time ones.

Gina was to leave Svalbard on 17 January 1991, two days after the expiry of the UN's deadline for Iraq to withdraw from Kuwait and, although I was feeling distanced from the situation, for Gina it was closer to home.

I am pretty concerned about the situation in the Gulf and now Lithuania. It has been interesting hearing the different views of the folks here. The Norwegians don't seem to have too many problems with giving someone like Saddam Hussein what they believe he deserves. Norway is a small country with compulsory military service and the largest army per capita in the world. They were overrun by the Germans in the Second World War, even Svalbard was taken over, so they still bear the scars of that. Our Scotsman, Alistair, who is approaching retiring age, keeps drawing parallels to Hitler and pushing for nipping things in the bud while you still can. Meanwhile I have problems condoning war. I was moved to hear from Tod that Liz Denham [a mutual friend from Hobart] has gone to the Gulf to protest. It hadn't occurred to me that some people may feel such a deep conviction. When there's thousands of people prepared to go and die in the name of war, a few people prepared to do the same thing for peace isn't such a surprising thing. For some reason Alistair couldn't believe it and kept saying to me, 'What does she think she's going to achieve?'. The more he said this, the more I realised that Liz was actually achieving something by making people like Alistair think about it in a new light.

We have been getting on amazingly well as a group and I enjoy the diversity. It is just as well because we have been spending so much time together. However, I'm looking forward to getting back to Fairbanks.

Our correspondence resumed after Gina had returned to Fairbanks and Paul and I had settled in Hobart. We were staying at the Antarctic Lodge, a group of self-contained flats to accommodate expeditioners during their time in Hobart. Paul and I had to readjust to 'normal' life, driving cars, handling money, shopping and cooking again. Both of us had much to learn about doctors, hospitals and illness.

Paul's physical and mental strength carried him through this period and masked the severity of his illness. Some of our fellow expeditioners were around Hobart for debriefing before leaving for other parts of Australia. Two good friends of mine from undergraduate university days in Armidale, Chris and Robyn, were also living in Hobart and we were to spend time with them and their 10-month-old son, Henry. Children and old people we had not seen during our sojourn at Mawson. Work was once again a 9 to 5 routine and not an observing schedule.

Gina and I experienced some problems with the electronic mail network in the next few months. We were using the same computers but at times messages did not get through until a new address was obtained.

17 JANUARY 1991

Hi Gina,
A quick message to welcome you home. Paul and I are staying at the lodge. It's quite convenient. I think Paul is on sickleave at the moment. I have to try and check with personnel today. Fred is happy for me to work here for a while. I have borrowed a friend's car and bicycle while he is on holidays. Paul and I are probably going to buy a car. Things are going OK at the moment. We are waiting for the infection to go before they'll operate on his neck.

Big hug, love, Pene.

22 JANUARY 1991

Well, I found this wasn't sent last week so I'll have another go today. Things are not going well here. Paul had a biopsy done last Friday and the cyst is cancerous, from a primary in the base of his tongue. This is really bad. He starts chemotherapy tomorrow. After the first dose we will have some idea of what the progress might be. In the best possible case he may be totally cured. In the worst possible case the treatment will have no effect and he will only have a couple of months to live.

So looks like we won't be over to visit as soon as I had hoped we might be. I haven't made any plans at all, except to say I'll stay here in Hobart with Paul. Still find it hard to talk about. Paul is not very positive as he's been in so much pain and not really happy for so long that he wonders if it's worthwhile even having any treatment. I try to be more positive and have some hope.

Thanks for the tape you sent me at Mawson. I find it really inspiring at times to hear such strong women singing. I have been listening to it often and especially think of you when they sing the song about 'Sunrise in my country, sunset in yours'. [1]

Hope things are going well for you.

Peace and happiness, love, Pene.

5 FEBRUARY 1991

Well, Gina, I have a new address to try for you so this might eventually get through. Things are going OK. Paul had the first lot of chemotherapy a couple of weeks ago and it looks like he'll be having the next lot next week, all being well. It is debilitating stuff and he is not looking forward to it at all. The last lot did have some effect and the swelling in his neck has gone down considerably. The worst of the pain has gone but he still has some headaches.

As soon as it was diagnosed as cancer they changed his pain-control drugs and put him on morphine. They worry that morphine can be addictive if not used properly and Paul is concerned about this too. If it's cancer, though, they prefer to use morphine as the dose can be increased steadily if required. (If you stop taking it when the pain stops, then it's not addictive.) Morphine comes in a few forms. As a liquid Paul says it makes him nauseous despite the masking flavours. At the moment he's taking tablets during the day; and in the evenings, when the pain gets worse, I give him an injection. Once he goes to sleep it tends to be more manageable, although in some positions the pain is worse than in others.

It's pretty hard giving needles. The sisters at the hospital showed me how and Paul rates each one on a 1–10 scale: 10 is good and < 5 means I've done something wrong and it hurts. I am improving and not doing too many < 5s. They're only subcutaneous–intramuscular injections so it's not as though I have to get into a vein or anything precise like that. Anyway, at least if I can do these things Paul can stay at home and will only have to go into hospital for the chemotherapy treatments. We still don't have any long-term prognosis yet.

We bought a car and we are still in the flats, although we're thinking of buying a house. It's hard to know if it's the best thing to do. If Paul can't have a job and I can't get a good job in Hobart then it may become difficult to meet mortgage payments, although Paul has enough money that we probably wouldn't need a huge mortgage. If all goes well we may still get to visit but it's likely to be later in the year.

Anyway, things are going OK. We've been doing a few afternoon walks, at least Paul has recovered enough to do that. He's been coming in to do some clerical work for the engineering section at the division, just to fill in the time. He was getting really bored at home by himself.

Love, Pene.

6 FEBRUARY 1991

Dear Pene,
Well, great to get your conglomerate of mail messages today, but also a shock. I was very sorry to hear that Paul's lump was cancerous but it's good to hear that the chemo seems to be doing something. Boy, not nice news to return to!

Well, it's been a long time since I've written. I've been back for three weeks now. Work is a lot more fun now, knowing the folks I was in Svalbard with so much better. But gee, it's taken a while to feel at home here in this way, a year to be precise. There have been almost record snowfalls in Fairbanks, so there is an abundance of snow, and we had a week of hot, balmy (about 0°C) weather when I returned so the skiing has been great and I'm skiing to work most days.

Art came to visit soon after I returned. He ended up being sick then having a minor collision in his truck and so stayed for nearly two weeks. His stay was just long enough for me to get used to having him around again, then he left looking much happier while shortly afterwards I collapsed into an unmotivated and depressed state. His visit has introduced a lot of confusion around the place as to what we are doing. I was also feeling confused and finally asked him what he wanted from me. I think Art carries some guilt and has some need to assure himself that I'm going OK. In fact I'm probably doing better than him as he looked pretty depressed for a while but had cheered up by the time he

189

left. I now realise how much stronger and more independent I'm feeling and how much more emotionally stable, as I don't really feel that I would now choose to get back with Art if it was a real option.

I'm feeling a bit more directed at work, too, and a bit more enthused but I guess underneath also a bit worried by the fact that I really should get something out, and soon.

I'm still feeling fairly rattled by your news, and feeling for you in your position as much as for Paul. You didn't sound like the fact that it's going to be hard for you to plan ahead for a while is bothering you. You are so patient and giving, Pene, and so good with your men. I hope you're remembering to save some for yourself. That is important, I think.

Well, hugs and kisses, Pene. I hope I get to give you one in person sometime this year. Gina.

I felt shocked and helpless at the news of Paul's cancer, confirmation of my greatest fear and no doubt Pene's too, although we hadn't mentioned it. I was coming to recognise a tendency towards selflessness in myself, and I was acutely aware of Pene's difficult position in the face of this crisis. I could do nothing but be there: standing guard at my terminal, to channel what empathy I could through the vacuity of the computer network.

In Svalbard I had been reflecting on my year and my grieving process. I had grieved a lot; about one day every month I had been crippled by grief. I was becoming quite accomplished at grieving since learning of the process used by some of the Alaskan natives. I imagine these green hairy balls of grief nestled deep in my belly and I bring them up and spit them out, just like cats with their fur balls. I spit them out into a huge river, the Tanana or Yukon; they are washed away down to the sea and eventually on to a beach where they dry out in the sun and are picked at by the birds. Sometimes there are reams of little ones, and other times one or two big ones that take some work to get out, but I always feel much better afterwards.

In some ways I enjoy the depths of feeling to which grief takes me. There is a certain comfort to be found when snuggling in the warm, green belly of life. The richness of these experiences demanded to be expressed in many creative forms. I wrote a poem entitled 'Birth or burial', presenting the paradox of Sophie's birth: that it took a life to end a love. No one here knew Tod or could appreciate my grief. I had separated myself from all who knew us together. I needed time to process this alone.

I had first met Sharon some months after moving to Fairbanks. I had been apprehensive about meeting her as she was a former girlfriend of Art's. She came to dinner one night but it wasn't until Art had returned for good to Chitina that I really got to know her. It was a desperate week for me, the biggest comfort being a very unseasonal rainstorm. It simply poured for five days continuously: I was sure it was in sympathy for me. Work was a huge effort, I had to take long walks at lunchtime to get through the day. During one of these walks, I was sheltering under the birch and spruce trees through which the ski-trails wound. I was crying as hard as it was raining when I decided on what I needed: to stand within a tight circle of women. I called them my healing circle. It gave me such comfort to imagine the concentrated caring of my favourite women that I hung on to this image and came to the great realisation that I didn't actually need them to be physically present.

Sharon, whom I hardly knew at this stage, was one of the women I had chosen for my healing circle. Surprisingly she rang later that week and 'No, Art isn't here' so we had an excuse to talk. We decided to go to a women's folk festival, which I found to be revealing as the lesbian community was well represented. Although I usually felt comfortable with lesbians here I was disappointed to find women playing obnoxious male roles; out to chat you up with a beer and a poor come-on. It was wonderful talking with Sharon. On the way home she told me about the women's circle of which she was a part. I then told her of my healing circle and I was inspired to find she understood completely and immediately thanked me for the honour of including her.

I went to the next women's circle and I have been going ever since. The circle has a life of its own and is a different experience every time. There is some observance of pagan traditions which honour the Earth and mirror the cycle of the seasons. Ritual is an important part of the women's circle; the autumnal equinox celebration may commence in the evening sun with the release of the jubilant energy of summer, followed by a retreat inside for quiet solitude and fireside stories typifying winter. Some of the women see themselves as 'white witches' but others, like me, shy away from this term. Whatever the label, the female acknowledgment to the planet, the seasons and the spirit world feels positive, and a lot of nurturing and healing energy is generated in the process.

I was brought up surrounded by a neighbourhood of strong 'spinsters'. My oldest brother and I visited these women, receiving sweets and a good dose of their wonderful presence. Otherwise I was happily surrounded by my three brothers. At my all-girls high school I resented the gossip and bitching. On the weekends I'd prefer to spend time with my elder brother and mixed friends, which included the family next door. After leaving school I made few good women friends until meeting Pene, six years later. Tod noticed that I always returned from Adelaide charged; I was so thrilled to find a woman I could talk to about anything and everything. It took another seven years and going to Fairbanks to find more — and suddenly I was inundated. There were good women in abundance and I instantly related and fitted in. They began with Kim at Hidden Hill and extended through the women in the Quaker community, to the women's circle, and even to the mother of one of my male colleagues. The place was alive with a resounding throb of female energy, readily identifiable in the quiet of the winter landscape.

I tried to share some of this energy with Pene as she emerged from the male world of Antarctica. In her current situation I wished I could muster for her more of the support on which I was thriving.

18 FEBRUARY 1991

Hi, Gina,

I only received one message from you last week, but two copies so think perhaps some items went astray. Paul had his second treatment last week. It is horrible stuff, vomiting all the time and not being able to eat, but he's home again and it's a little better than last time. Have to see the doctor on 1 March and no doubt discuss the next steps and get a bit better idea of what may happen. Yeah, I guess at times things all seem to come at once. I'm trying not to look on this as something to drag me down or stop me from doing things. I may have to change some of my plans but that is not necessarily a negative thing. At the moment I am trying to write an application for an ARC postdoc. position. There are 50 offered Australia-wide, each for three years. Gary Burns [Australian Antarctic Division UAP program manager] is very interested in this and I would be based here at the Antarctic Division [in Hobart, Tasmania] with possibly some commitment and teaching at IASOS [Institute of Antarctic and Southern Ocean Studies] at Tas. Uni. I should have a 50–50 chance of being successful. Of course they aren't deciding who will be successful until December, so will be on tenterhooks for a while.

I've been going home early, at lunchtime today, while Paul's ill. At times it's a bit frustrating when I have things I need to work on. I think we'll get a dog and/or a cat if we get a house.

Love from Pene.

21 FEBRUARY 1991

Dear Pene,
I have just had a wonderful four days away skijoring in the White Mountains [about 40 miles north of Fairbanks]. We had pretty mild weather, travelled about 70 miles and saw some lovely country. The White Mountains are not huge and impressive but still a nice region to explore, with some nice rock formations and little gullies and open plains. Dogs are the ideal way to enjoy it as the distances are too long to ski comfortably. Skijoring is the perfect way to take them in, particularly when you travel with some teams to carry your stuff. With two dogs pulling me on skis I had no trouble keeping up with the teams, and with one dog and a little more work you could also keep up. I went with William from Hidden Hill, Simon, the New Zealander, and Sue. (Sue's about 6 feet tall and big but with a personality to match and she has a wonderful rapport with each of her 21 dogs. Visiting her house with dogs running everywhere I think of Old Mother Hubbard.) Mostly I was using Sue's favourite old lead dog, Tucker, who is the most handsome, strong, intelligent dog I think I've known. We also had a few puppies running loose. The sun is returning with a vengeance and everyone is suddenly busy planning their spring trips.

Well, cause for some celebration for me today. Finally I have had my first two papers accepted for publication in JATP. Feels great — do you realise they've been in the pipeline for almost 18 months?!

This must have boosted my self-esteem because then I went on to

ring Tod and tell him I didn't want to be Sophie's godmother. This is
an important step for me. Decided I need distance and that I don't want
to start receiving baby photos, etc. I told Tod that I didn't think I was
the person he should be sharing his fatherhood experience with and that
if he wanted to he should have thought about it a while ago. Instead I
feel like I'm being lumped with the consolation prize and frankly I think
I'm better off without it.

Lots of love, Gina.

The trip to the White Mountains had given my free spirit a
chance to speak. I had wanted to do such a trip since hearing of
William's adventures soon after arriving in Fairbanks. I loved it
out there and grinned from ear to ear as Tucker and I flew along
the trails keeping up with the team. Tucker was as determined
to maintain the pace as I was and she ran as hard as I skied.
Skiing keeps you warm and as long as we were moving I didn't
feel the cold. (Mushing is hard work at times when driving the
sled in difficult terrain or heavy snow, but when the going is
good you can become quite chilled.) On the final run down the
gentle slope of Wickersham Dome, Sue was hootin' and hol-
lerin' her team along, riding the sled like a bucking horse. Tucker
and I had a wild time keeping up and I was laughing and hoot-
ing too as we careered along behind.

Sue was fun to be with. She had a good understanding of and
easy manner with her dogs, and most importantly she really
enjoyed all of them. She came alive out on the trail with an
array of dogs, both in harness and running freely. Sue had difficulty letting go of any dog that was a poor worker as she could
always find some compensating characteristic in its personality.
These dogs would therefore get to run along by the sled, tag-
ging along with the puppies. Sue had been working for the
Bureau of Land Management since heroically breaking out a
trail to a new hut that had been installed by helicopter one
summer. They were impressed by her skill in the bush, and her
artistic talents. She knew the country and had become involved
with the development of the cabins throughout the area. In
good company and with Sue's team and sled to carry my gear,

this was the way to begin in the doggy world before taking on the commitment of a team.

I came home from the White Mountains and made my major step towards letting go of Tod. When Mum heard of my decision not to be Sophie's godmother she was most relieved. I had sent her my poem and although she could hardly bear to read it, she thought it was wonderful that I could write it. She couldn't express her thanks at receiving it; it seemed she had felt the precariousness of my situation over the previous months more than I had been able to feel it myself.

22 FEBRUARY 1991

Dear Gina,
I have received a letter and fax today and you obviously haven't received my e-mail. So, 'Hello, hello, hello . . .'

Paul and I are looking at buying a house. It is a bit daunting taking on a mortgage but I guess I can get some sort of job here in Hobart and if that means getting out of atmospheric physics, then so be it. At this stage I'm not sure if Paul will be able to work or not. I guess if the right place comes up then we'll be happy about it. He had his second lot of chemo last week. In the meantime I am getting practice at giving morphine injections. Illness and hospitals are a whole other world. Well, I won't keep on raving on.

Love, peace and happiness, Pene.

5 MARCH 1991

Hi Gina,
Paul went in to hospital last night after a busy day organising mortgages. The agent rang last night and it looks like the person selling the house is just not prepared to negotiate much at all, which is very pigheaded of him. So we may just wait for a while. Am finding this all a wee bit tiring. Anyway, I'll ring the agent today and see what she thinks. It's odd but I do feel more comfortable dealing with a woman agent than a man.

Peace and happiness, love, Pene.

9 MARCH 1991

Dear Gina,

Well, we are now the prospective owners of the house in Taroona. We eventually settled on a price of $92 000. It's a really big block, quarter of an acre. It has no water views, but should be a nice quiet area. Paul was really pleased to get it.

I am glad this house business is finalised. I hope it ends up a good investment and a nice place to live, although I don't think of living here for the rest of my life, just the foreseeable future, which at the moment is not very far.

Well, I hope you have a good weekend.

Love, Pene.

11 MARCH 1991

Dear Pene,

Thanks for your two messages received 5/3 and 11/3. I'm attempting a vertical-wind campaign at the moment but after a week's perfect weather while the moon was up it's been terrible, with only two clear nights and one partly clear night being when I had commitments and so couldn't run. Fortunately Joe ran things for me on the clear nights. The FPS runs all the time but the other instruments need starting each night. Hence the trips out to Poker. We can't operate when the moon is up.

I have actually been feeling fairly flat lately. There has been a conflict brewing within the community which is making it difficult for everyone. The parties directly concerned don't seem to be prepared to confront things, so they are stewing away. With the return of the sun the old hormones seem to be getting stimulated and being single is suddenly not as much fun as it was before. Oh well, I guess I'll have to work harder to get my mind off it. It would be nice to get productive.

The weekend at Hutlinana hot springs was interesting. Pretty good fun but I think we scared ourselves a bit with the effects of jumping into a hot pool with tired bodies at $-20°F$ plus a wind. It ended up with Kim, who has long, thick, slow-drying hair and a poor sleeping-bag, getting really chilled and almost hypothermic. Fortunately Cathy had a good bag and acted quickly to warm her up. I, on the other hand, stayed in far too long as I was worried about freezing like those who got out before me. I almost had heat exhaustion and was really dehydrated. I ended up lying around taking a lot of aurora photos.

Getting in there was hard going. Skijoring with a good dog like Tucker is one thing, but with Zeb it was hopeless. Zeb is one of those dogs who does all his pulling before you even get moving, jumping at his lead and barking with excitement. His non-stop energy meant you had little control, and with a lot of trees and roots over the trail we were falling over a lot. Even then Zeb wouldn't stop pulling, so no sooner would you find your feet than you'd be over again. It was exhausting and hopeless, but Kim and I kept swapping and we got there in the end. Cathy, who was skiing alone, made better time than we did.

Lots of love, Gina.

9 APRIL 1991

Hi Gina,
Things not going smoothly for Paul. He went into hospital on Sunday night for some chemotherapy in conjunction with the commencement of the radiotherapy, and yesterday they managed to give him an over-dose of morphine. He's been on a fairly new form of oral morphine and somehow they managed to double his dose AND give extra to counter the effects of the chemo. So he spent the day totally out of it, on oxygen and being given withdrawal drugs every few hours to counter the effects of the morphine so that he didn't stop breathing. Jesus Christ!!! Some-times I just wonder whether the hospital can get anything right. The main problem was that when they gave him the withdrawal injections it totally counteracts the effects of the morphine and he was in excru-ciating pain for a few minutes. He was also given amnesiacs, which they apparently always administer with the chemo, so he may not have very good recollections of what went on. Next time I'll make sure I'm there when the doctors admit him so that I make sure they get the doses right.

Otherwise it's hard to say how things are going. The doctors say that the pain should be fairly quickly controlled by the radiotherapy. I guess we'll just have to wait and see. I certainly hope so.

Hope spring is treating you well.

Love, Pene.

10 APRIL 1991

Hi Pene,
Sorry to hear of the hospital stuff-ups with Paul. I was thinking of you today as I got a copy of the *Independent Monthly* and, lo and behold, there is an article about Antarctic expeditioners, including a picture of you. I like that paper. It's a nice way to keep in touch from over here as I haven't found any decent news source for international coverage and

Australia rarely hits the local press. (Except when Miss Australia breaks her collarbone bungy jumping!) I liked the article as it touched on the real side of what goes on in Antarctica, including the hopes and expectations of returning expeditioners, while minimising the glamour. American media is sickeningly over glamorised.

Well, spring is going great. I'm having another vertical-winds campaign at Poker during which I've seen and photographed some great aurorae. The other night was exciting. I went out to Poker Flat where, as well as running the FPS like in my thesis work, I have the support of some extra experiments including an all-sky auroral video and a meridian-scanning photometer which I have been given a 'licence' to operate. Once I have everything going I often catch an hour or so sleep but I like to keep checking things. I did doze off on one particular night and was woken suddenly from a dream of being in a dog-sled race. I went straight outside to see the most fantastic auroral 'corona' [when the aurora is straight overhead and the rays extend back to a point directly above you] I have seen. It was like being in a huge ballroom with a monstrous chandelier which extended from above right down to the horizon, with rays of glittering and twinkling light. This was about 3 a.m. It was there for about an hour. On top of that, when I looked at my data the next day I found that a stray burst of protons entered the atmosphere just prior to the corona and caused a huge and undeniable upward wind for about 20 minutes at both 120 and 240 km altitudes (i.e. in both the green and red emission data).

This is just the event I have been waiting for and the data are very convincing and definitely better than anything else I have seen or collected myself. So at last I feel my work is paying off. I want to try and model this event and get some physics into these vertical wind observations.

I've been making the most of the spring weather. We have had record snow up here so we may well be skiing and mushing into May. Last week I spent four days in the White Mountains with Sue and Simon; Dale, who also wintered at McMurdo, came with us. We had two 7-dog and an 8-dog team and one skijorer. I skijored for two days and mushed for two. Mushing is quite different from the Mawson experience with trails and trees to contend with, so you are constantly throwing the sled around to keep it upright and on course. It was hot and sunny, so much so that it got too hot for the dogs (about 10°F). We were forced to bask in the sun over the 'heat' of the day and take some leisurely lunches on the trail with wine and sandwiches.

Sue is a great storyteller and it was over one of these leisurely lunches, with Sue's favourite lead-dog Tucker lying in the sun with us, while all the other dogs were in the shade, that the Tucker stories came out. 'Tucker's problem is that she's too hard-headed and strong-willed, and she loves people' says Sue, as if describing herself. It is no surprise that this has made for many clashes between the two of them, as they've stood at a trail intersection, lancing at each other with their iron wills. When asked who usually wins, Sue claims that she does, although adds that sometimes she's had to put Tucker back in the team to get her way; so perhaps that's a Tucker win, she admits.

She tells a story of when she was in a 300 mile race, the Tour de Minto, with Tucker as lead. The word was getting around that at one of the check-in points, Bill Cotter, who had just won the Yukon Quest, was to be there. The Yukon Quest is a well-respected race among mushers, possibly more so than the Iditarod as the mushers have to carry all they need and cannot depot on the way, over 1000 miles. There is stiff competition and a tremendous amount of prestige in the mushing world in winning such a race, so Sue was pretty excited to meet this fellow and of course wanted to make a good impression. Well, as she pulled into the checkpoint a local boy came up offering to help, so Sue stuck in her snowhook and asked the boy to keep an eye on her team while she checked in. Two sets of swing doors formed the entrance to the cabin in which Bill Cotter was sitting. Sue entered and made her presence felt (as she can't help but do) and was in the process of introducing herself when the first of the swinging doors flung open, followed by the second, and there they were: Tucker, with the rest of the team trailing along behind, followed by the boy, 'And hi! I'm Tucker!' was the strong statement written across her face.

I'm off to Juneau this weekend. Since the war there have been a lot of cheap airfares around so I'm taking advantage of these and going to a folk festival which is being held down there. Life has been feeling very full lately. There seems to have been a lot of conflicts within the community which somehow seem to surface with the return of the sun. Meanwhile it is nice to have a wee romantic interest developing with one of the postdocs at work. We have been to a Green Party meeting together and now I've been invited around for dinner next week. It's added a nice touch of spice to life at the moment. I don't know if it will go anywhere serious. It is rather nice to be kinda courted for, you know, probably the first time in my life. I'm not in a hurry to get involved again and in fact I'm feeling fairly cautious about the whole thing. So it's nice to take things real slow and not have the emotions jump in and take over before I've had a chance to really suss out the situation.

Lots of love and thoughts, Pene, and best wishes to Paul, Gina.

Externally spring was an exciting time but internally it was often intense and revealing, and I would learn to prepare for this time of re-emergence. Residual conflicts that were hidden in the darkness and severity of winter tended to surface and seek attention. Frictions within the community, personal conflicts at work and even issues with my mother at home all appeared at this time. It is a recognised medical disorder for people living in high latitudes known as seasonally affective disorder (SAD). Statistics show a strong increase in the number of suicides and bouts of violence in March and April which are attributed to the SAD complex. Easter occurs near this time when the inner darkness is being exposed and addressed and we are starting to emerge refreshed and ready for the intensity and joy of summer. I came to appreciate the fundamental need for a symbolic rebirth, and finally this cornerstone of Christian tradition started to make some sense, although it made me realise how blindly we had mirrored these seasonal traditions in the southern hemisphere.

12 APRIL 1991

Hi Gina,

Boy, your mushing–skijoring sounds great. What wouldn't I give to have a bit of a run with the dogs at the moment. Just to get out and leave behind some of my worries for a while. Often think about Goohaw and Oscar and Merlin and Cocoa and all the boys at Mawson.

Well, Paul should be out of hospital on the weekend, probably Sunday. He has one more dose of chemotherapy to go and then they keep him in for at least 12 hours afterwards for nausea and fluid control. They've been pumping a lot of fluid into him this time and his drip sites are failing nearly every day!!! The tumour has swollen up this week, possibly due to chemo and/or radiotherapy, and it's been suggested that that's a good sign.

The radiotherapy is to continue for six or so more weeks but we'll just have to visit the clinic (at the hospital) twice a day. By the end of all this it is going to take at least another few months for everything to be fixed up, and that's if all goes well. My job officially finishes soon, 22 April. At least Comcare have said they'll take on Paul's case now so he'll continue to be paid until he is better and able to work.

Hope to get stuck into the garden this weekend, maybe plant a few grevilleas and bottlebrush in the front yard. Yeah, that article in the *Independent Monthly* was a bit of a surprise. Tania was on the trip home and I had a bit of a talk to her. It was Paul's photo of me taken at midwinter and the island behind the iceberg is the peak of Ufs Island near Colbeck. We climbed it a couple of times on later trips.

Have a good weekend.

Peace and happiness, love, Pene.

23 APRIL 1991

Dear Pene,
Well, just got back from Juneau Folk Festival, or should I say USA in the '60s. A place I felt I shoulda, coulda, mighta been, sorta was a part of. Basically it was just three days of raging on top of a night at Poker. Juneau is a pretty city, with mountains and water limiting its size. It's small, so you can walk everywhere, yet with the legislature there it supports a good number of restaurants and coffee shops which Fairbanks lacks. It was so nice to smell water, trees and greenness again, although with the rain and the wet cold it actually felt colder than here. I did some workshops on writing political satire songs, singing harmonies and Cajun dancing.

It's taken me a week to catch up with sleep and life and finally get back to some serious work, as I wasn't getting much done when I was going out to Poker each night either.

Spring is certainly here. We now have enough sunlight to keep you awake at night. I'm back on my bike after what I think should be my last attempt at skiing in yesterday. People are starting to disappear for the summer, and the first mosquitoes have arrived. Personally I miss the winter. It is my favourite time of the year but I guess it's nice to have the change and the freedom of summer and not have to rug up before heading out the door.

My romantic endeavours didn't get very far. We still intend to enjoy the friendship and he's coming around for dinner this Thursday. I'm a little worried about this as Art's on his way up for a visit and a wedding we are both going to, and what's the bet he'll arrive on Thursday. Oh well, I'll see what happens. Actually Art is staying with our next door neighbour following my initiative. I'm looking forward to having him accessible but not on top of me. I have felt a bit drained and confused after his previous visits.

I hope Paul's latest treatment went as well as you were hoping. How are you coping with it all? I wish I could be a bit closer so as to give you back even a fraction of the support I imagine you are giving to Paul. I hope you are looking after yourself at the same time as I'm sure you must be bearing some of Paul's suffering. This is not meant to underrate what Paul must be going through and I wish I knew him and knew you together. But the fact is, I don't, so my feelings and concerns are more for you. You give so much, Pene, a common female failing I think sometimes. It is much easier for women to slip into selflessness than men. Anyway, I wish I could feel closer to you but I've been thinking about you.

I'm going to the IUGG [International Union of Geodesy and Geophysics] meeting in Vienna. I'll be spending some extra time in Europe with my folks. Suddenly I'm a little worried that we may be overdoing it as they are coming to Vienna also. Oh well, we'll see how things pan out.

Much love and springtime thoughts, Gina.

1 MAY 1991

Hi Gina, Mark Conde here.

Well, first some bad news. Pene's friend from Mawson, Paul Myers, died yesterday morning. You probably knew he was suffering from cancer, which they thought had a good chance of being cured. Well, it turned out to be worse than first expected and to be untreatable. He only found out last week. He could not eat or drink. Then he caught pneumonia. Rather than be kept alive by drips he opted to stay at home and take what came. They knew for several days beforehand that it would mean he would die, but he wanted it that way. Anyway, Pene is pretty upset of course. If you could give her a call or a telex or something I'm sure she would appreciate it. She's at a bit of a loss as to what she's going to do now too.

Sorry this message carries such horrible news. Let's know how life in Alaska is going.

Look forward to hearing from you, Mark.

Mark's telex stopped me in my tracks. Coming through Mark I knew it was serious. I reread it, gazed at the words, then read it again to be sure. Then I hopped on my bike and rode straight home to collapse in Art's arms. I was glad Art was around then, and the next day I phoned Pene. It was hard — nothing could be done, nothing could be said. All I had to offer were our years of friendship and the assurance that I was still here.

At times of trauma and loss, e-mail was not enough. It was impersonal, the words could not be held, and feelings and emotions were shrouded. Our messages were pounded out on a keyboard, delivered by high technology and viewed on a monitor. What could I do to bring myself closer to Pene and feel at least something of what she was going through? I made a printout of all her letters and digested them in the quiet of my cabin away from the influence of computers and the world of work. I wrote a card, an offering, that would transcend the distance between our homes at a palpable pace and arrive in entirety; encompassing penstrokes, words, flowers and fingerprints.

9 MAY 1991

Dear Pene,
Where do I start and what can I say to help you in this time of your huge loss? In trying to feel closer to you right now, I started flicking back through your letters from last year (a copy of which I am in the process of sending to you). They cover your time with Paul from when you first got together over a tipped sled going up Gwamm. I noted your comments on not letting yourselves talk about the future, and yet at the same time you never seemed to question your love.

'Paul's pretty special and treats me really well. Quite different to how any other man has made me feel.' The romance of Antarctica itself, I'm sure, added a unique spice to your relationship, not to mention all the dog-trips you shared. Especially the Kloa trip, running alongside each other and looking after each other when you are being physically and mentally pushed and yet, on your return from Kloa you talked of having trouble readjusting to not being with Paul 24 hours a day.

I can't believe all that you two must have been through together, in a relatively short time, and all since I last saw you. You must have seen sides of each other which neither of you could have shared or could ever share with anyone else, and sides which many of us don't even know in ourselves.

I felt sad reflecting on your dreams of visiting San Fransisco and Alaska, and goat farming in New Zealand together, and for myself I'm sorry that you won't be filling your reservations for *two* spots on my floor. And when Paul's health was deteriorating you remained strong and positive and, above all, devoted. I could see that nothing was going to budge you from Paul's side. I'm sure your strength, love and dedication must have been a great comfort to Paul.

Looking back over your letters I was struck by the wisdom of what you have written to me during my troubled times, but which perhaps I should throw back at you now. When I was struggling with Tod and Art affairs you wrote: 'It's hard to come to terms with the ends of things'. Although death is a well-defined ending it is *so* final that it is almost inconceivable and may feel like an impenetrable brick wall.

I hope that when you are ready you will be able to move on — move on a stronger, wiser and richer person for having known Paul, and to be thankful for the love you have shared.

Peace and happiness, Pene, and love always, Gina.

Paul's death was sudden. The swelling we had thought was a side effect of radiotherapy was actually rapid growth of the cancer. This type of growth is uncontrollable and untreatable. It made it impossible for Paul to eat, and drinking extremely painful. He had almost completely lost his voice. He was admitted to hospital overnight to rehydrate and I took him home next day. Hospitals had come to be places that made Paul ill rather than curing or helping him. He did not like the rules and regulations and the whole atmosphere is generally depressing for people used to health and freedom. The hospital could not provide any effective treatment and, as nursing and palliative-care sisters would make home visits, we could cope much better there in a much happier environment.

We had regular visits from Albert Bruehwiler who had since returned from Mawson and was working at the division in Hobart. Elwood (Peter Mantel), a friend of Paul's from the year he spent at Casey in 1987, came and helped by just being there. Paul's parents were able to come to Australia and spend a few hours with him in the days before he died. My mother, who works with the chronically ill, came and helped me manage in the last few days. Time became a blur and death, as for us all, an inevitability.

Paul died on 29 April 1991. We had a simple civil funeral at the crematorium two days later. Although these facts describe in a concrete manner what happened, it is impossible to write about or describe what I felt during that week and the weeks that followed. The sun rises and sets regularly and predictably and life goes on no matter what you feel. I appreciated a haven in physical and mental exercise; I could work or run or cycle without having to justify it to myself.

Gina and I had a long telephone conversation and I could feel that she wanted to give me support but the distance between us became more tangible. I sought time and isolation to put my feelings and life into context in the world.

ALASKA

Prudhoe Bay

CANADA

Wiseman

Arctic Circle

Koyukuk R.

2

Yukon R.

Circle   Dawson

C

Circle Hot Springs

Nome

6

Fairbanks

Tanana

3

4   McCarthy

B

A

Chitina

Anchorage

Valdez

Haines

1

Juneau

Homer

0   100   200

Miles

Highways

Alaska Peninsula

2 Dalton

National Park and Preserve

6 Steese

A Wrangell-St. Elias

3 George Parks

B Denali

4 Richardson

C White Mountain

1 Glen

MAP: JOHN COX

PART SEVEN

SANDHILL CRANES

The seasons in Alaska are orchestrated by the most dramatic of composers, with a brilliance bordering on schizophrenia. The only point of continuity is the evergreen spruce. On the permafrost, tall and elegant white spruce give way to scrawny black spruce daring to grow where nothing else will, surviving in only inches of soil. In windswept passes they withstand a windchill factor reaching –75°C and below. There they are like warriors, growing all of 1.5m in 100 years — survival defined. The spruce provide a dark-green backdrop highlighting the brilliant green of new life during the spring. In the fall the contrasting green and rich gold create a patchwork covering vast horizons, unlike anything in Australia. And in the winter the spruce are the lifeblood of the land, the only vestige of green in the deadly stealth accompanying the lowest temperatures of 30°, 40°, and 50°C below — at times standing tall adorned in a fresh white veil, at others bowing down like a yoga class under the weight of metres of heavy snow. Committed, reliable and steady, these evergreens provide the promise of life which is so lacking in Antarctica.

Summer in Alaska brings a joyful flush of vitality as flowers and greenery transform the scene. The pasque flowers lead the parade, appearing soon after the retreat of the snow in late April, just as the rivers are opening up and canoeists emerging. On the first weekend in June the whole of Fairbanks visits the greenhouse to pick up plants and seedlings for their gardens. One by one flowers appear along verges and in flowerboxes throughout the town. Even the vast tundra joins in the celebration with an assorted array of small flowers best appreciated by lying down and examining a few square metres in area. White, yellow, red, blue and purple, they are all there. By the middle of summer the fireweed blossoms in a brilliant magenta with blooms beginning at the base of a central stem and progressing upwards as the summer ticks on. Smothering roadsides and any previously disturbed ground, the fireweed clock is a constant reminder that the days of summer are numbered.

The fall is short, brilliant and foreboding: two weeks can see you go from paddling a canoe in a T-shirt to the first snow. Berries ripen as hunting, gathering and preparations for winter begin. Those with wood stoves frantically chop and assemble huge piles of wood to get them through the long winter. Freezers are filled with bags of blueberries and cranberries and, with a bit of luck, a moose or caribou. The hunting season is limited and only the bulls can be legally taken. The meat is sought after and even the animals killed on roads are reported and allocated to someone's freezer. The high tundra leads the annual display of red, orange and gold which progresses southward. The deciduous trees take their cue and within days the flush of fall has reached its peak. Occasionally the first snow moves in before the leaves have fallen, leaving them frozen on branches, awaiting a warm spell when they may be released and finally buried.

Winter always comes too quickly, leaving behind the mask of summer as the system reverts to its seemingly more normal state. The first winter nights are the darkest as the sun is gone but the white snow has not yet settled. Like a child tottering in its first pair of shoes, adjusting to the winter mode of living feels awkward. On and off come the jackets, boots, hats, gloves and scarves every time you pass through the door. The migratory birds, the tourists and family visitors disperse and a sense of community grows among those that are left. Winter is a time of coming together, which is recognised in the Thanksgiving feast held in late November. It is also a time of retreat and reflection and, for many, a sacred time. During the depths of winter the sun moves backstage as the waxing and waning moon calls the tune and the aurora ripples the strings of the violins.

Spring is the most exhilarating time of the year. The vigorous re-emergence of the sun brings an increase in daylight of up to 15 minutes a day at the equinox. The combination of daylight, frozen lakes and rivers, and a solid base of winter snow makes it the prime time for getting out with dog-teams, skis and snow machines. Trails that have been maintained throughout winter become hives of activity. Community attention focuses on the Iditarod and Yukon Quest dog-sled races, as the media tracks the progress of teams across a thousand miles of unyielding terrain.

Excitement builds and bets are placed on the day, and time, that rivers will break out from the binding ice of winter. The arrival of the first birds brings assurance that summer is on its way, and that of the first mosquitoes, a sense of reality. The crescendo builds as the buds swell on the aspen, birch and cottonwood trees. Finally the leaves burst forth in perfect unison, creating a luminous glow of new life.

14 MAY 1991

Hi, Gina,

Well, I've come back to work for the time being. My mum was here for a week and then my sister Prue. Prue and I did a bit of tourist-type things like looking at Port Arthur and we visited a cousin of ours who is living in Devonport. Prue flew back home yesterday so I am on my own for a while. I have a lot of sorting out and assessing to do. Not sure where my life goes on from here but I guess I'll find out sooner or later.

Last week I found out that the Director of the Antarctic Division said that we'd pull the dogs out of Mawson. 1994 is the definite cut-off. I had a chat to Rod Ledingham about it this morning. He's not sure yet if we should fight it or accept that this decision is inevitable. One possible solution would be sending them to Alaska. It would be best if they could be kept in their teams rather than splitting them up. This all just seems like another thing I have to cope with. I don't like the idea of the boys being taken out. It's like removing the lifeblood from Mawson.

I am thinking of the possibility of coming to visit you later in the year. At the moment I feel like I need to stay put for a while. I will have to go to Adelaide and Perth in the near future to collect all our gear but I'll leave it for a few weeks.

It's hard to know what to say and what to do.

Take care, peace and happiness, love, Pene.

13 MAY 1991

Dear Pene,

Nice to hear from you today and know that you are there and back on the air. Yeah, it is hard to know what to say and what to do. In fact it's enough just to try and feel or empathise when someone is bearing a loss of an order that you can't comprehend. I have been generally depressed, partly thinking of you, partly from having Art up, partly thinking of me, and with some family turmoil. I just don't know what to do!

On the weekend I was showing some of my Mawson slides and in fact was asked whether there was any chance of the dogs being taken from Mawson. I said no. I was quite shocked to hear of the plans. Boy, I'd love to have them up here. So much of me would love to stay up here and have a dog-team but then the other side of me just wants to go back where I feel I belong, preferably WA. I'm worried that I won't find my type of people there like I have found up here. This is my current inner conflict.

I don't want to rave on with my problems. The last two weeks have seen the snow disappear and vivid green leaves appear on the trees. It's been time to put the skis away and bring out the bike and shorts. It's just such a drastic change, blows me away.

Love you, Pene, Gina.

17 MAY 1991

Dear Pene,

Friday afternoon and my analysis programs can't handle the noise I have just put into my simulated profiles and I don't feel like tackling the problem. I have been trying to put these programs together for weeks now, just head down into the grunt work and not getting anywhere terribly fast. At the end of next week I'm going to the spring AGU [American Geophysical Union] meeting in Washington DC, for a week. I'm presenting the radar data from my thesis. I gave a talk to the GI about it the other week and I was pleased to get a good turnout. The week I gave the talk was the week Paul died. A lot happened that week as the weekend was spent at a wedding, and Kim's graduation. All it lacked was a birth.

I'm having a quietish weekend. The weather is so wonderful that I just feel like having some time at home on my little balcony soaking it up. We have started having barbecues outside at least one night a week at William's cabin, which is on the end of our little ridge. While I was sitting out there last night two sandhill cranes came circling overhead. They are huge, with an eerie call, sort of like pterodactyls. The two friends who just got married both study birds and for their honeymoon went to watch the birds migrating north near a pass in the mountains. They saw thousands of these cranes. It must be a magnificent sight.

Lots of love, Gina.

21 MAY 1991

Dear Gina,

Thanks for your Friday message. I almost wrote Friday but realised I didn't have a lot to say. Work-wise I have been trying to sort out a few problems which have been plaguing the sodium D-line analysis. If we can solve them it may answer some of the riddles presented by the results. It's a slow process though. Next year's UAP expeditioners start tomorrow so it will be interesting to meet them.

Last weekend was my first weekend by myself. It doesn't bother me being by myself. I would get someone in to share my house but I don't want just anyone and right at the moment I feel like I need a bit of space and don't feel like rushing out madly looking for someone. However, I've told a few people so someone may turn up.

I did some work in the garden on Saturday. I haven't got much vegie garden going. Think I'll concentrate on getting fruit trees and natives in and limit my vegie garden to planting heaps of potatoes where the veggie garden will go next summer. It's almost overwhelming, there's so much work to be done in the garden. You don't achieve much in an afternoon.

Well, I hope you've had a good weekend and feel like tackling your computer problems again.

Love, Pene.

20 MAY 1991

Dear Pene,

If you're thinking of coming over here, September is when the trees change, birds leave, berries ripen and the snow starts. By October it's getting pretty crisp. It takes a little while for there to be enough snow for mushing–skiing. In that respect it's not a prime time of year for doing things but there's always something to do.

Well, I solved the first of my computer problems but of course they have been replaced by some new ones. I was tickled when a few weeks ago Poker Flat made it into 'Good Morning America' with a story on aurorae, including a glimpse of me. Well apparently that story was shown in Australia at some very off-peak time in the middle of the night and (trust Tim) my brother was up late with a mate and saw it.

Well, better get home, good luck with your plans.

Lots of love, Gina.

24 MAY 1991

Dear Gina,

I am writing to ask you a favour. Could you write a letter to the minister (Ros Kelly is currently the minister for DASETT) complaining about the decision to remove the dogs from Mawson? I had a talk to the director of the division yesterday. He's keen to be seen as doing the right thing and wanting to justify his decision without actually entertaining the possibility that he may have to change or even discuss it. It may also be worthwhile writing to the Antarctic bod in the US government too.

Apparently the main concern was the possibility of introducing distemper viruses into seal populations down there, principally from unvetted dogs going down with private expeditions. It would seem that they decided a blanket ban on all dogs would be easier to manage than trying to be more specific and only allowing properly vetted animals in. It is impossible for the Mawson dogs to have any diseases as they have been in effective quarantine for 30 or so years. Britain still has dogs at Rothero base and Argentina also has teams on one of their stations, Esperanza. Britain came up out of the blue and said it would remove its dogs. Argentina was talked into it also and by the sounds of it the Australian delegation just didn't have the guts to stand its ground or even ask for time to consider its position. I see it as a totally political decision with no logical basis. Unfortunately the Australian and British delegations weren't talking to each other as one was pro-mining and the other, anti-mining. I think it shows poor preparation on the part of the delegation that they weren't aware that the issue of dogs was to be raised. There's also a suggestion that some of the radical environmental groups were behind the lobbying for this move. It is my firm belief that if they want to protect the Antarctic environment that much then they should not allow any humans there either. People and dogs are ideally suited for working together in such an environment.

I'd better stop raving on. I hope your conference talk goes well.

Peace and happiness, love, Pene.

4 JUNE 1991

Dear Gina,

Well, I hope your conferencing went well. Not a great deal is happening here. Keating challenged Hawke for the Prime Minister's position and lost, so I suspect that all that has been achieved is that a great doubt has been sown as to how long Hawke will last. It is unfortunate as I think they were a good team. Now Keating has been relegated to the back bench. Hawke is 62 so can't expect to continue as leader for too much longer. I think it's unfortunate that Keating had to challenge and couldn't wait for Hawke to retire at an appropriate time, especially while the Labor Party continues in power.

The Labor left has come out in power though, with Brian Howe as deputy leader and Kerin, the ex-primary industries minister, as the new treasurer. So with all this political toing-and-froing our little stories about the dogs are not making it to air in prime-time TV shows.

Vicki came around on Sunday night for tea.[1] We were going to the pictures but were talking too much so didn't make it. Her cancer has progressed into her lungs now and she has refused any more radical chemotherapy treatment. I can understand her. It may give her another three or six months to live, at the cost of all the side effects. Continuing the sort of treatment she's getting now, she'll probably live about six more months. It is good to be able to talk about what happened to Paul with her. Although nothing seems to make it make sense.

Hope things are going well for you.

Peace and happiness, love, Pene.

PS: Gina, looks like you have not received either of my last two messages yet so I'll try resending them. There appears to be a problem somewhere in the mailer. They've been sent back to me.

11 JUNE 1991

Dear Pene,

Well, just got back to a nice pile of mail, and good to get your messages too. I had a great time sea-kayaking and as for the AGU, I put all that in a snail-mail letter which (if you haven't got it by now) should be there soon. Coming home is always a bit difficult and coming back to work I am wondering how much longer I want to continue in this scene.

Sea-kayaking with Cathy and Sharon was excellent. We had a lot of sunshine, saw lots of seals, sea-otters, eagles and a puffin. We had a fire on the beach each night, with fresh mussels eaten out of their shells and also fresh greens from the surrounding forests — very interesting and delectable. We also did lots of talking about everything and anything, as only women can do. It was new to me, to experience the feelings of emotional nakedness with a couple of women. I've only got to that level within relationships with men before.

We had one double kayak, the big pig, and one single kayak, the latter being much faster and more manoeuvrable than the former. The person in the 'little boat' seemed to get into this 'little boat' mentality, zipping off lost in her own thoughts and world, sometimes to the concern and safety worries of those in the big pig. This all led to feelings of reprimand and awkwardness of what the number three can be. Eventually it brought us a lot closer and we appreciated the other more positive aspects of being three people. We did a few hikes — the sound is surrounded by beautiful mountains and glaciers, most spectacular. It was always nice to stretch the legs after some time in the kayaks.

Better go, I'll write some more at the end of the week.

Lots of love and hugs, Gina.

Sharon, Cathy and I formed a dynamic threesome; bound by a willingness to explore our strengths, our vulnerabilities, and the assumptions that both we and society had put on us as women. Paddling kayaks in the sheltered waters of Kachemak Bay, and hiking the mountain slopes that rose above it, the environment beckoned many forms of exploration. This was Sharon's stomping ground and she knew the area; the weather, the tides, and the respect demanded by their changeable nature. We were also bound by a mutual respect for each other's spiritual journeys, and I benefited from the distinctly different styles presented by the two of them. While Sharon had introduced me to the women's circle, Cathy provided me with an important inroad into Quakerism.

Cathy had received a Catholic upbringing and had been

involved in the Quaker meeting since moving to Fairbanks. Spirituality was an integral part of her nature and she was becoming committed to the Quaker form of expression. She had a strong sense of self and was in touch with her internal state of being. If you asked how she was at any time, Cathy could actually tell you; I was continually impressed.

Cathy was at ease with a conventional religion, whereas I had not been involved with any formal religion since leaving school. My first experience of the Chena Ridge Friends meeting was a memorial service for a young woman. The service lasted all afternoon. I attended briefly, walking into a wall of grief, as friends, family and the community shared thoughts and memories. Everyone came away with a better understanding of this person, her inner struggles and the importance of one life in touching so many. An ability to care for its members at the turning points in a life is an important function of any spiritual community. I liked the strong feeling of oneness which lingered in the meeting for some time afterwards.

Quakers encourage a high level of social responsibility and historically have taken a strong pacifist position through the major wars. The practice is embodied in a peace testimony. During the gulf crisis, letters were written opposing the war effort and some people chose the direct action of withholding the portion of their tax that would be tagged for military expenditure. Quakers are prepared to act on their beliefs, a shortcoming of other arms of the Christian tradition.

On a personal level Cathy and Sharon's friendship gave me a new way of looking at my inner struggles and enlightened me on my spiritual journey. We would do further trips together in different combinations, enjoying the physical challenges and stunning beauty of the Alaskan landscape, from the mountains to the oceans. We would talk endlessly; time with Cathy and Sharon was affirming and grounding.

13 JUNE 1991

Dear Gina,
Hope all is going well. I saw Tod at a seminar yesterday. He said he had rung you. Hope that's not made you too angry.

One, possibly good, thing we have found out was that the British dog people, as distinct from the polly types at the Madrid meeting, were also totally unaware that Britain had any intention of pulling out their dog-teams and were caught as much on the hop as we were. So I have hope that there will be enough groundswell from those actually living and working with dogs that the politician types may change their stance. The seminar yesterday, by a person from foreign affairs, was on the draft protocol of the treaty. He said that persons with Antarctic experience had been on the delegation in Madrid and had been consulted about removing the dogs. He was referring to the director of the division, who has been on a round trip for a couple of weeks, and a member of the policy section who has done a couple of round trips. What an absolute joke! It makes me angry that these people with no real experience of Antarctic affairs are making decisions, with no consultation with those whom the decisions affect. Without actually living and working with the dogs you can't appreciate their benefits.

I've spent some time sorting out my slides and photos from Mawson. I took a sequence of photos of East Bay over six months and I've been using my journal to date them properly. I get engrossed in reading my journal and find I've read a month or two. I wonder how much of that would be of interest to others? I went to bicycle in to work yesterday and found I had a flat tyre. A spot that had a patch on it had totally perished, as though the glue had eaten the rubber. I don't like feeling totally dependent on a car, although I have driven so much this year. Paul didn't like driving as he was on morphine the whole time once we got back. The doctor did say it would be OK for him to drive but if he started feeling sick and had to vomit immediately it would be hard to cope. Paul did drive on a couple of the longer trips we did. He was a good driver too and obviously had a much better idea of the real dimensions of the car than I do.

Peace and happiness, love, Pene.

17 JUNE 1991

Dear Gina,

Your kayaking trip sounds fantastic. I went orienteering yesterday, which was good, and then tree-planting in the afternoon. Paul's parents gave some money to the Hobart City Council to plant some trees and they put it into the extension of the Rivulet Park. I think with the current lot of extensions it will join Cascade gardens with the lower park so will cover the whole length of the Rivulet. In some places it won't be really wide. So there's some trees down there for Paul.

On Friday the US said they won't sign the Madrid protocol in its present form. They want an option to mine in 50 years without having to renegotiate the treaty. The bit about the dogs may be able to be renegotiated when the redrafting occurs. Hence I think it is useful to continue writing to politicians.

Peace and happiness, love, Pene.

PS: I've tried to send this yesterday but it wouldn't go. Hopefully will get through sometime.

18 JUNE 1991

Dear Pene,

Great to get all your letters tonight. It feels terrible when our lines of communication appear to close up. It's nice to hear from you because I've been thinking about you and I guess I've been doing my share of worrying about you too. Nice to hear titbits of Paul creeping into your letters again. The tree-planting sounds great. I know where you mean and I'm glad there's been efforts to make the Hobart Rivulet area nice again. I remember walking all the way into town along it one Sunday evening to go to the State Theatre and being very surprised to find some lovely secluded little houses hidden away there in the heart of the city.

I'm glad you've caught up with Tod and I appreciate your comments. Don't worry, I have been developing the fine art of getting angry and there's plenty in my journal to show for it, and a lot directed at Tod. This last time was the first time we had spoken for about three months and there was no way I was going to instigate it. You know, I am pleased to say that I put down the phone to realise I wasn't feeling emotionally wrenched by the experience.

I had some interesting talks with Cathy and Sharon about the situation with Tod while kayaking. They shed some new light on it all when I told them of him and Claire wanting me to be godmother, and Claire's letter to me one week after the birth telling me about it. It is like they were still hanging on to me. In other words, Tod was, at the same time as not wanting our relationship, not capable or willing or able to let go of it either. This was OK for him, having Claire; it's rather a case of wanting to have your cake and eat it too. So this left me with not only losing the relationship but having to take control of terminating it, when it wasn't me who wanted to do this in the first place. So, humph!!

217

This has given me plenty of good fuel for anger. I'm yet to see what I may get out of it all in the long run.

I am excited at the thought of you visiting. It would be great and perhaps further incentive for me to take on looking after a small team this winter, so we could make the most of them while you were here. Meanwhile I dream about not working, or having a shorter working week and a less open-ended job. That was the nice thing about teaching, so well defined.

Lots of love and thoughts, Gina.

24 JUNE 1991

Hi, Gina,

Good to get your last letter. I had a pretty miserable week with a flu but I think I am over the worst of it now. One good thing was, I finally got the last bugs out of the fitting programs (well, more or less). Now I'm just tidying it up a bit and doing a few simulations to make sure it works properly. So hopefully by the end of the week when I'm packing up to go to Adelaide and Perth I may be starting to get somewhere.

I had a pleasant weekend with a friend, Chris, and his wife Robyn and their little baby Henry. Chris is studying rat kangaroos, bettongs, and does field work in the state forest out near Campania/Colebrook. I got to see some of his bettongs and one which had just given birth to this tiny young one about 1.5 cm long. Mind you, the adults are only small animals weighing 1.5–2.0 kg. They eat truffles which grow on the roots of eucalypts, and the forests out there have masses of small diggings. It is most interesting.

We did get rain a few times, though. Chris has a pop-up caravan he takes out, so we stayed dry and had a big fire outside. Henry is quite a good baby but you have to watch him 24 hours a day. No time to yourself. Think I'm just too used to having some peace and quiet.

Chris and I went off to check the traps at night and on Sunday set up the screens Chris puts out to stop the truffle digging in some spots. He does this to try and estimate growth rates of the truffles. Robyn stayed and looked after Henry. Chris is very good with Henry and does his share of baby-minding too. I guess it's only the first couple of years that they need so much attention.

Well, not much more news. Are you planning more observations for the coming winter?

Peace and happiness, love, Pene.

27 JUNE 1991

Dear Pene,

Well, it sounds like we had similar weekends as I was off hiking with a friend and her 2.5 year-old, Arial. We had to carry Arial most of the 4.5 miles in then we camped a few miles from the granite tors, impressive and eerie rock formations. That evening I hiked up to the tors themselves, on my own in the midnight sun. It was just wonderful and much needed. As much as it was nice to enjoy some young company it was also kind of exhausting for me. Art had rung that morning just before I left. He wanted me to be the first person to know that he was now seeing someone else. I was feeling a strange combination of happy and sad, so it was nice to walk it all off. I guess it was just the next step, which I think I was ready for.

The next day Arial was just fantastic hiking out. She ran ahead of us most of the way down, picking herself up every time she fell, and being a real delight. It was a hot weekend with temperatures in the eighties and nineties. When we got back down Arial wanted to swim in the river. We were watching her by the side of the river and suddenly, when she had been in up to her knees one minute, she was then up to her waist and then right under. She was probably under for five seconds before her mum grabbed her and had her upside down. It was quite a shock for us all. It was pretty cold water and it took a while to warm her up again. I guess it's one of those things that all parents go through at some time.

I hope Perth ain't too hectic/difficult for you. If it gets messy or you feel like the contact give me a ring, any time, and I will ring you back.

Lots of love and hugs and a safe trip, Gina.

24 JULY 1991

Hi Gina,

Got your last message today. Sorry I didn't write from Adelaide. I thought I would have heaps of time but as usual with last-minute things to do I didn't manage to write. The Mawson Institute just doesn't exist any more. It's really sad. Don't think I could go back to Adelaide Uni to work, too many old memories. Also I can't help feeling that the university just didn't give a stuff about Mawson and the Mawson Institute. They don't value true scientific work; too concerned with preserving their bureaucratic empires.

Then I had three weeks in Perth. I stayed with some friends of Paul's who looked after me. Things went fairly smoothly although at times I have felt that I've run out of energy. I wondered what I was doing in Perth and what I was trying to achieve there. I was glad I saw Paul's ex-wife Louisa. I got along well with her and I felt she knew Paul in the same way I knew him. She told me a lot about their time together and showed me photos of Paul, some of which had caught him in some of his characteristic gestures and moods. I don't have all that many photos of him.

While in Perth I had a phone interview for the two jobs I applied for at the Antarctic Division. No decisions will be made about them, at least until next week. Fred seemed fairly positive about these jobs at the division so I have high hopes that I will get one of them.

Hobart has had lots of snow. I was feeling pretty exhausted when I got home and I wonder if it will be a good idea for me to travel to visit you? If you are coming home, then I should put in an extra effort before you return. Life's a bit dismal at times.

I need some space or something. Not quite sure just what it is I need. Maybe just to settle down and have a boring life for a while. If I get a job then I'll definitely try and come and visit you before I start work.

While I was in Perth I went orienteering a couple of times. It was good but last Sunday I got a xanthorrhoea leaf up my nose and then 500 m later one went into my ear. I went to the doctor last night as I was feeling pretty crook. He said I'd damaged my eardrum but right on the bone spot, so it wasn't perforated, or if it had been perforated it was very small and had healed up again. I've got a bad headache again today; if it continues for more than a day or two I'll have to go back and have some more investigations made.

Well, I won't keep on writing. Good luck with the working, love, Pene.

23 JULY 1991

Dear Pene,
It's almost a month since I've written or heard anything from you and I'm thinking surely you must be back by now. I leave for the UK and Vienna the day after tomorrow, so I am a little bit frantic as usual. My talk is all prepared. It is basically just vertical winds from Mawson, but I am preparing a poster on the spring large vertical-winds event which is not ready yet. I have been working hard but still don't have my analysis going so I am using Roger's and Jim's. They each give slightly different results. There is definitely a lot more than meets the eye in this analysis stuff. In fact there is a paper in someone putting down the nitty-gritty.

My current plans are that I am going home in December for Christmas and then coming back to finish off and do some mushing in spring before returning for good.

Good news, after a night at the pub with Sue, Dave and the rest I have organised some dogs for the winter. Sue has been saying for a while that she needs a break from her dogs as the time and financial commitments are getting a bit much. This is a common feeling in summer as dogs still need to be fed and cared for while the rewards of running them aren't there. Well, Dave and I leapt to the rescue, agreeing to take six of them off her hands for the winter. She'll supply boxes, harnesses and her spare sled and we'll feed, care for and work them. We are rapt and will share the responsibility of feeding and running them and take turns in doing trips in the spring. All we need is the community's permission for a second dog-team.

So now we'll be able to run some dogs together when you visit. This is further incentive for me to cut down to four days of work a week and I definitely think I want to if I am going to make the most of having the dogs.

Lots of love, Gina.

Conferences are a vital part of research. They offer lectures by senior scientists in the field, and sessions where people can request to give talks. When working in a university department or research group there may be one or two others who have a sound knowledge of your research area. There are possibly several times that number who may be able to offer specific advice on particular problems without relating to your research as a whole. By talking to someone with more experience or a different perspective you can often gain a better understanding of a problem. Presenting your work at a conference gives you the opportunity to tell others what you have learned; they can come forward and offer suggestions or criticisms of what you have done. Your future research can be discussed with others and plans for coordinated efforts are often made. It is usually very refreshing to attend conferences (in moderation).

The main advantage of conferences over publishing articles in journals is that at a conference you can present work which may not be sufficiently polished for written publication. The publication process takes anything from four to 18 months so by the time of actual publication you've probably moved on to a new problem and so do not benefit as much from discussion.

Gina had recently attended the American Geophysical Union (AGU) spring meeting in Baltimore, Maryland. The AGU has biannual meetings; international meetings occur less frequently. She was also about to go to Vienna for the 20th General Assembly of the International Union of Geodesy and Geophysics (IUGG) to present papers in the International Association of Geomagnetism and Aeronomy (IAGA) workshop. The IUGG conferences occur every four years and IAGA every two years. The Australian Institute of Physics (AIP) has biennial meetings at which the national Solar Terrestrial and Space Physics group meets. Gina and I were at a stage in our careers when international conferences were important as they provided opportunities to meet our peers and learn about the current developments in atmospheric physics. New developments are aired at conferences and discussed, sometimes years before results are published. Participation in such discussions at this stage can lead you in new directions.

Ray Morris, a colleague at the Antarctic Division, was also going to the Vienna conference. The day before he left he was offered the program manager's position and I, the five-year contract at the Antarctic Division. It was good news for him to pass on to Gina in Vienna. I also gave him a letter for her, outlining my plans to visit Alaska and suggesting we use our letters as the basis for a book.

From this point until our reunion our letters tended to become less descriptive and more disjointed. We were saving details for real conversations. I had trips to make to Melbourne and a visit to my family in north Queensland before leaving for Alaska. I would only have intermittent access to the computer network. We still tried to keep in touch, however.

29 AUGUST 1991

Dear Pene,

Well, back at work with period pains and all. Yesterday I gave the group a summary of the high points of the conference. It proved worthwhile and I'm glad I did it on the first day back. I know that if you don't do things like that then, you will never do them.

Well, Pene, yesterday I made a big move for me and a small but significant move towards a saner society. I'm down to three-quarters time and bloody hell, I'm proud of it. Roger isn't impressed; said he admired me in a sense but also that I'd never make a top scientist. As I understand it, 'top scientist' status is one of those unachievable goals. There'll always be someone just a little bit 'topper' than you. You'll always be stressing out wondering if you're there yet and then working and stressing out harder. If you do manage to convince yourself that you are there, then you start worrying that you're slipping off your little pinnacle or someone is going to sneak up behind you and push you off. I'd much rather be cruising along the fertile valleys of life doing my little thing and happy in the stability of being firmly grounded, knowing that one can always venture up a hill if one chooses.

So there — take that, society — at least I'll be happier.

Actually the nuts and bolts of it all is that there is this big rocket campaign coming up for which Roger is deploying his rapidly-coming-together new portable instrument down at Fort Nelson. I'm feeling a bit sorry that I haven't been getting my hands dirty in the development. Roger is in his element putting it together. I was the obvious candidate to go down and install and run it with him. His wife didn't fancy the two of us being together in a 12 by 6 foot caravan 24 hours a day. I get a wee bit upset when I find my sex holding me back. So it looks like I'm down as one of the operators to be out at Poker each night, which actually suits me better, so I'm not going to stir about it. Not sure that I'll be needed that much but I am keen to be in on the action. The first window is October 2–19, then the second is the moon down-time in November.

The bureaucratic side of going part-time is just too easy. Now I get paid for whatever I work between 60 and 80 hours a fortnight. If I work five days a week, I get paid for five days. Fantastic, eh?

Well, better go because I'm aiming for increased productivity in the four days that I do work. Hope this gets to you.

Lots of love and have fun in the snow, Gina.

30 AUGUST 1991

Hi, Gina,
Yesterday I went in and booked some tickets. I have a flight booked for October 14th. I plan to stay a day or two in Anchorage and then get the train or a bus up to Fairbanks. I will have to fly out from Vancouver to start work on December 2nd. I have booked a flight on Tuesday 26th

because there are not flights from Vancouver to Sydney every day.

As I left the travel agent's I realised that the Thursday of that week is Thanksgiving and maybe it would be worthwhile staying for Thanksgiving, which would just give me time to get back for work on Monday. (You lose a day going backwards over the dateline.) The red herring in all of this is whether I am to visit Paul's parents in Arizona. I think I'll give them a ring next week if I still haven't heard from them.

I have been wondering just what I hope to get out of this trip and why I'm doing it. Here's my list:

- I want to catch up with you
- go through our letters with you
- see a bit of Alaska
- talk to some bods about OH observing
- maybe get some inspiration for work
- learn to ski better
- do some Alaskan mushing
- have a break from my current environment.

How's that for being truly logical about things? So the nuts and bolts of exactly what I end up doing are fairly irrelevant and will have to tie in with your plans.

With regard to your comments about me wanting to write because Paul died, I agree, that is part of my motivation. If Paul had lived I know I would never have found time to write anything. My life is like a pond and his death has created huge waves, which are totally swamping everything else at the moment and will take some time to damp out.

Well, I'd better get some work done today, love, Pene.

PS: Good on you cutting back on your work hours! It is a really hard thing to do but you're right about never getting to the goal of being a 'top scientist'. You can be a good scientist without being a 'top' scientist. Sort of like the difference between a lead dog and a top dog.

9 SEPTEMBER 1991

Hi Gina,

Spring is on its way here. We've had a week of warm weather. All the snow is melting and flowers are out and most significantly the days are so long. It's light from before 6 a.m. to after 6 p.m. I guess the reverse effects of that are being felt your way.

On Saturday I went skiing up Mt Field with a few division bods. Skiing was good. It was a bit wet and slushy but still heaps of snow lying around. I didn't try and do anything I wasn't confident of doing, so I didn't damage myself too much.

I spent yesterday cleaning the house and sewing. I'm making a jacket out of wool. I'll be going to North Queensland to visit my family in just over a week's time.

Peace and happiness, love, Pene.

11 SEPTEMBER 1991

Dear Pene,

Hi again! The leaves have started falling. The 10 days the folks were here saw the colours turning, then peaking last weekend when we drove down the Richardson Highway to Summit Lake to see the vivid red of the alpine tundra. The weather had closed in down on the flat. As we drove up Isabel Pass at about 8 p.m. the sun burst out through the patches in the clouds, bringing alive the tundra and playing on the peaks. It was just brilliant!

The following day we drove back down into the gold of the woods and helped some friends who were banding raptors (eagles, hawks) as they were migrating south. Dad and Mum got such a thrill out of that, particularly with the large red-tailed hawk that was caught while we were there. I was given the job of letting this beautiful bird go while Mum paused ready with the camera. She was a bit close and the hawk almost flew right into her. She's probably going to have a great picture of belly feathers of a hawk, very close up.

All in all I think the folks got a very good taste of Alaska in their 10 days here. I took them canoeing down the Tanana on the first weekend, which was still warm and sunny. Mum looked very regal sitting calmly in the middle of the canoe, whereas Dad was much happier once he had a paddle in his hand and could be of some use. There were six of us altogether and on our arrival at the take-out point we discovered that the keys for one of the cars was back in a car at the start. We had to leave the folks, smiling bravely with a fire and in company of the river and the rising moon, while we drove back and forth. By the time we got back to them a few hours later they had settled in. It was such a beautiful evening.

I was really sad to put them on the bus on Sunday as we realised that the past six weeks is probably the most time we've spent together since I left home some 13 years ago. For me I enjoyed them most back here where I have some of my own space. It was great to share them with

225

the people I know. It's decided me on going back to WA. I want to live near them while there is so much there to enjoy.

Take care, enjoy the spring. It's funny hearing you getting excited about all your sunshine when we still have heaps more than that, and yet knowing that it is diminishing is sending me into a panic. The nights are so dark at the moment without any snow. It's the darkest time of the year.

Lots of love, Gina.

17 SEPTEMBER 1991

Dear Pene,
Well, I hope I haven't missed you. That extra day always gets me! Wanted to wish you a happy time with your family. *Eennjjooyy* the tropics a bit for me too.

I had a pretty low-key weekend, which I haven't had for a long time. The weather continues to be mild, just so beautiful. It's pleasant to be outside without mosquitoes and watch aurorae without hats and gloves. Everyone is asking, 'How long can it last?'

I'm enjoying having productive Fridays, getting other things done. I'm getting excited to think you're kinda on your way 'cause you've got a full schedule from here on.

Happy travels, lots of love, Gina.

8 OCTOBER 1991

Hi, Gina,
All went pretty well at home although had a few very busy days. Pam, my sister living in Germany, was home for most of the time I was there. Her daughter, Louise, had her first birthday last Monday. She is not quite talking, not quite walking, and a handful. Mum and Dad are both well. They enjoyed having all of us there. A family gathering doesn't happen very often; we are all too far spread.

I had a message from Maria. She had just returned from a trip to Kloa. They got there but sounds like it was a bit of a torrid trip; no dramas, though.

I have had to rebook my flights. I'll be flying into Fairbanks on Sunday 20 October about midnight. Yuk, that's a pretty horrible time to meet someone at the airport! Well, I'll save my news until I see you then.

Love always, Pene.

PART EIGHT

GEEING AND HAWING
IN ALASKA

i spent a week with Paul's parents in Arizona. They were most hospitable, taking me to many places of interest including the Grand Canyon and Sonora Desert Museum. Arizona had some beautiful and spectacular scenery and I enjoyed my time there, including my first encounters with hummingbirds. However it was my first real taste of the USA and quite a cultural shock. It was with some trepidation that I took to the air again across America from south to north to meet with Gina in Alaska, flying from one haven to another.

I arrived at Fairbanks airport on Sunday 20 October, but to my surprise Gina was not there. She was weathered in, along with Cathy, at Circle Hot Springs. Although it was one of the most luxurious places to be stranded, as she said later, it was one time when she badly wanted to be in Fairbanks. In the comfort of the small hotel, with good meals and a telephone, she could at least organise a proxy to be at the airport. And so, rather appropriately, Sue and Tucker were there to greet me and take me to Hidden Hill. Tucker rode, as always, in the cab of Sue's big Dodge pick-up with the eight dog-boxes on the back; she studied the snow, ice, and road conditions continuously as she never had come to trust Sue's driving.

The wind and first snow of the season continued to keep Gina snowed in and the road over Eagle Summit closed for another few days. There is no point in ploughing a road when the wind causes the snow to drift over it again within half an hour. On the second day Cathy was becoming anxious to return to work, and Gina anxious about me. After several phone conversations it was decided that I would fly out to the nearby town, Circle Central, and Cathy would take the flight back to Fairbanks the following day. I had a spectacular flight in the co-pilot's seat of the small plane used to service remote Alaskan communities. First we delivered groceries at Circle on the mighty Yukon river, which could be seen winding its way through the hills. Circle Central lay about 50 km to the south-east. As the plane taxied its way towards the cars it was easy for Gina to recognise me, the only passenger, and vice versa, as Gina was the only person waving furiously among the small collection of service vehicles.

Two days were spent lounging in the hot pool, sharing stories. By road we visited Circle and the pioneers' cemetery. A trapper, hitchhiking from nowhere to Circle, entertained us with stories of the bush. He said he was looking for a mechanic to fix his snow machine but we guessed he was also in need of some company after too long alone in the bush. On this side of the summit there was very little snow, barely enough to ski on. By the next day the wind had subsided and the road over the summit was cleared. A line of traffic followed slowly behind the snowplough. Whiteout conditions still prevailed at Eagle Summit, where Gina and Cathy had stopped for a carefree ski under sunny blue skies only days before. The road would have to be ploughed again that afternoon.

For Fairbanks this was the first decent fall for the season — just what all the mushers had been waiting for. Gina and Dave had established a dog-yard within earshot of their cabins (and within earshot of everyone else's as well) after obtaining permission from the community. Sue had relinquished six of her dogs: Jasper, Rex, Maimi, Zeb, Dune and Sasha, one of the Glasnost puppies. The first run, with all six dogs harnessed up and barely enough snow, was as exciting as it was terrifying. We careened around the corner near William's cabin, taking a young spruce tree with us and almost ploughing into William's dog-yard — an inevitably rough start to the season, given the state of the trails, and the adrenalin the dogs had stored away over the sedentary summer months.

In Alaska I noticed many differences from my Antarctic sledging experiences. The Alaskan dogs could be fussy eaters and were more highly strung, prima donnas compared to the Mawson chorus lines. They were pampered to improve performance, being fed in bowls and watered once or twice a day. This meant that considerable fuel was required for melting snow on longer trips. Mawson dogs ate snow and frozen food and were only ever asked to perform at a fraction of their ability, although they could continue at that level for long periods with minimal attention.

It was just getting light at 8 a.m. We established a new routine for getting Gina to work, by dog-team. We had settled upon using four dogs until our skills and the trails improved. The panic-line was tied to a tree to hold the sled as the wildly excited dogs were harnessed and hooked up. This was another contrast to Mawson, where the sled was secured by ice-pegs, which could not be relied upon to hold seven or nine leaping dogs. The dogs at Mawson were therefore trained to start from a sitting position. We had the use of Sue's toboggan-type sled, a sheet of plastic on runners with handlebars and a brake.

Alaskan sleds are built quite differently to Mawson sledges. At Mawson the sled base sits on bridges arching some 20 cm above the runners, which are curved at both ends. Because of this, standing on the runners is discouraged as it heavily weights the end of the curve, risking damage to the sled. The runner is ridden only when the brake is required, for example when travelling on icy slopes or over sastrugi. Both people travelling with the sledge either walk, ski or run alongside. If the sledge is unladen then two or more people can sit on it. Alaskan sledges are flat at one end for the driver to stand on the runners. It is not usual for more than one person to travel with each sled. Alaskan teams usually travel faster and it would require a marathon athlete to keep up with them.

Travel with dogs brings the same pleasure whether in Antarctica or Alaska: the freedom to embrace the wide open spaces common to both landscapes.

It took 15 minutes to get down to Sheep Creek Road, with

me sitting in the sled, ducking the grass and sticks that lined the trails. The sky glowed orange behind the trees as the sun clawed its way over the southern horizon. 'Come haw, Jasper!' we'd cry, mimicking the American accent ('Jaspurrrrrr'), rather than the Australian staccato ('Jaspa'). Jasper would double back on the rest of the team, turning them through 180°: an unheard-of feat at Mawson, where there are no trails as such. Once turned, Gina would jump off with skis and pack, to make her way up the ski-trails to the Geophysical Institute. Not liking to linger, the boys and I would be off with a quick wave. I was glad the boys stuck to their tracks on the return trip. It takes a few weeks to gain a sense of direction and recognise one trail from another, and spruce trees all look very similar to the uninitiated.

Like Gina in her first few weeks in Alaska, I became absorbed in *Race across Alaska*, an account of the 1985 Iditarod, when Libby Riddles became the first woman to win this 1770 km dog-race.[1] Through her descriptions of footsoldiers, overflows and sweepers, Alaska and the experiences to be had mushing were brought to life. The Iditarod and Yukon Quest are useful in generating interest and investment in dogs. Winning champions are pictured in most feed shops, along with their sponsors' food and equipment. Gina took me on a feed-shop crawl to see the vast array of gear available for handlers and dogs. For me this was far more exciting than the paraphernalia sought out by the regular tourist.

Our next trip away from Fairbanks was to visit Art in Chitina. The morning we were to leave, Art phoned to announce that his father had died the night before. We would still go and be there to support him at this time of loss. Gina felt some reluctance about falling back into a supportive role and would not have chosen to visit Art at such a time had fate not intervened. We made a hasty departure.

The Richardson Highway passes through Delta, Isabel Pass and other small towns along the way. The high mountains around Isabel Pass are very spectacular and in patches along the road a heavy hoarfrost dressed the tree limbs, grasses and footsoldiers on the hills. We arrived in Chitina in time for tea. Art was packing the goods in his gallery to return to the artists and boarding up the shop windows, as he planned to spend some time in Texas. He would not be able to organise his usual travelling Christmas sale. Art left late the next day in order to catch a 6 a.m. flight out of Anchorage the following morning. We left in his wake, returning to Summit Lake for the night.

Time on the road was time for contemplation and reflection. For the first time, we were both single. It was just over three years since we'd completed our theses and it was as though only now were we beginning to face the future with a balanced perspective. During the last years of postgraduate work, many other aspects of our lives were put on hold. We had to make amends for this in the years that followed as we both found our personal lives disintegrating for various reasons; perhaps they would have disintegrated earlier if we had not been so absorbed in our work. In proceeding to new phases, we had plenty to share. Writing this book gave us a structure by which we could examine our lives more closely. It made us laugh at times, sharing the lighter moments. The tears from the tougher times were not so easily shared.

The following weekend Gina decided to enjoy some quiet time at home, giving Dave and me the opportunity to take the team out for an overnight run. We spent the morning preparing while Gina baked us cookies for the trail. William and Sarah were to lead the way to Sue's place. From there Dave knew the trails out to a good camping spot in the Chatanika Valley beyond. The main trail would take us over an overflow which had caused Gina and I and the sled to become airborne on recent trips. The overflow point on the creek was marked by a fallen spruce — a perfect ski-ramp for the sled. As Dave and I didn't want to become airborne with a fully loaded sled, we decided upon the alternative route, across Ace Lake.

The extra few hundred metres were worth the effort although we had not counted on Maimi taking us on two laps of the lake while William and Sarah disappeared beyond the beaver dam. Rex was put in the lead with Jasper and soon we were under way again. By this stage I was on the brake driving and Dave was in the sled, it being too icy for either of us to run and keep up. There had been little new snow in the four weeks since my arrival, and the trails remained in poor condition. Soon after leaving the lake, the trip came to an abrupt halt when I was introduced to a so-called jumping spruce: somehow we were collected by a spruce tree, broke a runner and had to hobble home.

I joined Gina in her quiet weekend, which gave us more time to put into the book. A Sunday night book-reading was organised for the community and close friends. Huddled around a fire in the main cabin, we shared our letters and the start of our story. Sarah was captivated and keen to know more. 'How would the book end,' she asked, 'when your lives are going on and there is no obvious conclusion?' We discussed the dilemma late into the night over tea, cookies, and Sarah's fantastic English toffee.

Of all the different aspects of this story, what stood out was the fact that Gina and I were both multifaceted people, and that all these facets were used in our approach to both life and work. Such an approach to work is rather different to the more focused and narrow style usually befitting the classic male scientist. Women are more inclined to see things as a whole and take a more integrated approach.

We felt it was time that the women of ANARE got some recognition. Gina had attended the annual midwinter dinner in Melbourne, in 1988. Phil Law, past director of the Antarctic Division and leading figure in Australian Antarctic circles, gave the after-dinner speech, addressing the 'Men of ANARE ... men of ANARE ... *men* of ANARE'. Gina was fuming at his discourtesy in completely ignoring a number of overwintering women present. At the end of the speech she mustered all the tact and courage she could find to ask when the *women* of ANARE would be included. Although a number of people applauded her afterwards, it seemed that many would prefer that there were no 'women of ANARE'.

Here in Alaska, we two multifaceted women of ANARE were realising the value of each other. The uniqueness of our friendship was in the sharing of all the parts of our lives, from work, to men, to dogs, to the inspiration of the polar regions. It was a friendship unlikely to be replaced. From here we would strive for the same acceptance of women in Antarctica as we found in Alaska. In a land where women have come to terms with lives that incorporate raising children, flying planes, wintering alone on traplines, and even winning the Iditarod, this was a place where women were accepted along with their achievements.

We had one last trip to do together; a visit to Wiseman, a small town about 400 km north of Fairbanks. Simon, who had left Hidden Hill in the summer, was now spending the winter there trapping. Gina had not been there and felt apprehensive about taking her little truck up the icy Haul Road, so named because it was the domain of large trucks that service the Prudhoe Bay oil fields. It would be a big trip just getting up to the Brooks Range, and then the temperatures could easily fall to 40°F or 50°F below. Extensive preparations were required.

The week before our departure was extremely hectic. I borrowed bunny boots and an expedition-weight sleeping-bag and sleeping mats from various residents at Hidden Hill. An evening visit to Sue's had us further decked out as we carried away ruffs to sew on to hoods and many other pieces of cold-weather apparel. Gina found a huge pair of beaver-skin mitts in one of the feed stores and decided to treat herself to them. She named them 'Geelong' on the right hand and 'Hawthorn' on the left hand, after two Australian Rules football teams; more importantly they were shortened to 'Gee' and 'Haw', the Alaskan commands for turning the dogs to the right and left respectively. The mitts would come into their own if temperatures dropped: a chilled face could be warmed in the soft outer fur and hands in inner gloves could be slipped inside them when moving on the sled. Warm extremities lift the spirit, and furs are the best way to keep warm in the extreme cold.

Preparations to Gina's pick-up were next: a thorough 'winterisation' at the garage, an extra spare tyre, a new battery, and anchor points and chains to secure the dogs in the small space in the tray back. Simon had three sleds and eight dogs so only four dogs were needed to give us each a small four-dog team. The last day of preparations coincided with the day that I was to give a seminar to a Friday afternoon gathering at the Geophysical Institute. I spent the day working on my talk while Gina shopped for supplies. We had a modest list of provisions that Simon had requested: pilot bread, butter, and flour bought in cartons from the bulk food store. With a trapper's income

Simon was living on a frugal diet, so we added quite a few goodies we knew would be appreciated.

We packed until the wee hours; dog food, human food and gear. Frozen dogmeat was chopped into bite-size morsels, and 'fat-pills' were made by freezing individual globs of fat in a muffin tray. After five hours' sleep we finally hit the road at 10.30 a.m. on Saturday morning; tired, but content to be on our way to explore new territory.

Spectacular scenery unfolded ahead of us. Above the tree-line the full moon rose between snow-clad mountain peaks, while a brilliant orange twilight was left behind. We crossed the Yukon River then proceeded over the more infamous sections of the road; down 'Beaver Slide' and over the 'Roller Coaster', the well-earned names given by the truckers. The road appeared to be in good condition and we had no need to go through the routine of putting on chains, as practised the night before. We were now over the Arctic Circle, a first for me, and we were pleased we'd decided to come north.

Arriving at Wiseman we were greeted by choruses from the resident dogs, over 100 dogs among a handful of people. The largest kennels had 50 and 35 dogs, used for guiding tourists in the spring. Simon was pleased to see us and keen to show off the charming abode he was looking after. It had an air of history, with its museum of relics out the back, having been the old community hall. First priority, however, was to unload Jasper, Maimi, Dune and Zeb after the long haul. All seemed quiet in the back but when we opened the door Dune shot out like a bullet, having detached himself from the chain. He was easily caught but he had left an ugly trail. The window was red with blood and Zeb had been the victim. He had sustained several injuries, limped, and looked a very sorry sight. Checking him over and spoiling him with time in the warmth of the cabin, we decided to see how he looked next day. We fell asleep early while Simon stayed up sewing his furs, contentedly. He looked at home and seemed well adapted to the trapping lifestyle.

At about 10 a.m. morning light gently beckoned us from our beds. It was an enticing and balmy morning, the temperature just below zero and low cloud around the mountains suggesting the possibility of snow. After a good breakfast of pancakes we packed the sleds, prepared thermoses and dressed on the lighter side for the warm temperature. We decided that Zeb was in no condition for the trip, but after a short walk around town we had left him in caring hands and found a replacement. Grotto was an enormous pack dog, with a large proportion of St Bernard and Siberian husky blood. He had short legs and was a champion puller in the forward direction, but was vertically retarded as he could barely lift a foot off the ground.

Simon led the way out of the yard, along the river and down the road out of town. Simon's eight dogs were well-trained animals, essential for a trapper working alone in the wilds. These he split between himself and me. Simon led with Ex, followed by Lune, Spot and Werkum. Five of the dogs, including Ex and Spot, were only two years old and from a litter of Lune's. I travelled behind Simon with three more of the litter, Shiska in lead, Dan and Ruff, and then Grotto. Gina followed with Jasper in lead followed by Maimi, Dune and Alex. Alex, a big black house-dog with a long shaggy coat, didn't look the part at all. However, there was no room for house-dogs up here so he had been retrained for sled work and coped surprisingly well.

The trip to the Igloo was 48 km, 20 along the pipeline from Wiseman to Linda Creek then 28 up Linda Creek Trail and down into the valley. We had left at 1.30 p.m. and mushing was extremely pleasant in the warmth of the afternoon. We would be able to get on to the Linda Creek Trail by dark. As we headed up the middle fork of the Koyukuk River a flock of ptarmigans rose, their black tails stark against the snowy scenery. Spirits were high as we were all pleased to be heading out again with a team of dogs and a trail unwinding before us. It took an hour and a half to travel the 20 km to Linda Creek Trailhead, not bad for four-dog teams pulling reasonably heavy sleds. We were all carrying extra dogfood for Simon to depot at the Igloo for following trips. The bare mountains unfolded as we travelled up the valley. Spruce trees clad the river valleys and lower foothills. Simon and a friend had broken the trail three weeks earlier. Little snow had fallen since but there was enough to make for good travelling conditions.

We stopped at the Linda Creek cabin. It was empty, abandoned; a wind chime still tinkled in the wind. We had a drink and some biscuits, and gave the dogs a fat-pill to prime them for the climb up the ridge ahead. We had been able to ride the runners travelling along the river valley and pipeline, cruising at a speed too fast to pedal. From here we'd have to work, walking behind the sleds and pushing them when stopped, to help the dogs with the load. The best strategy was to keep the sled moving. We climbed slowly, hitting the worst section of trail, a patch of overflow on a steep gradient a few kilometres past the cabin. Simon went ahead swiftly, tilting his sled to put all the weight on the uphill runner. We were less graceful, briefly losing traction and control of the sled on the slick ice.

Simon stopped occasionally to check his traps. He'd plant his snow-hook, sit the dogs and leave them waiting patiently on the trail, watching his every move. We were continually impressed, being forced to turn our sleds on their side in order to hold the less obedient teams. The dogs worked well and distance quelled the extra energy of Jasper and the excitable rearguard. As we continued up the Linda Creek Trail, polar twilight ended as mountains and trees slowly melted into the darkness. Each of us could only just discern the moving shadow of the team in front. Thin cloud covered the sky, keeping the temperature from plummeting and filtering the moonlight. Occasionally on downhill stretches the teams clustered together. This prompted Jasper to leave the trail and run beside me, while Alex, unwilling to deviate, would slip his head unabashedly between my legs.

The trail skirted a large lake, visited in summer for fishing and hunting. Riding the sled in the dark was more difficult as we couldn't anticipate the bumps and ridges. Taking the descent into the Igloo on Glacier Creek, I had further problems due to a bow in one runner which caused my sled to pull to the left. It had run reasonably well on the main trail, but on the narrow and more overgrown trail there were a lot more trees to negotiate. I became stuck, my sled wedged over a small spruce. The dogs were keen to keep moving as they knew they were close to the Igloo and the end of the day's run. Eventually I managed to manoeuvre the sled from one side to the other and disengage it from the spruce.

We arrived at the Igloo about 9 p.m. Simon had helped construct the tiny sod cabin the previous year. A plastic vapour-barrier allowed the inside to be heated with a small wood stove, which was also used for cooking. It was a big job to melt enough ice from nearby Glacier Creek to feed and water the dogs, and then do the same for ourselves. A few mice could be heard and seen scurrying along tunnels between the sod and plastic. All were enjoying the warmth and we soon fell into an easy sleep.

The next day was spent exploring. Simon had heard of an old cabin in the vicinity, but had never come across it. We spread out and spent a couple of hours combing the area, but were unsuccessful. It was hard to believe that we could miss a small cabin amongst the spruce. The few hours of light passed quickly and the low sun never broke through clouds on the horizon. The next day we would be heading out and I would be starting on my return south: seven hours by dog-sled to Wiseman; eight hours' drive down the Haul Road to Fairbanks; farewells and Thanksgiving at Hidden Hill; and 38 hours of airports and planes to Hobart. Hobart seemed a long way from the Igloo, a different reality.

The return trip was slightly faster as it was mostly downhill. We kept a steady pace in order to maintain control of our sleds, especially on the approach to the overflow. Again Simon crossed with ease and grace. Our trailing teams lacked style, but managed the crossing without too much loss of control. We passed Linda Creek cabin and crossed the Dalton Highway to travel along the oil pipeline. Once on the open trail the Wiseman dogs raced for home and Simon and I jostled for the lead. Gina's city dogs, lagging in fitness, posed no threat to the competition. Racing up to a blind corner with Simon in the lead we almost collected a second team coming in the opposite direction; Joe from town was out with 12 dogs. Few words were exchanged as we quietly coaxed the dogs on as quickly as possible. The longer the rival teams were in sight, the more tempted they would be to fight.

We arrived back in Wiseman by 7 p.m. and got the stove going again to feed and water all. Tired and hungry after a good day on the trail, we relaxed by the warmth of the fire. After dinner a string of locals visited. (Few people make it to Wiseman in winter so outsiders are a novelty, especially those from Australia and Antarctica.) We were told trapping stories until the wee hours; stories of survival and of the animals they trapped and respected. Unlike tourist game hunters they were in touch with the local animal populations and kept track of variations in their numbers. Maintaining these populations was of primary importance. The environment could be tough but life was pleasant in this small supportive community.

Next day we all squeezed into the front of the pick-up, as Simon was going to spend Thanksgiving in Fairbanks, joining the celebrations at Hidden Hill. He nursed his contribution to the feast, a bowl of sourdough to be used as a bread starter, which also took front seat in the cab. As the cabin warmed up and the miles rolled by, Simon nodded off and soon there was sourdough all over Simon, me and the floor. It was a while before Gina could discern what had happened from the laughter and exclamations of 'Oh no, oh no . . . oh no!' We stopped at the Yukon for some chilli beans and a quick shower. It was several more hours to Fairbanks. On arrival Simon was dropped off at the end of Sue's driveway, as the weary travellers were not going to risk getting bogged as we had done the last time we ventured down the drive. Back at Hidden Hill we unloaded and fed the dogs, then went straight to bed.

In the loft of the main cabin, I was woken next morning by sounds of William and Sarah putting turkeys in the oven. Tables had been set the night before for Thanksgiving. I rolled over to sleep for a bit longer as it would be a long day. Careful discussion had managed to keep the Thanksgiving dinner to 19 guests. It seemed everyone wanted to have Thanksgiving at Hidden Hill, but more than 20 guests and there wouldn't be room for everyone to sit down. Dinner was to be at 4 p.m. to allow everyone the chance to make the most of the few hours of daylight for skiing or mushing.

I was to make the requisite mashed potatoes and Gina a lentil loaf and an American marshmallow salad. (Gina was constantly intrigued by what Americans would serve up in the name of a salad and was barely overstating the point with this sugary concoction.) It was a Thanksgiving for all to remember. Food, laughter and tales were shared. I had met most of the guests previously and was made to feel part of the circle of friends: a pocket of warmth within the cold outside. The four-footed crowd comprising Tucker, Whacko and Moladyets joined in the fun through the window, later sneaking in through the door when unwary visitors left. It was late when Sue and Simon finally departed. Dave had the sauna going so we relaxed in the heat then took the traditional roll in the snow: a good way to wind down after the excitement and festivities.

I had just got to bed when I remembered the car heater; if we were to get the car going I'd have to make a cold dash in my pyjamas. Gina was not in a hurry to see me off and so had given me responsibility for getting the show on the road in the morning. After four hours' sleep my first job was to make the required cup of tea to winkle Gina out of bed, then load the luggage into the car.

Fairbanks in winter looks much the same at 5 a.m. as it does at 8 a.m. Dark, stars, a hint of aurora in the sky, and steam hanging over the river as we drove past. There was time for another cuppa before the plane left — Gina thinking of work later in the day; I mentally preparing for the long journey via Juneau, Seattle, Los Angeles, Auckland, Melbourne and finally Hobart and the summer.

Parting was hard. We'd had a good time renewing our friendship, working, learning from and about each other.

'Let me know how the boys go.'

'Yeah, I hope your new job goes well.'

'Take care and keep in touch.'

'Yeah, I'll send you a message when I get back . . .' — pause, then jokingly — 'but we'll delete them from now on!'

Laughter and tears and waving from the walkway.

EPILOGUE: PENE

My job with the Antarctic Division saw me heading south again for the 1992–93 summer. I set out to do some modifications to the Mawson FPS and preliminary observations of another sky emission from near 85 km. It was also my job to train the expeditioner staying to run the FPS through winter. On a personal level this trip allowed me to revisit Mawson and the experiences I had there. I had hoped to run with the dogs again before their removal, but this was not to be. After sitting at the ice edge for three days waiting for snow showers to clear, I flew by chopper over the teams as they were running out to the ship. Somewhere below me Cocoa, Merlin, Oscar, Goohaw, Jedda and my other favourites were heading off on a journey that would take them far from the land they knew.

With me on this trip I took Paul's ashes. He had travelled far in his life, but I felt his spiritual resting place should be where he had met his final challenges; a land which had given him the best and worst experiences in life. Albert had also returned to Mawson, to winter again through 1993. Together one day we climbed Mt Henderson, a trip Paul and I had once set out on only to be foiled by a blizzard and miserable conditions; we didn't get another opportunity to climb that peak. In 1993 the weather was perfect, blue skies and not a breath of wind. The

241

snow petrels had nested and left with their young so only the odd bird reeled overhead.

Albert and I took our memories to the top of the mountain. We sat there talking for what must have been an hour, sharing an orange, a cider, and the experiences we had with Paul in 1990. All of Antarctica was spread out around us. Ufs Island and Chapman Ridge were beckoning to the west, the white expanse of the plateau to the south, and to the north, nestled into the coast, lay Mawson and the islands Paul and I had often visited with the dogs.

Although I have climbed Mt Henderson many times, this particular trip will be etched eternally in my mind. The peace and stillness of the day were like a gift from Antarctica. The winds which normally whip the mountain top were absent. This gave me the time to properly contemplate what had brought me to this place and this moment.

Finally we had to go back down the mountain. I'd make it back to Mawson in time to start observations when it got dark at 10.30. Somehow life must go on.

POSTSCRIPT: GINA

As I reflect on my tale of this time I see it is more of an internal than an external journey, and I feel I have covered some important ground. Day-to-day life can be quite turbulent but on a longer timescale the highs and lows seem to smooth out. From time to time I like to delve into my diaries and appreciate both the chaotic and more ordered components of my life. At times I think I can almost make out a trace of meaning; then I hit some turbulence and lose the thread. But I know the thread is there.

After all the wonderful women I had met in Alaska it felt good to know that one of my best female friends was another Aussie. Being able to share our Antarctic and Alaskan experiences, I was putting things in context. I felt an affinity with the high latitudes and the aurorae, but I now realised it would be Alaska I would be coming back to; it had many of the elements of Antarctica but with more life and a more tangible soul.

One night during her visit, Pene and I sat in front of a tape recorder and talked: of our friendship, our similarities, and our differences. It seemed like a good start to writing a conclusion, except that these two high-tech scientists had not managed to successfully operate the tape recorder! Two years later we are still trying to recover the essence of our combined tale. The answers lie in our story and perhaps are more clear to those who are not a part of it.

It snowed an inch a day during the week after Pene left, and soon the trails were perfect and even the creek was do-able. Alone, I harnessed up six dogs. We screamed out on to the familiar trail system, then settled down to a steady pace. With moonlight showing the way, the dogs content and responsive, me standing on the runners, I was in my element and in control. The sled purred on the new snow. I would tell Pene about it on the e-mail tomorrow.

APPENDIX 1 :
PEOPLE (BY PLACE)

Mawson Institute for Antarctic Research, University of Adelaide
Dr Fred Jacka, Director
Eleanor Jacka (together with husband, Fred Jacka, co-edited *Mawson's Antarctic Diaries*)
Don Creighton, engineer (wintered Mawson, 1963)
Richard Ferguson, research assistant
Heather Duff, secretary
Damian Murphy, research associate (wintered Mawson, 1991)

Post-graduate students
Phil Wilksch
Peter Jacob   (wintered Mawson, 1981)
Norm Jones   (wintered Mawson, 1981)
Rod MacLeod   (wintered Mawson, 1981)
Paul Wardill   (wintered Mawson, 1983)
Mark Conde   (wintered Mawson, 1984, 86, 92)
Andre Phillips   (wintered Mawson, 1984)
Gina Price   (wintered Mawson, 1985)
Maria de Deuge   (wintered Mawson, 1987, 91)
John French   (wintered Mawson, 1989)
Pene Greet   (wintered Mawson, 1990)
Steven Argall

Other Australian physicists mentioned
Dr Peter Dyson, La Trobe University
Prof. Neville Fletcher, University of New England
Dr Frank Hibberd, University of New England

Australian Antarctic Division, Kingston, Tasmania
UAP section
Dr Gary Burns, program manager
Dr Ray Morris, physicist
Dr Andrew Kleckociuk, physicist
Other
Tom Maggs, Mawson Station Manager 1990 (voyage leader)
Rod Ledingham, Field Operations Officer, responsible for dogs
Graham Robertson, biologist (wintered Mawson, 1988)

Mawson Base
1984 expeditioners mentioned
Mark Conde, Mawson Institute physicist
Andre Phillips, Mawson Institute physicist
Alistair Urie, UAP engineer

1985 wintering expeditioners
(complete listing; not all mentioned by name in text)
Enid Borschmann, chef
Peter Bourke, maintenance electrician
Paul Chesworth, Bureau of Meteorology technical
officer (met. tech.)
Jim Cooper, cosmic ray physicist
Dennis Day, maintenance plumber
Gavin Day, construction plumber
Robyn Downey, radio operator
Tony Everett (The 'Bear'), construction carpenter
Roger Gauthier, medical officer
Alan Holmes, radio operator
Dave Jewell, radio technician
Peta Kelsey, geophysicist
Mark Loveridge, Ionospheric Prediction Service officer
Paul Lytwyn, construction electrician
Neil Miller, senior diesel mechanic
John McIlwham, meteorological observer

Grant Morrison, construction plumber
Al O'Neill, maintenance plumber
Danny O'Reilly, construction foreman
Dave Pottage, senior meteorological observer
Gina Price, UAP physicist
Kevin Pritchard, diesel mechanic
Allen Rooke, senior radio operator
Bill Singleton, plant inspector
Mark Spooner, radio technician
John Stanborough, construction carpenter
Judy Turner, radio operator
Ted Upton, officer-in-charge

1989 expeditioners mentioned
Peter Crosswaite, PC, BMR geophysicist, 1989 dog handler
Mike Dymond, UAP engineer
John French, UAP physicist

1990 wintering expeditioners
(complete listing, not all mentioned by name in text)
Grant Brightman, radio operator
Albert Bruehwiler, plant inspector (PI)
Patrick Butler, diesel mechanic (dieso)
Malcolm Campbell, Mal, UAP engineer
John Colley, radio technical officer (RTO)
Bill Collins, electrician (sparky)
Dr Lloyd Fletcher, medical officer (doctor)
Leighton Ford, plumber
Dave Freeman, meteorological observer (met.)
Paul Gigg (Giggles), radio technical officer
Pene Greet, Mawson Institute physicist, 1990 dog-handler
Dave Harrison, radio operator
Alex Hindle, senior radio operator
Craig Hunter, senior radio technical officer (SRTO)
Andrew Lewis, BMR geophysicist
Bob Libbiter, carpenter (chippy)
Paul Myers, diesel mechanic
Scot Nichols, chef (cook)
Ian Palmer, diesel mechanic

Bob Parker, station leader
Dave Shaw, Bureau of Meteorology technical officer (met. tech.)
Shane Spriggins, radio operator
Lionel Whitehorn, diesel mechanic
Graham Whiteside, senior meteorological observer

1991 expeditioners mentioned
Louise Crossley, station leader
Maria de Deuge, BMR geophysicist, 1991 dog-handler
Stuart Hodges, Stu, carpenter
Rob Kiernan, glaciologist, Lambert traverse leader (summer)
Andrew Kleckociuk, Klucky, UAP physicist (summer)
Micheal Craven, Duk, Antarctic Division UAP physicist
Damian Murphy, Murph, Mawson Institute physicist
Tony Otterli, Tonyo, UAP engineer

Alaska
Geophysical Institute, University of Alaska
Prof. Roger Smith
Joe Minow, graduate student
Jim Conner, graduate student

Other
Prof. Gonzalo Hernandez, University of Washington
Kathy Price (wintered South Pole, 1991)

Hidden Hill
Residents
Art Keoninger
William and Sarah Walters
Scott Wilbur
Tim and Anne Walker/Sudkamp
Kim O'Brien
Dave van den Berg
Marin Kuizenga

Associates
Sue Steinacker
Simon McLaughlin (New Zealander)
Cathy Walling
Dale Pomraning

APPENDIX 2:
DOGS (BY PLACE)

Mawson (two teams)
Pedro; Nanok; Mandy (bitch); Blackie; Welf; Otis; D-Day; Oscar; Goohaw; Kamik (spayed bitch); Choofer; Merlin; Cocoa (bitch); Broka (bitch); Jedda (bitch).

Brendan; Arne; Elwood; Jake (Gentleman Jake); Io (bitch); Luvan; Morrie; Ursa; Fanny (bitch); Zipper; Bear; Kirsty (bitch); Bundy (bitch); Bonza.

Hidden Hill
Dipper (bitch); Jasper; Rex; Maimi (bitch); Sasha; Dune; Zeb. *Pets:* Moladyets (bitch); Kodi; Whacko.

Sue's dog mentioned
Tucker (bitch)

Wiseman dogs
Shiska; Xi; Ruff; Lune (bitch); Dan; Spot; Alex; Werkum; Grotto.

A P P E N D I X 3 :
M E T R I C – I M P E R I A L
C O N V E R S I O N S

Temperature

$$t_C = \frac{t_F - 32}{1.8}$$

degrees Celsius	degrees Farenheit
−80°C	−112°F
−70	−94
−60	−76
−50	−58
−40	−40
−30	−22
−20	−4
−10	14
0	32
10	50
20	68
30	86
40	104
50	122

$t_F = (t_C \times 1.8) + 32$

degrees Farenheit	degrees Celsius
$-100°F$	$-73.3°C$
-50	-45.5
0	-17.8
50	10.0
100	37.8

Lengths

1 kilometre = 1000 metres
1 metre
100 centimetres = 1 metre
1 000 millimetres = 1 metre
1 000 000 micrometres = 1 metre
1 000 000 000 nanometres = 1 metre
1 000 000 000 000 picometres = 1 metre

1 inch = 25.4 mm = 2.54 cm
1 foot = 0.305 m = 30.5 cm
1 yard = 3 feet = 0.914 m = 91.4 cm
1 mile = 1609 m = 1.609 km
1 Nautical mile (Nm) = 1852 m

Mass

1 pound = 0.454 kg = 454 g

Wind velocity

1 knot = 1 Nm/hr = 1.852 km/hr = 0.514 m/s

APPENDIX 4 : BEAUFORT WIND SCALE

Force	Description	Wind Speed (knots)
0	Calm	0–1
1	Light air	1–3
2	Light breeze	4–6
3	Gentle breeze	7–10
4	Moderate breeze	11–16
5	Fresh breeze	17–21
6	Strong breeze	22–27
7	Near gale	28–33
8	Gale	34–40
9	Strong gale	41–47
10	Storm	48–55
11	Violent storm	56–63
12	Hurricane	63+

Note: 1 knot = 1 Nm/hr = 1.852 km/hr = 0.514 m/s

GLOSSARY

AAP   Australian Associated Press.

ACS   Construction at Australian Antarctic bases is carried out by 'Australian Construction Services', an Australian Federal Government body. The stations have been largely rebuilt by a reconstruction program which has been in operation since the early 1980s and should be completed before the end of the century.

aerosol counter Aerosols are small colloidal particles in the atmosphere (e.g., smoke, dust). The counter measures the number of such particles in the air. Mawson is an important station for such measurements as it has one of the cleanest atmospheres in the world.

AGU(meeting)   American Geophysical Union. This professional body hosts biannual conferences in the earth, atmospheric, oceanic, hydrologic, and space sciences.

AIP   Australian Institute of Physics

airglow   Emission of light from the sky. Differs from aurora only in that the source of the emission is photochemical rather than energy

	from the solar wind. Airglow occurs at all latitudes at subvisual intensities.
all-sky camera or ASC	Used for auroral photography. Photographs the whole sky through a fish-eye lens at one-minute intervals.
all-sky video or ASV	A modern version of the all-sky camera which records images on video camera.
ANARE	Australian National Antarctic Research Expeditions.
Anaresat	satellite communications facilities for ANARE, part of Intelsat.
ANZAC	Australian and New Zealand Army Corps. Anzac Day, 25 April, is a celebration of the stand made by Australian and New Zealand troops at Gallipolli, Turkey, in 1915 during World War I.
apples (she'll be)	Everything will be fine (Australian).
ARC	Australian Research Council, the body responsible for distribution of research funding for universities within Australia.
arvo	afternoon.
aurora	Bright emissions visible in the polar night sky. The light is produced by the interaction of the atoms and molecules in the upper atmosphere and energetic charged particles entering the atmosphere from the sun (solar wind).
Aus, Aussie	Australia, Australian.
Austpac	A telephone link between computer installations within Australia.
avagoodweekend	Slang, derived from an insect repellant commercial.
BA	Breathing apparatus.
blizz static	Electric charge built up between objects during blizzards due to the combination of a dry atmosphere, high winds and blowing snow.
blizzard	When the winds are greater than 35 kt, visibility is less than 100 m, and the temperature

	is less than zero Celsius for at least one hour. Colloquially called 'blow' or 'blizz'.
BMR	Bureau of Mineral Resources, a department of the Australian Federal Government, now the Australian Geological Survey Organisation (AGSO).
bod	Person.
bonnet	Hood of car.
bugger	Term of endearment or abuse (Australian).
cable tray	As Mawson is built on rock, electrical cables cannot be buried. To protect such cables they are laid in trays connecting the buildings.
CAE	College of Advanced Education. These colleges grew out of institutions for teacher training and have recently been amalgamated with or made into universities.
CCD	Charged-coupled devices: extremely sensitive detection system used in low light conditions.
CEDAR	Coupling Energetics and Dynamics of Atmospheric Regions, a program coordinating atmospheric research in the United States. CEDAR organises an annual conference for discussion of issues, presentation of results and organisation of research programs.
chemo	Chemotherapy, drugs used for cancer treatment
chippie	Carpenter.
choofer	Small portable pressurised stove for camping, Optimus stove.
chook	poultry, chicken (Australian).
comms	Communications: both satellite and radio communications are used on Australian Antarctic bases.
contra dance	Although referring to a particular style of folk dancing in America, contra dance can be used to refer to folk dancing in general.
crack	Crevasse (see also slot).

crook	Ill (Australian).
CSIRO	Commonwealth Scientific and Industrial Research Organisation, a research organisation funded by the Australian federal government
cubby, cubbyhouse	Child's playhouse (Australian).
cuppa	Cup of tea or coffee, more usually tea.
D5, D7	Models of Caterpillar bulldozers.
DASETT	Department of Arts, Sport, Environment, Tourism, and Territories, a Federal Government body responsible for the Australian Antarctic Division (Australia claims about a quarter of Antarctica as territory).
dayglow	Light emitted from the sky during the day (not visible against the background of scattered sunlight).
deadman	An aluminium plate for anchoring in snow, plural: deadmen.
Denali	(or Mt McKinley) at 6194 m is the tallest mountain in North America.
DHC	Construction at Australian Antarctic bases is carried out by 'Australian Construction Services' an Australian Federal Government body. ACS was previously known as DHC, Department of Housing and Construction.
dieso	Diesel mechanic (Australian–Antarctic).
dog-line	In general refers to place where dog-teams are tethered; in particular at Mawson the dog-lines are chains which can be moved vertically on poles as snow accumulates (sited just to west of main station).
e-mail	Electronic mail, used for communication between computer users. Provides almost instant transfer of messages from one computer to another.
entropy	The concept of entropy is used to describe the tendency of all systems to move towards a state of increased randomness or disorder. Work must be done to reverse this tendency.

equinox	When day-length equals night-length and sun is over the equator, nominally 20 March and 22 September.
etalon	See FPS.
F.A.	Means fuck all, in expression 'sweet fuck-all' = 'nothing', more polite when left as abbreviation.
fast ice	Sea-ice connected to the continent or islands surrounding Antarctica.
5577	Wavelength of an atomic oxygen emission in airglow and dominant in the aurora. The airglow originates from a layer near 97 km; the auroral emission is produced over a broad height range typically centered about 120 km.
flat chat	At full speed (Australian).
FPS	Fabry-Perot spectrometer, in essence a pair of optically flat glass plates, a Fabry-Perot etalon, enabling the instrument to scan in wavelength. FPSs can be used to observe atmospheric emissions; from such data winds and temperatures in the source region of the emissions can be determined.
frostnip	A mild version of frostbite.
g'day	Salutation, good-day (Australian).
gash	Garbage (Australian–Antarctic).
GI	Geophysical Institute, University of Alaska.
gun team	Best team (Australian).
gunna	Going to (Australian).
Gwamm	A traverse fuel depot at the top of the steep ascent on to the plateau above Mawson.
Hagglunds	A tracked all-terrain vehicle used on Australian bases. (The vehicle is made in Sweden by the Hagglunds company.)
ham	Amateur radio operator.
Hendo	Mt Henderson, 20 km south of Mawson. A refuge hut is located at the base of the mountain.
IAGA	International Association of Geomagnetism and Aeronomy, a body of the International

Council of Scientific Unions (ICSU), which organises a biennial conference on atmospheric physics and associated disciplines.

IAMAP   International Association of Meteorology and Atmospheric Physics.

IASOS   Institute of Antarctic and Southern Ocean Studies.

Icom radio   An Icom M700 transceiver was taken on the Kloa trip to provide reliable high frequency (hf) radio communications with Mawson. This unit is more powerful than standard Codan hf radio. A solar panel was required for charging the Icom batteries. The Icom also made it possible to listen to international news broadcasts from Radio Australia and the BBC World Service.

Inmarsat   Satellite communications for ships at sea. Each Australian Antarctic base has facilities to enable use of Inmarsat.

IPD   Intensified photon detector, a sensitive detection system used in low light conditions. First used in military nightglasses.

IUGG   International Union of Geodesy and Geophysics.

JATP   *Journal of Atmospheric and Terrestrial Physics.*

jillaroo   Female station-hand (or in US ranch-hand), female of 'jackaroo' (Australian).

jolly   Usually refers to any trip away from an Australian Antarctic Base, more particularly for trips for rest and recreation.

karabiner   A spring-loaded metal clip typically used for mountaineering and climbing.

Kloa Point   Named by a Norwegian expedition, 'Kloa' means 'claw'. There is an emperor penguin rookery nearby which has been monitored regularly over the last two decades. Most of the trips to Kloa, approximately 300 km west of Mawson, have been by dogsled as Kloa Point is on the western edge of Edward VIII

	Gulf, a large gulf which has unreliable sea-ice and so is unsuitable for vehicular travel.
knockers	hostile critic or doubter (Australian).
kombi pop top	Volkswagen camper van with expandable roof (Australian).
lash out	To be extravagant (Australian).
lidar	Acronym for 'light detection and ranging', similar in principal to radars except using lasers, or light, instead of radio waves.
light-on	Insufficient, less than required (Australian).
lower 48	From an Alaskan point of view the 48 contiguous states of the USA.
magnetometers	Used to measure the intensity of the Earth's magnetic field.
MBT	Mawson Bastard Time, a non-standard time on which Mawson operates, 6 hours ahead of Universal Time, and 1 hour 48 minutes ahead of real local time. This time was chosen so that morning work hours at Mawson would coincide with afternoon work hours in eastern Australia.
MCP	Male chauvinist pig.
melt lake	An area where ice has melted, usually around exposed rock or in a depression in the plateau ice. The ice is a different colour from plateau ice having less air pockets. In contrast to the rippled surface of plateau ice melt lakes often have a smooth polished surface.
melt stream	At the height of summer the plateau ice can melt. The resulting water runs in streams or 'melt streams'. These streams are only to be found on the extremities of the Antarctic plateau.
met.	Meteorology, specifically the Bureau of Meteorology, a department of the Australian Federal Government.
met. string	A strong braided string supplied to Antarctic bases for balloon flights and frequently used for other purposes.

met. tech	Meteorological technician.
MIAR	Mawson Institute for Antarctic Research, formerly a department within the University of Adelaide. MIAR opened in 1961 to honour the Antarctic explorer Sir Douglas Mawson who had been a professor in geology at the university. It was closed in December 1990. (Sometimes referred to as MI.)
MSP	Meridian-scanning photometer, used to measure intensity of atmospheric optical emissions along a meridian of the sky (i.e. north to south).
MT	Mt Torrens. The Mawson Institute had a field station at Mt Torrens in the Adelaide Hills. Pene completed the field work for her PhD thesis at this field station.
mush	An Alaskan term to describe running with dog-teams.
nip	See frostnip.
NSW	New South Wales, a state of Australia.
NZ	New Zealand.
OH	Hydroxyl, chemical symbol OH, which exists as a free radical in the atmosphere. It produces one of the brightest airglow emissions in the night sky. A layer of OH molecules exists near 87 km.
OIC	Officer-in-charge. Despite attempts to change this label to 'station leader' the term OIC persists.
OICery	OIC or station leader's office.
OS	Overseas (Australian slang).
outside	Alaskan term for parts of America outside Alaska.
Oz	Australia.
PCM	Prince Charles Mountains.
pemm	Pemmican. A cake of dried meat and fat providing a balanced diet. At Mawson in 1990 only the huskies ate pemm. A human pemm preparation was used for field operations in earlier days.

photometers	A generic term for describing instruments which measure the intensity of light emissions from the sky. (See specific descriptions of 3FP, MSP.)
PI	In scientific context, principal investigator. In Antarctic context, plant inspector, in charge of the vehicles and engines from base.
plateau	The Antarctic ice cap rises abruptly behind Mawson Station to a level of about 800 m. It continues to rise steadily beyond. Any ice which is part of the ice-cap is referred to colloquially as 'the Plateau'. Near the coast and through mountainous regions the plateau divides into faster flowing glaciers.
PM tube	Photomultiplier tube which converts photons to electronic pulses; can be used to detect very low light levels.
PMT	Depending on context, pre-menstrual tension or photomultiplier tube (see PM tube).
polly	Australian slang for a politician.
port-o-gaff	A drink of stout and lemonade.
pressure ridges	When sea-ice or fast ice is under pressure it buckles forming pressure ridges.
quikes	Four-wheeled motorbikes. These are more useful in some parts of Antarctica than ski-doos as they travel better on blue ice, although they will bog easily in soft snow.
rafted ice	Pieces of sea-ice jumbled together. This usually happens when the ice is broken up soon after it forms and is then blown into a heap.
rapt	Pleased, thrilled.
'ron	Short for 'later on' (Australian slang).
RSL	Returned Services League, an organisation for Australians who have participated in active military service.
RTO	radio technical officer.
Rumdoodle	A mountain in the Masson Range with a refuge at its base. (Named after the book *Ascent of Rumdoodle* by W. Bowman.)

run-in	Argument (Australian slang).
SA	South Australia, Australian state.
SAB	Special Antarctic blend, a blend of fuel for very low temperatures.
SAR	Search and rescue.
sastrugi	Wavelike structures in snow, formed by wind. Sastrugi can be from centimetres to metres in depth, and the snow is compacted in the process.
SDI	Strategic Defense Initiative or 'Star Wars', a US defence program initiated by the Reagan Administration.
sea-ice	When sea-water temperatures fall below $-1.8°C$ sea-ice starts to form. At Mawson the sea-ice reaches a thickness of 1 to 2 metres. Islands by the coast hold it fast to shore, so once it is properly formed it rarely breaks out before January. On the wall of the Mawson dog-hut, which was originally a glaciology van, is written: 'The sea-ice will form on the first calm day after March 21'.
sked	Radio schedule or appointed time for radio contact between two parties.
skijoring	Being pulled on skis by one or more dogs in harness.
SL	Station leader, previously known as OIC or officer-in-charge.
sledgies	High protein biscuits specially designed for Antarctic field operations. Used in a similar fashion to a cheese biscuit or cracker.
slot	A crevasse, also known as a crack. A vehicle is slotted if it is driven into a crevasse. This usually happens accidentally when the crevasse is concealed by snow cover.
slotty	Adjective to describe a crevassed area.
slushy	Kitchenhand (Antarctic slang).
solstice	Winter or summer solstice, which occurs when the sun is furthest from the equator, nominally 21 June and 22 December.

SPA	Specially protected area, a designated area protected for environmental reasons.
speccy	Spectacular (Australian slang).
SRTO	Senior radio technical officer.
sweet F.A.	Slang (see F.A.).
sweets	Candy.
tankhouse	A building over a large water tank, Mawson's water supply. The tank holds sufficient water for several days and a reserve is kept for fire fighting.
Tas, Tassie	Tasmania, the island state off south eastern Australia.
tea	Evening meal (Australian).
thermos	Vacuum flask for storing drinks.
3FP	Three-field photometer, an instrument which measures the intensity of optical emissions from the sky from three closely spaced regions. From the data recorded, the speed and direction of atmospheric gravity waves can be determined.
TLC	Tender loving care.
traverse	A convoy of vehicles travelling together (in Antarctica) across a vast distance.
UAP	Upper atmospheric physics.
UT	Universal Time, equivalent to the old Greenwich Mean Time.
ute	Short for utility (Australian); American equivalent is a 'pick-up'.
UTI	Urinary tract infection.
WA	Western Australia, an Australian state.
whacker/wanker	Someone who makes out they're better than they are (Australian), similar to American 'jerk'.
willy-willy	Spiralling wind (Australian Aboriginal).

ENDNOTES

Part Two

1 A traverse is a convoy of vehicles covering long distances in Antarctica. The Lambert traverse comprised three tractor-trains carrying glaciology experiments to measure the thickness and rate of flow of ice on the Lambert Glacier, the biggest glacier in the Antarctic. The traverse is circumnavigating the glacier basin over a period of years to determine the ice movement through the area.

2 Libby Riddles & Tim Jones, *Race Across Alaska: The First Woman to Win the Iditarod Tells Her Story*, StackPole Books, 1988.

3 One of the old dongas, named after an early explorer. The dongas originally housed six expeditioners with a communal shower and urinal. Each expeditioner had an area about 2.5 m by 1.5 m with a bed above a desk and cupboard-storage area. Curtains screened the doorways. The modern accommodation provides reasonably large single bedrooms for wintering expeditions.

4 IPD, intensified photon detectors, like CCDs, are extremely sensitive detection units for use in very low light conditions. IPDs were first used in military night-glasses.

5 A precise measurement of the distance between the plates of the high-resolution etalon, which is the heart of the FPS.

This distance must be determined within half an observing wavelength, about 300 nm or 0.0003 mm.

6 Magnetic midnight is a time calculated from the geomagnetic coordinate system. The Earth's magnetic poles do not coincide with the geographic poles and if these magnetic poles are used to define a coordinate system a new time can be defined from magnetic longitude.

7 As secretary of the NSW branch of the Builders Labourers Union (BLF) in the early 1970s, Jack Mundy was instrumental in imposing a series of union 'green bans' on Sydney building projects to protect historically important sites.

8 Nightwatch is a common duty done by all expeditioners. Starting at 9 p.m., the person is expected to stay awake and alert all night principally as a firewatch and to make three-hourly checks on the powerhouse to ensure the engines are running properly. He or she also mops out and cleans up the kitchen, mess and club areas and arranges the breakfast tables and servery. Depending on the weather, routine tasks usually occupy only part of the night hours, leaving some time for other things. Saturday nightwatches were carefully rostered as the club usually hosted a party and cleaning there became somewhat more time consuming. Nightwatch can go to sleep after the 0600 powerhouse obs by which time two met. observers and a radio operator have started work.

9 Kloa Point was named by a Norwegian expedition; 'kloa' means 'claw'. There is an emperor penguin rookery nearby which has been monitored regularly over the last two decades. Most of the trips to Kloa have been by dog-sled as Kloa Point is on the western edge of a large gulf, Edward VIII Gulf, which has unreliable sea-ice and so is unsuitable for vehicular travel.

10 A dichroic filter splits light, in this case by reflecting longer wavelength light and transmitting shorter wavelength light.

11 Usually the FPS is used to measure line-of-sight winds when looking at a 60° zenith angle, i.e. 60° off vertical or 30° above the horizon. Such measurements have a vertical wind component and the vertical wind campaign involved looking continually in the zenith to monitor how frequently the vertical wind is non-zero. The vertical wind measurements

in routine observations are required for a zero wavelength reference to measure the Doppler shift.

12 The space between the interferometer plates is varied or 'scanned' by altering the voltage on peizo-electric ceramic mounts on which the plates sit. The piezoelectric mounts vary in height by about 0.0005 mm. This changes the wavelength transmitted through the plates and allows the interferometer to scan in wavelength through the emission feature of interest. 'Turbo-scanning' was a termed coined by Mark Conde to describe a fault in the system when scanning occurred more quickly than it should.

Part Three

1 The laboratory lamp emits the oxygen green line which is the dominant emission in the aurora. The emission is reliant on very low pressures, as exist at 100 km where the aurora begins, difficult to create in a laboratory lamp. In fact, the lamps have to be flushed out on a vacuum system for a month and then there is a high failure rate, hence the high cost.

2 Ions are charged particles and because of their charge move along magnetic field lines which lie close to the vertical at high latitudes.

3 Soft precipitation has low energies, hundreds of electron volts (eV) as compared to the hard precipitation which is high in energy, keV and MeV.

4 Fred Bond was involved in Australian upper atmospheric research in the Antarctic for many years.

5 Infra-red detectors are sensitive to slightly longer wavelengths of the electromagnetic spectrum than visible light.

6 In America time on the mainframe computers is charged to users. This is not the case in Australia.

7 The CEDAR (Coupling Energetics and Dynamics of Atmospheric Regions) program has an annual workshop–conference in Boulder, Colorado.

Part Four

1 Special antarctic blend, a blend of fuel with a low freezing point for Antarctic operations.

2 Presents for expeditioners can be given to station leaders for distribution at nominated times. Most expeditioners receive birthday and Christmas presents from relatives and friends in Australia.

3 Breathing apparatus (a group of expeditioners is trained to use it for firefighting).

4 A katabatic wind is any wind blowing down an incline. The air above continental Antarctica is cold and dense so it sinks, causing a high-pressure system to form over the ice-cap. The air sinks further, rolling down the slopes of the plateau and producing a katabatic wind, which is strongest at stations at the base of the plateau. At Mawson the katabatic blows on most days, typically 15–30 knots for 12–15 hours. The katabatic falls off quickly as you travel from the plateau (Davis base, 15–20 km from the plateau, experiences little katabatic wind).

5 Island 45 is an island in the Stanton Group about 60 km west of Mawson. The spot height, 45 m, on the map distinguishes it from other islands in the group. It is the furthest north-west and provided us with a good point to set off to negotiate the rafted ice around the Jelbart Glacier.

6 Due to the large number of bitches on the base if Cocoa had all bitches the whole litter would be put down and she'd be able to come on the long Kloa trip with us.

7 In mid-August 1985 a huge rafting of ice occurred, in what had been the centre of Auster rookery. When it was visited a short time afterwards an estimated 600 dead chicks and abandoned eggs were found. Many adult birds appeared agitated as they paraded on the edge of the rafted area, which covered $500 \, \text{m}^2$.

8 Power logic controller, a computer-controlled system which manages the station powerhouse and power distribution.

Part Five

1 Summer is referred to as the 'silly season' because with all the comings and goings of the ships and with the many visitors, including bureaucrats, politicians and journalists, the bases do not seem to run along sensible lines. (Chaos is the word which comes to mind.)

2   Macey Island hosts an Adelie penguin rookery in summer so there is nowhere to stake out the dogs on arrival. Adelies, unlike emperor penguins, are very territorial and even if the dogs are a reasonable distance from any birds the birds will accost them to establish their territorial rights.

3   Scattered sunlight produces background in the sky observations. The sunlight in the spectral range concerned contains the sodium Fraunhofer absorption features.

4   This is a very weak emission to try to observe using an FPS. It can be compared to auroral emissions which are measured in kilo-Rayleighs (i.e. 1000 times brighter).

Part Six
1   The lyrics of 'Cradle of Dawn' by Libby Roderick are reproduced at the front of this book.

Part Seven
1   Vicki Aitken was a mutual friend. She had been south twice as a chef in 1983 and 1987. On the second occasion she was repatriated in May due to the diagnosis and rapid development of breast cancer. The last Australian ship had left some months earlier so Russian helicopters and ships provided transport from the station to civilisation. She continued her involvement with the Antarctic Division, working at head office in Kingston at times from 1987 until her death in January 1992.

Part Eight
1   Libby Riddles & Tim Jones, *Race Across Alaska: The First Woman to Win the Iditarod Tells Her Story*, StackPole Books, 1988.